The Open University

MST209 Mathe

C000225612

Block 6

Contents

The Open University, Walton Hall, Milton Keynes, MK7 6AA.

First published 2005. Second edition 2008.

Edited, designed and typeset by The Open University, using the Open University TeX System.

Printed and bound in the United Kingdom by Charlesworth Press, Wakefield.

ISBN 978 0 7492 5286 1

1.1

UNIT 21   Fourier series

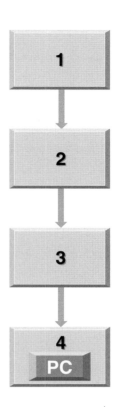

Study guide for Unit 21

This unit is concerned with the technique of expressing a periodic function as a sum of terms, where each term is a constant, a sine function or a cosine function. There is a strong analogy with the technique, studied in *Unit 12*, of expressing a (non-periodic) function as a Taylor series, which is a sum of terms that are powers of the independent variable(s); in both cases, working with just the first few terms generally gives a useful approximation.

The unit assumes the following background knowledge:
- the definition of the period (*Unit 7*);
- forced oscillations and resonance (*Unit 17*);
- integration by parts (*Unit 1*).

The methods of this unit will be required later in the course, particularly in *Unit 22*.

The sections should be studied in their numerical order if possible. The first three sections should each occupy one study session, while Section 4 (which involves working with the computer) should need rather less.

Introduction

In *Unit 12* you saw that many functions can be approximated by a Taylor polynomial

$$f(x) \simeq f(x_0) + (x - x_0)f'(x_0) + \tfrac{1}{2}(x - x_0)^2 f''(x_0) + \cdots$$
$$+ \tfrac{1}{n!}(x - x_0)^n f^{(n)}(x_0).$$

It is often the case that a small number of terms gives a useful approximation, and it is tempting to ask whether the approximation may be made exact by taking an *infinite* number of terms – in other words, is it true that

$$f(x) = \sum_{r=0}^{\infty} \frac{1}{r!}(x - x_0)^r f^{(r)}(x_0) ?$$

In general, the answer is 'no', but for a wide class of functions the result is true. For example, with $f = \exp$ and $x_0 = 0$, we have $f^{(n)}(x_0) = e^0 = 1$, so

$$e^x = \sum_{r=0}^{\infty} \frac{1}{r!} x^r,$$

for any real number x.

In this unit we are primarily concerned not with polynomial functions (which, if not constant, become numerically very large as $x \to \pm\infty$), but with *periodic* functions, such as $\sin x$ and $\cos x$. A great deal of beautiful mathematics has arisen from the analysis we shall describe, but there are also important practical benefits.

One example arises directly from *Unit 17*, where you studied differential equations modelling forced and damped oscillations. You saw how they could be used to predict the response of various mechanical and electrical systems. In particular, you saw how these responded to a sinusoidal forcing term like $\cos t$, with graph as in Figure 0.1.

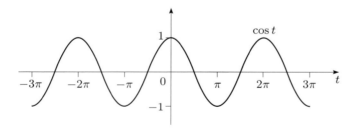

Figure 0.1

Such forcing terms occur frequently in applications; for instance, they model the force acting on the suspension of cars travelling on bumpy roads and the effect of radio signals acting on electrical circuits. Such a model leads to a differential equation of the form

$$m\ddot{x} + r\dot{x} + kx = P\cos(\Omega t),$$

with steady-state solution

$$x(t) = P\cos(\Omega t + \phi)/k^*.$$

The factor k^* and the phase angle ϕ are rather complicated functions of the forcing frequency Ω, which we need not consider here.

However, a forcing term, though periodic, may be more complicated than a purely sinusoidal function. Figures 0.2, 0.3 and 0.4 depict periodic functions $c(t)$, $g(t)$ and $h(t)$ that are reasonably easy to visualize and describe.

For dimensional consistency, k^* and k have the same dimensions and both are measured in newtons per metre.

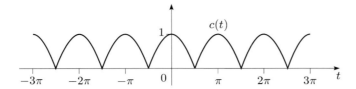

Figure 0.2

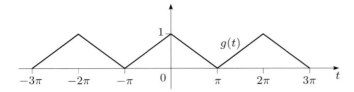

Figure 0.3

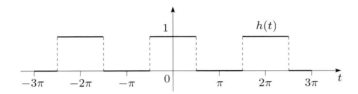

Figure 0.4

The graph in Figure 0.2 is similar to that of $\cos t$, except that all the values are positive. The function $c(t)$ is described by

$c(t) = |\cos t|$.

This graph differs from that of the cosine function, which turns smoothly. Here the direction changes abruptly every time the graph reaches the t-axis. However, $c(t)$ is still continuous in that there are no sudden jumps in the function value as t increases smoothly; it is possible to draw the graph without taking the pen off the paper.

The graph of $g(t)$ in Figure 0.3 is also continuous, but with abrupt changes of direction at both the highest and lowest values. Between the points where the direction changes, the graph is a straight line. The whole graph looks rather like the blade of a saw, so $g(t)$ is known as a **saw-tooth function**. You will study this function quite intensively in *Unit 22*, and in the next unit you will meet a saw-tooth function as a model of the initial displacement of a plucked violin string.

The graph in Figure 0.4 shows a function that takes the value 1 whenever t lies in the interval $[(2k - \frac{1}{2})\pi, (2k + \frac{1}{2})\pi]$ for some integer k and the value 0 otherwise, i.e.

$$h(t) = \begin{cases} 1 & \text{if } (2k - \frac{1}{2})\pi \le t \le (2k + \frac{1}{2})\pi \quad (k \in \mathbb{Z}), \\ 0 & \text{otherwise.} \end{cases}$$

This graph differs quite radically from those of $\cos t$, $c(t)$ and $g(t)$. Here there are abrupt jumps in the function value itself (rather than merely abrupt changes of direction) at the points $t = (k + \frac{1}{2})\pi$. The function $h(t)$ is discontinuous, while $\cos t$, $c(t)$ and $g(t)$ are continuous. The function $h(t)$ is known as a **square-wave function**.

At present we have no way of predicting the response of a mechanical or electrical system to a forcing function like $c(t)$, $g(t)$ or $h(t)$ (although such systems are extremely common). Fourier series provide the answer.

The differential equation

$$m\ddot{x} + r\dot{x} + kx = P\cos(\Omega t)$$

is *linear*. Therefore the superposition principle tells us that if

See *Unit 3*.

$$x = P_1\cos(\Omega_1 t + \phi_1)/k_1$$

is a solution of

$$m\ddot{x} + r\dot{x} + kx = P_1\cos(\Omega_1 t),$$

and

$$x = P_2\cos(\Omega_2 t + \phi_2)/k_2$$

is a solution of

$$m\ddot{x} + r\dot{x} + kx = P_2\cos(\Omega_2 t),$$

then

$$x = P_1\cos(\Omega_1 t + \phi_1)/k_1 + P_2\cos(\Omega_2 t + \phi_2)/k_2$$

is a solution of

$$m\ddot{x} + r\dot{x} + kx = P_1\cos(\Omega_1 t) + P_2\cos(\Omega_2 t).$$

If we could express $c(t)$ as a linear combination of cosine functions, then we would be able to apply this idea to find a solution of

$$m\ddot{x} + r\dot{x} + kx = c(t)$$

(and similarly for $g(t)$ and $h(t)$). This is precisely what we shall do in this unit, except that the linear combinations will involve an *infinite* number of terms.

As you will see, the functions $c(t)$, $g(t)$ and $h(t)$ introduced above correspond, respectively, to the infinite sums

$$C(t) = \frac{2}{\pi}\left(1 + \frac{2}{1\times3}\cos 2t - \frac{2}{3\times5}\cos 4t + \frac{2}{5\times7}\cos 6t - \frac{2}{7\times9}\cos 8t \right.$$
$$\left. + \cdots\right), \tag{0.1}$$

$$G(t) = \frac{1}{2} + \frac{4}{\pi^2}\cos t + \frac{4}{9\pi^2}\cos 3t + \frac{4}{25\pi^2}\cos 5t + \frac{4}{49\pi^2}\cos 7t + \cdots, \tag{0.2}$$

$$H(t) = \frac{1}{2} + \frac{2}{\pi}\cos t - \frac{2}{3\pi}\cos 3t + \frac{2}{5\pi}\cos 5t - \frac{2}{7\pi}\cos 7t + \cdots. \tag{0.3}$$

We call infinite sums like these **Fourier series**. Successive terms in the sum are functions that belong to a family of sinusoidal functions whose frequencies are related. The sums are infinite in the sense that they do not stop after a finite number of terms, though, in practice, we take only as many terms as are needed to make the result as accurate as we require.

Fourier series are not just of interest in the analysis and application of damped forced oscillations, but are widely applicable and are of fundamental theoretical importance. Whenever a system exhibits variation at a range of frequencies, it is sensible to see if this variation can be explained by some combination of sinusoidal terms.

In *Unit 22* you will be looking at transverse vibrations of violin strings and at the conduction of heat along metal rods. These effects will be modelled by differential equations involving the partial derivatives that you met in *Unit 12*. In the case of the vibrating systems, there are sinusoidal solutions with a range of frequencies corresponding to the normal modes of *Unit 18*. These can be combined to find particular solutions. However, it is not so obvious that solutions to the heat-conduction problem can also be found as sums of sinusoidal terms. This was one of Fourier's many great discoveries.

Fourier realized that by considering series of sinusoidal functions, he could approximate most periodic functions. It is these series that we introduce and explore in this unit. You have already studied the mathematics that you need. Here all we have to do is to draw it together to obtain powerful results.

The traditional approach to Fourier series was fairly analytic. If, however, computers had been generally available, it would have been possible to obtain Fourier series numerically, without any of the analysis contained in this unit. This would have been a great loss to science. Though the mathematical approach is indirect, it reveals properties that would have otherwise remained concealed. In particular, the sizes of successive terms in Fourier series often fit into interesting algebraic patterns. Here we shall attempt to combine the numeric and the algebraic approaches.

In Section 1 we introduce Fourier series. This first involves a discussion of families of periodic functions and their periods, frequencies and fundamental intervals, and of even and odd functions. In Section 2 we find general formulae for the Fourier series of both even and odd functions with any given period. In Section 3 we extend these formulae to deal with functions that are neither even nor odd. Finally, we apply the formulae to functions that are defined on only half the fundamental interval. This is the technique that will be of most use in the next unit. In Section 4 you will explore Fourier series on the computer.

1   Finding Fourier series

In this section we ask: 'what functions can be expressed as Fourier series?' You will see that a requirement is that the function is periodic. You will look at families of periodic functions (cosine functions), and at odd and even functions. For a periodic function, we discuss the period, angular frequency and fundamental interval. Also you will see how to obtain the Fourier series for the saw-tooth and square-wave functions.

1.1   Families of cosine functions

Suppose that we *define* the function $G(t)$ by the following Fourier series (an infinite series of cosine terms):

$$G(t) = \tfrac{1}{2} + \tfrac{4}{\pi^2}\cos t + \tfrac{4}{9\pi^2}\cos 3t + \tfrac{4}{25\pi^2}\cos 5t + \tfrac{4}{49\pi^2}\cos 7t + \cdots. \qquad (1.1)$$

We now investigate some properties of $G(t)$, *without* assuming any connection with the saw-tooth function $g(t)$.

The individual cosine terms in the sum are periodic, so it is not surprising to find that the sum $G(t)$ is also periodic.

*Exercise 1.1 _____

Let $G(t)$ be defined as in Equation (1.1). Find $G(t + 2\pi)$ and $G(t + 2n\pi)$, where n is any integer, in terms of $G(t)$.

_____

You saw in Exercise 1.1 that the function $G(t)$ defined by Equation (1.1) is periodic with period 2π, just like the cosine function $\cos t$. But what of the individual terms in the sum?

Apart from the constant term, they are multiples of

$$\cos t, \quad \cos 3t, \quad \cos 5t, \quad \cos 7t, \quad \dots . \tag{1.2}$$

Exercise 1.2 ────────────────────────────────

What are the angular frequencies and the periods of the functions in sequence (1.2)?

───

Hence we have a family of cosine functions where all the angular frequencies are integer multiples of the smallest angular frequency 1, and whose periods are integer fractions of the *fundamental period* 2π. We have seen that this is the period of the function $G(t)$, since all the component functions will have repeated after this time — some having repeated several times.

More generally (as you may recall from *Unit 7*), any function $f(t)$ is said to be **periodic** if it repeats regularly, i.e. if there is some positive value λ such that, for all t, $f(t + \lambda) = f(t)$. In this case, it is also true that, for all t, $f(t + 2\lambda) = f(t + \lambda) = f(t)$, so 2λ could be taken as a period for $f(t)$ instead of λ and, in general, $r\lambda$ could be taken as the period (where r is any positive integer). The **fundamental period** of such a function is the *smallest* possible (positive) value for the period.

The phrase 'fundamental period' is usually shortened to 'period'.

Example 1.1

Let $f(t) = \cos 4t + 3\cos 6t$. What are the angular frequencies and corresponding periods of the component functions? What is the period of the function $f(t)$?

Solution

The angular frequencies of the component functions are 4 and 6. Their corresponding periods are $\frac{\pi}{2}$ and $\frac{\pi}{3}$, respectively. Hence the period of the combined function $f(t)$ is $\tau = \pi$ (as this is the shortest time that is a multiple of both $\frac{\pi}{2}$ and $\frac{\pi}{3}$). After this time, the first cosine term will have completed two cycles, while the other cosine term will have completed three. ∎

Throughout most of this unit, time is the independent variable of functions, and τ is used to denote the period of a periodic function.

In Section 3, which looks forward to *Unit 22* and the analysis of plucked strings, it will be more natural to consider the period as a length, and there we shall use a period $2L$, which is twice the length of the string.

Example 1.1 suggests that the period of a sum of sinusoidal terms is the least common multiple of the periods of the component functions. This period gives the first time after which *all* the component functions repeat.

Exercise 1.3 ────────────────────────────────

Let $f(t) = 2\cos \pi t + 3\cos \frac{3\pi t}{2} - \cos 2\pi t$. What are the angular frequencies of the component functions and the corresponding periods? What is the period of the function $f(t)$?

───

A Fourier series is an infinite sum of sinusoidal terms, each of which is periodic, so, as has been exemplified above, a Fourier series is also periodic. Hence a sensible restriction on a function that is to be described by a Fourier series is that it should itself be periodic. However, as you have seen above, if you are interested in obtaining Fourier series for a function with period τ, then you must consider not only sinusoidal functions with period τ in the infinite sum, but also sinusoidal functions with fractional periods

$$\frac{\tau}{2}, \frac{\tau}{3}, \frac{\tau}{4}, \frac{\tau}{5}, \dots ,$$

since functions with these periods also repeat after time τ.

Corresponding to the periods $\tau, \frac{\tau}{2}, \frac{\tau}{3}, \frac{\tau}{4}, \frac{\tau}{5}, \ldots$ are the angular frequencies

$$\frac{2\pi}{\tau}, \frac{4\pi}{\tau}, \frac{6\pi}{\tau}, \frac{8\pi}{\tau}, \frac{10\pi}{\tau}, \ldots.$$

So, for example, for a Fourier series of cosine functions, you must consider the family of functions

$$C_r(t) = \cos\left(\frac{2r\pi t}{\tau}\right), \quad \text{where } r \text{ is a positive integer.} \tag{1.3}$$

Since these functions repeat after a time τ, we do not need to draw their graphs for all values of t. We can restrict our attention to any interval of length τ. We shall choose the interval $\left[-\frac{\tau}{2}, \frac{\tau}{2}\right]$ as it has the correct length and is centred on the origin. In general, any interval whose length is the fundamental period can be chosen as the **fundamental interval** for functions of that period. The graph of the function $C_1(t)$ is shown in Figure 1.1.

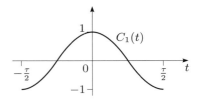

Figure 1.1

Exercise 1.4

Sketch the graphs of the functions $C_2(t)$, $C_3(t)$ and $C_4(t)$ on the fundamental interval $\left[-\frac{\tau}{2}, \frac{\tau}{2}\right]$.

What happens if you try to define $C_0(t)$ using formula (1.3)?

We have now obtained a family of cosine functions that repeat after a time τ, including the constant function $C_0(t) = 1$. (Whatever period τ is chosen, it is trivially true that a constant function repeats after that period.) You will see in Subsection 1.3 how this family can be used to obtain Fourier series. But first, in Subsection 1.2, we need to digress to discuss even and odd functions.

1.2 Even and odd functions

The previous subsection dealt solely with cosine functions, but sine functions are also periodic, so why have we not used them? In fact, there is a distinguishing feature that separates these two families of functions.

Figure 1.2 shows the graphs of a cosine function and a sine function, namely

$$C_1(t) = \cos\left(\frac{2\pi t}{\tau}\right), \quad S_1(t) = \sin\left(\frac{2\pi t}{\tau}\right).$$

They both have period τ and hence the same fundamental interval.

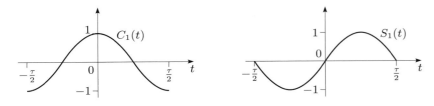

Figure 1.2

Both graphs exhibit symmetry. If you look at the graph of the cosine function $C_1(t)$, then you will see that it takes the same values at corresponding points on either side of the vertical axis. We say that the function is *even*. By contrast, if you look at the graph of the sine function $S_1(t)$, then you will see that the values at corresponding points on either side of the vertical axis have the same magnitude, but opposite signs. We say that the function is *odd*.

11

Definitions

The function $f(t)$ is an **even function** if

$$f(-t) = f(t) \quad \text{for all values of } t;$$

it is an **odd function** if

$$f(-t) = -f(t) \quad \text{for all values of } t.$$

A function need not be either even or odd, as you will see below.

Example 1.2

Suppose that the function $f(t)$ is defined by $f(t) = t^2$. Is this function even or odd?

Solution

Since $f(-t) = (-t)^2 = t^2 = f(t)$ for all t, the function is even. ■

*Exercise 1.5

Suppose that the function $g(t)$ is defined by $g(t) = t^3$. Is this function even or odd?

The graphs of the functions $f(t)$ and $g(t)$ defined in Example 1.2 and Exercise 1.5, and shown in Figure 1.3, should make the definitions clearer.

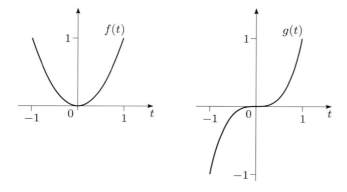

Figure 1.3

For the even function $f(t)$, the same values appear on either side of the vertical axis, so the graph appears to be reflected in this line. For the odd function $g(t)$, the values on either side of the vertical axis have opposite signs, so the graph is rotated through π about the origin.

Polynomial functions where *all* the powers are even are themselves even functions. Polynomial functions where *all* the powers are odd are themselves odd functions. A function need not be either even or odd, but you will see shortly that restricting attention to even and odd functions can reduce the computations needed to construct a Fourier series.

*Exercise 1.6

(a) Is the function $C_0(t)$, given by $C_0(t) = 1$ for all t, either even or odd?

(b) Is the function $h(t)$, defined by $h(t) = t^2 + t^3$, either even or odd?

The way that even and odd functions combine is similar to the way that positive and negative numbers combine. That is:

- the sum of two even functions (positive numbers) is even (positive);
- the sum of two odd functions (negative numbers) is odd (negative);
- the product of two even functions (positive numbers) is even (positive);
- the product of two odd functions (negative numbers) is even (positive);
- the product of an even function (positive number) and and an odd function (negative number) is odd (negative).

The exception to this analogy is the sum of an even function (positive number) and an odd function (negative number), which is neither even nor odd (either positive, negative or zero). In the next example and exercise, we use the first two properties in this list to demonstrate the last two properties.

Example 1.3

If $f(t) = t^3 + 2t^5$ and $g(t) = t - t^3$, show that the function $h(t)$ defined by $h(t) = f(t)g(t)$ is an even function.

Solution

Calculating explicitly,

$$h(t) = f(t)g(t) = (t^3 + 2t^5)(t - t^3) = t^4 - t^6 + 2t^6 - 2t^8 = t^4 + t^6 - 2t^8.$$

This is a polynomial where all the powers are even, therefore $h(t)$ is an even function.

Alternatively, since both $f(t)$ and $g(t)$ are odd functions, we know by definition that

$$f(-t) = -f(t), \quad g(-t) = -g(t).$$

Hence

$$h(-t) = f(-t)g(-t) = (-f(t))(-g(t)) = f(t)g(t) = h(t),$$

so $h(t)$ is an even function. ∎

*Exercise 1.7

If $f(t) = t^3 + 2t^5$ and $g(t) = 3t^2 - t^4$, show that the function $h(t)$ defined by $h(t) = f(t)g(t)$ is an odd function.

For much of this subsection we have been concerned with even and odd functions that are not periodic. If a function $f(t)$ *is* periodic, of period τ, then an advantage of choosing a fundamental interval $\left[-\frac{\tau}{2}, \frac{\tau}{2}\right]$ centred on the origin is that we can tell whether $f(t)$ is even, odd or neither by seeing whether it is even, odd or neither on $\left[-\frac{\tau}{2}, \frac{\tau}{2}\right]$.

> **Even and odd periodic functions**
>
> Let $f(t)$ be periodic of period τ. Then:
>
> $f(t)$ is even provided that it is even when considered as defined only over $\left[-\frac{\tau}{2}, \frac{\tau}{2}\right]$;
>
> $f(t)$ is odd provided that it is odd when considered as defined only over $\left[-\frac{\tau}{2}, \frac{\tau}{2}\right]$.

An important fact about an odd periodic function is that its values must be zero both at the origin and at each end of the fundamental interval. You are asked to prove this in the next exercise.

*Exercise 1.8

Let $f(t)$ be an odd periodic function of period τ with a fundamental interval $\left[-\frac{\tau}{2}, \frac{\tau}{2}\right]$. Show that

$$f\left(-\tfrac{\tau}{2}\right) = f(0) = f\left(\tfrac{\tau}{2}\right) = 0.$$

If you look back at Figures 0.3 and 0.4, you will see that the saw-tooth function and the square-wave function are both even functions. Looking back at Figure 1.2, you will see that the cosine function is even, but the sine function is odd. The suggestion is that, to approximate an even function as a sum of sinusoidal terms, we ought to ensure that the approximate function is even, and the only way to do this is to ensure that only cosine functions appear in the sum. This idea is developed in the next subsection.

1.3 Finding Fourier series for even functions with period 2π

In Subsections 1.1 and 1.2 you saw that there are certain useful things that can be said about series (1.1), namely that it is periodic of period 2π and that it is an even function. But this does not tell us why this particular series corresponds to the saw-tooth function $g(t)$ on page 7. In this subsection we find the Fourier series for the saw-tooth function $g(t)$ by a mathematical argument. Then we ask you to do the same for the square-wave function.

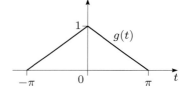

The graph of $g(t)$ (see Figure 1.4) coincides with the line $g(t) = \frac{t}{\pi} + 1$ in the range $-\pi \leq t \leq 0$ and with the line $g(t) = -\frac{t}{\pi} + 1$ in the range $0 \leq t \leq \pi$. The interval $[-\pi, \pi]$ is a fundamental interval for $g(t)$, on which it is defined as

$$g(t) = \begin{cases} \frac{t}{\pi} + 1 & \text{if } -\pi \leq t \leq 0, \\ -\frac{t}{\pi} + 1 & \text{if } 0 < t \leq \pi. \end{cases} \tag{1.4}$$

Figure 1.4

*Exercise 1.9

What are the period and angular frequency of the saw-tooth function $g(t)$?

You saw at the end of Subsection 1.2 that to write $g(t)$ as an infinite sum of sinusoidal terms, we need consider only cosine functions. You saw in Subsection 1.1 that a suitable family of cosine functions is given by formula (1.3). From the solution to Exercise 1.9, the value of τ in this family needs to be 2π. Hence a suitable family of sinusoidal functions for the saw-tooth function $g(t)$ is $\{C_0(t), C_1(t), C_2(t), \ldots\}$ defined by

$$C_r(t) = \cos rt \quad (r = 0, 1, 2, \ldots).$$

We now consider a series

$$G(t) = A_0 C_0(t) + A_1 C_1(t) + A_2 C_2(t) + A_3 C_3(t) + \cdots$$

$$= A_0 + \sum_{r=1}^{\infty} A_r \cos rt, \tag{1.5}$$

and ask: 'how can the coefficients A_r be chosen so that, as we add successive terms of the series to obtain the approximations $G_0(t), G_1(t), G_2(t), G_3(t), \ldots$, the values approach $g(t)$ for any chosen value of t?' That is, how can A_r be chosen so that $G(t) = g(t)$ for all t?

The argument that we are going to use is quite general, in that it works for *any* even function with fundamental interval $[-\pi, \pi]$. Thus, for the remainder of this section, we shall use the symbol $f(t)$ to refer to a general such function, and

$$F(t) = A_0 + \sum_{r=1}^{\infty} A_r \cos rt \qquad (1.6)$$

for the corresponding series whose coefficients $A_0, A_1, A_2, \ldots$ we are trying to find. We shall then apply the general argument to the saw-tooth function (in Examples 1.4–1.6), and ask you to apply it to other functions, including the square-wave function (in Exercises 1.11, 1.13 and 1.14).

The easiest coefficient to find is A_0. The technique is based on the observation that all the functions $C_r(t)$, some of which are illustrated in Figure 1.1 and the solution to Exercise 1.4, oscillate, and the positive contributions to the integral exactly cancel out the negative contributions. This means that if you integrate the cosine functions over the fundamental interval $[-\pi, \pi]$, then you obtain 0; that is,

$$\int_{-\pi}^{\pi} \cos rt \, dt = 0 \quad (r = 1, 2, 3, \ldots). \qquad (1.7)$$

Exercise 1.10

Verify that the integral in formula (1.7) is zero (for each $r = 1, 2, 3, \ldots$).

If we integrate both sides of Equation (1.6) term by term over the fundamental interval $[-\pi, \pi]$, then we find that

$$\int_{-\pi}^{\pi} F(t) \, dt = \int_{-\pi}^{\pi} \left(A_0 + \sum_{r=1}^{\infty} A_r \cos rt \right) dt$$

$$= \int_{-\pi}^{\pi} A_0 \, dt + \sum_{r=1}^{\infty} A_r \int_{-\pi}^{\pi} \cos rt \, dt.$$

In this course we assume the validity of term-by-term integration and differentiation of infinite series. The process is valid in all the practical cases that concern us.

Now all the terms involving integrals of cosine functions vanish, by formulae (1.7), leaving us with

$$\int_{-\pi}^{\pi} F(t) \, dt = \int_{-\pi}^{\pi} A_0 \, dt = 2\pi A_0 \quad \text{(since } A_0 \text{ is a constant).}$$

Hence

$$A_0 = \frac{1}{2\pi} \int_{-\pi}^{\pi} F(t) \, dt. \qquad (1.8)$$

The function $f(t)$ is assumed to be even, so $F(t)$ is also even, and the integral between $-\pi$ and 0 is the same as the integral between 0 and π. Hence

$$A_0 = \frac{1}{\pi} \int_{0}^{\pi} F(t) \, dt. \qquad (1.9)$$

The computer deals with formulae (1.8) and (1.9) equally easily. In Section 4 and the next unit, you will see examples of functions with simple formulae for positive values of t, for which formula (1.9) is preferable.

We do not know the coefficients of $F(t)$, but our aim is to ensure that $F(t) = f(t)$.

So to determine A_0, we replace $F(t)$ by $f(t)$ in formula (1.9) (or in (1.8)), to obtain

$$A_0 = \tfrac{1}{\pi} \int_0^\pi f(t)\, dt. \tag{1.10}$$

You can think of A_0 as the average value taken by the function $f(t)$.

Example 1.4

Find the value of A_0 when the general function $f(t)$ is replaced by the saw-tooth function $g(t)$.

Solution

Equation (1.10) becomes

$$A_0 = \tfrac{1}{\pi} \int_0^\pi g(t)\, dt.$$

The function $g(t)$ is given by Equation (1.4), so the above integral is

$$\tfrac{1}{\pi} \int_0^\pi g(t)\, dt = \tfrac{1}{\pi} \int_0^\pi \left(-\tfrac{t}{\pi} + 1\right) dt = \tfrac{1}{\pi} \left[-\tfrac{t^2}{2\pi} + t\right]_0^\pi = \tfrac{1}{2}.$$

Thus, for the case of the saw-tooth function,

$$A_0 = \tfrac{1}{2}. \quad \blacksquare$$

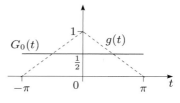

$G_0(t)$ $g(t)$

Figure 1.5

Figure 1.5 shows the graph of the original function $g(t)$ and this first approximation $G_0(t) = A_0 = \tfrac{1}{2}$. You can see from the figure that $A_0 = \tfrac{1}{2}$ is the average value of the function $g(t)$.

---

*Exercise 1.11

(a) Suppose that the general function $f(t)$ is now replaced by the square-wave function $h(t)$ of the Introduction, which can be defined on the fundamental interval $[-\pi, \pi]$ by

$$h(t) = \begin{cases} 1 & \text{if } -\tfrac{\pi}{2} \le t \le \tfrac{\pi}{2}, \\ 0 & \text{otherwise.} \end{cases}$$

Find the value of the Fourier series coefficient A_0.

(b) Now find the value of A_0 for the square-wave function $w(t)$ defined on the fundamental interval $[-\pi, \pi]$ by

$$w(t) = \begin{cases} 1 & \text{if } -\tfrac{\pi}{2} \le t \le \tfrac{\pi}{2}, \\ -\tfrac{1}{2} & \text{otherwise.} \end{cases}$$

So integration has enabled us to eliminate the coefficients A_n ($n > 0$) and hence to find the coefficient A_0. To find the next coefficient, A_1, we must somehow eliminate A_0 and all the other coefficients. The technique is to multiply both sides of Equation (1.6) by the term $\cos t$ to give

$$F(t)\cos t = A_0 \cos t + \sum_{r=1}^{\infty} A_r \cos rt \, \cos t. \tag{1.11}$$

If we integrate both sides of Equation (1.11) term by term over the fundamental interval $[-\pi, \pi]$, then we find that

$$\int_{-\pi}^{\pi} F(t)\cos t \, dt = \int_{-\pi}^{\pi} A_0 \cos t \, dt + \sum_{r=1}^{\infty} A_r \int_{-\pi}^{\pi} \cos rt \, \cos t \, dt. \tag{1.12}$$

Now we evaluate each of these integrals separately.

Exercise 1.12

(a) Using the trigonometric identity

$$\cos rt \,\cos t = \tfrac{1}{2}\left(\cos(r+1)t + \cos(r-1)t\right),$$

show that

$$\int_{-\pi}^{\pi} \cos 2t \,\cos t \,dt = 0.$$

(b) More generally, use the identity given in part (a) to show that

$$\int_{-\pi}^{\pi} \cos rt \,\cos t \,dt = 0 \quad \text{when } r \text{ is an integer and } r > 1.$$

(c) Using the trigonometric identity

$$\cos^2 t = \tfrac{1}{2}(\cos 2t + 1),$$

evaluate the integral

$$\int_{-\pi}^{\pi} \cos^2 t \,dt.$$

The trigonometric identities used in this exercise are based on more general versions in the Handbook.

Exercise 1.12 shows that most of the integrals on the right-hand side of Equation (1.12) evaluate to zero. The only remaining term involves the coefficient A_1, and we are left with

$$\int_{-\pi}^{\pi} F(t) \cos t \,dt = A_1 \int_{-\pi}^{\pi} \cos^2 t \,dt = A_1 \pi.$$

Hence the coefficient A_1 is given by

$$A_1 = \tfrac{1}{\pi} \int_{-\pi}^{\pi} F(t) \cos t \,dt.$$

Since the functions $F(t)$ and $\cos t$ are both even, with symmetry about the y-axis, we can simplify this to

$$A_1 = \tfrac{2}{\pi} \int_{0}^{\pi} F(t) \cos t \,dt.$$

We are trying to choose the coefficients so that $F(t) = f(t)$, so we replace $F(t)$ by $f(t)$ and obtain

$$A_1 = \tfrac{2}{\pi} \int_{0}^{\pi} f(t) \cos t \,dt. \tag{1.13}$$

Example 1.5

Returning to the saw-tooth function $g(t)$ defined by Equation (1.4), find the value of the coefficient A_1.

Solution

Substituting the definition of $g(t)$ from Equation (1.4) into Equation (1.13) and using integration by parts, we obtain

$$A_1 = \tfrac{2}{\pi} \int_{0}^{\pi} \left(-\tfrac{t}{\pi} + 1\right) \cos t \,dt$$

$$= \tfrac{2}{\pi} \left(\left[\left(-\tfrac{t}{\pi} + 1\right) \sin t\right]_0^\pi - \int_0^\pi \left(-\tfrac{1}{\pi}\right) \sin t \,dt \right)$$

$$= \tfrac{2}{\pi} \left((0 - 0) + \tfrac{1}{\pi}[-\cos t]_0^\pi \right)$$

$$= \tfrac{2}{\pi^2}(1 - (-1)) = \tfrac{4}{\pi^2}. \quad \blacksquare$$

So our second approximation to the function $g(t)$ (our first non-constant approximation) is

$$G_1(t) = \tfrac{1}{2} + \tfrac{4}{\pi^2} \cos t.$$

The graph of this approximation is compared with the graph of $g(t)$ in Figure 1.6. Already it is quite a reasonable approximation.

The scale of Figure 1.6 has been enlarged over that of Figures 1.4 and 1.5 in order to help distinguish $g(t)$ from $G_1(t)$.

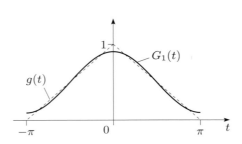

Figure 1.6

Exercise 1.13 _____

Suppose that $f(t)$ in Equation (1.13) is replaced by the square-wave function $h(t)$ of the Introduction, defined in Exercise 1.11(a). Find the value of the coefficient A_1.

1.4   Finding the general coefficients

We can continue in this way to find each of the coefficients A_r. Along the way to constructing the Fourier series, we find a sequence of functions that gives a better and better approximation to our even periodic function f. We have to evaluate many integrals, but, like those in Exercise 1.12, most vanish. Generalizing the results of that exercise, we find the following.

If f has discontinuities (for example, if it is a square-wave function), then we have to be careful about what is meant by a 'better and better approximation'. This point will be discussed further in Subsection 1.5.

Trigonometric integrals over the interval $[-\pi, \pi]$

For any positive integers r and n,

$$\int_{-\pi}^{\pi} \cos nt \, dt = 0, \tag{1.14}$$

$$\int_{-\pi}^{\pi} \cos rt \cos nt \, dt = 0 \quad (r \neq n), \tag{1.15}$$

$$\int_{-\pi}^{\pi} \cos^2 nt \, dt = \pi. \tag{1.16}$$

These results mean that if we multiply both sides of Equation (1.6) by $\cos nt$ and integrate over the fundamental interval, then all of the coefficients except A_n disappear. To see this, multiply both sides of Equation (1.6) by $\cos nt$, to obtain

$$F(t) \cos nt = A_0 \cos nt + \sum_{r=1}^{\infty} A_r \cos rt \cos nt.$$

Then integration gives

$$\int_{-\pi}^{\pi} F(t) \cos nt \, dt = \int_{-\pi}^{\pi} A_0 \cos nt \, dt + \sum_{r=1}^{\infty} A_r \int_{-\pi}^{\pi} \cos rt \cos nt \, dt,$$

and using formulae (1.14) and (1.15) gives

$$\int_{-\pi}^{\pi} F(t) \cos nt \, dt = A_n \int_{-\pi}^{\pi} \cos^2 nt \, dt.$$

Finally, formula (1.16) gives the value of the right-hand integral as π, so

$$A_n = \tfrac{1}{\pi} \int_{-\pi}^{\pi} F(t) \cos nt \, dt.$$

Since we are assuming that $f(t)$ (and hence $F(t)$) is even, and we know that $\cos nt$ is even, their product is also even. So we can simplify this integral to

$$A_n = \tfrac{2}{\pi} \int_{0}^{\pi} F(t) \cos nt \, dt.$$

We are trying to choose the coefficients so that $F(t) = f(t)$, so we replace $F(t)$ by $f(t)$ and we have

$$A_n = \tfrac{2}{\pi} \int_{0}^{\pi} f(t) \cos nt \, dt. \tag{1.17}$$

Example 1.6

Returning once again to the saw-tooth function $g(t)$ as defined by Equation (1.4), find the values of the coefficients A_2 and A_3.

Solution

Substituting the definition of $g(t)$ from Equation (1.4) into formula (1.17), and using integration by parts, we obtain

$$
\begin{aligned}
A_n &= \tfrac{2}{\pi} \int_{0}^{\pi} \left(-\tfrac{t}{\pi} + 1\right) \cos nt \, dt \\
&= \tfrac{2}{\pi} \left(\left[\left(-\tfrac{t}{\pi} + 1\right)\left(\tfrac{1}{n} \sin nt\right)\right]_0^{\pi} - \int_0^{\pi} \left(-\tfrac{1}{\pi}\right)\left(\tfrac{1}{n} \sin nt\right) dt \right) \\
&= \tfrac{2}{\pi} \left(0 + \tfrac{1}{\pi n^2}(1 - \cos n\pi) \right).
\end{aligned}
$$

If $n = 2$, $\cos n\pi = 1$, so $A_2 = 0$. If $n = 3$, $\cos n\pi = -1$, so $A_3 = \tfrac{4}{9\pi^2}$. ■

Hence, from Examples 1.4, 1.5 and 1.6, a better approximation to $g(t)$ is

Since $A_2 = 0$, $G_2(t) = G_1(t)$.

$$
\begin{aligned}
G_3(t) &= A_0 + A_1 \cos t + A_2 \cos 2t + A_3 \cos 3t \\
&= \tfrac{1}{2} + \tfrac{4}{\pi^2} \left(\cos t + \tfrac{1}{9} \cos 3t\right).
\end{aligned}
$$

The graph of $G_3(t)$ is shown in Figure 1.7(a) to the same scale as Figure 1.6. Figure 1.7(b) shows the graph of $G_3(t)$ superimposed on that of $g(t)$.

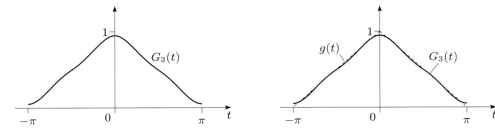

Figure 1.7

This shows a further improvement in the accuracy of the approximation, to the extent that it is hard to see a difference between the graphs of $G_3(t)$ and $g(t)$.

*Exercise 1.14 ──────────────────────────────

Suppose that $f(t)$ in formula (1.17) is replaced by the square-wave function $h(t)$, defined in Exercise 1.11(a). Find the values of the coefficients A_2 and A_3.

───

Examples 1.4, 1.5 and 1.6 can be generalized to find all the coefficients in the Fourier series for the saw-tooth function $g(t)$. We find that

$$A_0 = \tfrac{1}{2}, \quad A_1 = \tfrac{4}{\pi^2}, \quad A_2 = 0, \quad A_3 = \tfrac{4}{\pi^2} \times \tfrac{1}{9}, \quad A_4 = 0,$$
$$A_5 = \tfrac{4}{\pi^2} \times \tfrac{1}{25}, \quad A_6 = 0, \quad A_7 = \tfrac{4}{\pi^2} \times \tfrac{1}{49}, \quad A_8 = 0, \quad \ldots,$$

and a clear pattern has appeared. Hence the Fourier series for the saw-tooth function $g(t)$ is

$$G(t) = \tfrac{1}{2} + \tfrac{4}{\pi^2}\left(\cos t + \tfrac{1}{9}\cos 3t + \tfrac{1}{25}\cos 5t + \tfrac{1}{49}\cos 7t + \cdots\right),$$

confirming Equation (0.2). Notice that this Fourier series can be written equivalently as

$$G(t) = \frac{1}{2} + \frac{4}{\pi^2}\sum_{s=1}^{\infty} \frac{1}{(2s-1)^2}\cos(2s-1)t.$$

It is sometimes more convenient to write Fourier series in so-called **closed form** like this, using the summation symbol $\sum$.

Exercise 1.15 ──────────────────────────────

You have found, in Exercises 1.11(a), 1.13 and 1.14, the Fourier coefficients A_0, A_1, A_2 and A_3 for the square-wave function $h(t)$, defined in Exercise 1.11(a). In fact, as indicated in Equation (0.2), its Fourier series is

$$H(t) = \tfrac{1}{2} + \tfrac{2}{\pi}\cos t - \tfrac{2}{3\pi}\cos 3t + \tfrac{2}{5\pi}\cos 5t - \tfrac{2}{7\pi}\cos 7t + \cdots.$$

Write down this series in closed form.

───

┌───┐

Procedure 1.1   Fourier series

Given an even periodic function $f(t)$ with period 2π (and fundamental interval $[-\pi, \pi]$), its Fourier series

$$F(t) = A_0 + \sum_{r=1}^{\infty} A_r \cos rt$$

is found by using the formulae

$$A_0 = \tfrac{1}{\pi}\int_0^{\pi} f(t)\,dt, \quad A_r = \tfrac{2}{\pi}\int_0^{\pi} f(t)\cos rt\,dt \quad (r = 1, 2, \ldots).$$

└───┘

1.5 Further remarks on Fourier series

You have just tackled a substantial piece of work, and this has involved finding the Fourier series for several even functions. Having found them, you need to take stock of what you have done.

Using the computer, you could have integrated numerically and found values for the coefficients directly. However, obtaining the Fourier series algebraically shows that there is a simple underlying pattern. Such patterns have proved very important.

You have seen that just a few terms of the Fourier series for the saw-tooth function $g(t)$ give a very good approximation. However, the first few terms of the Fourier series for the square-wave function $h(t)$ do not give a particularly good approximation, as Figure 1.8 illustrates.

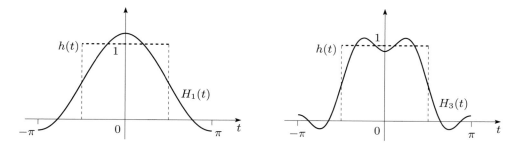

Figure 1.8

The situation improves only slowly for the square-wave function. Plotting the graphs for the sums as far as the $\cos 7t$, $\cos 11t$ and $\cos 21t$ terms, better approximations to $h(t)$ are obtained, as expected (see Figure 1.9).

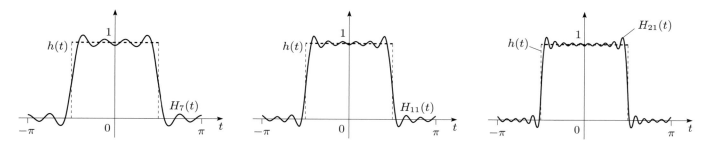

Figure 1.9

However, even $H_{21}(t)$ does not approximate $h(t)$ as well as $G_3(t)$ does $g(t)$. This is because of the discontinuities in $h(t)$. We cannot reasonably expect the sum of continuous sinusoidal functions to provide a good approximation to a discontinuous function. From the graphs you can see that the approximations to $h(t)$ are worse near the discontinuities, i.e. near the points where the value of $h(t)$ jumps from 0 to 1 and back again. Nevertheless, even for a discontinuous function such as $h(t)$, we can, remarkably, approximate reasonably well using Fourier series. At a discontinuity, the Fourier series takes the average value of the function at either side of the discontinuity.

There is a theorem (which we shall not prove) that guarantees the nature of the Fourier series for a wide class of functions.

Theorem 1.1

If, on the interval $[-\pi, \pi]$, the function f has a continuous derivative except at a finite number of points, then at each point $x_0 \in [-\pi, \pi]$ the Fourier series of f converges to

$$\tfrac{1}{2}\left(f(x_0^+) + f(x_0^-)\right).$$

Here $f(x_0^+)$ is the limit of $f(x)$ as x approaches x_0 from above, and $f(x_0^-)$ is the limit of $f(x)$ as x approaches x_0 from below. If f is continuous at x_0, then $f(x_0^-) = f(x_0^+) = f(x_0)$ and the Fourier series converges to $f(x_0)$.

End-of-section Exercises

Exercise 1.16

If $f(t)$ and $g(t)$ are both odd functions, show that the function $k(t)$ defined by

$$k(t) = f(t) + g(t)$$

is also an odd function.

Exercise 1.17

Find the Fourier series for the even periodic function $f(t)$ defined on the fundamental interval $[-\pi, \pi]$ by

$$f(t) = t^2.$$

(*Hint*: Symbolic evaluation using the computer algebra package for the course gives

$$\int_0^\theta t^2 \cos nt \, dt = \frac{1}{n^3} \left((n^2\theta^2 - 2) \sin n\theta + 2n\theta \cos n\theta \right).)$$

Exercise 1.18

A variant of the saw-tooth function can be defined on the fundamental interval $[-\pi, \pi]$ by

$$w(t) = |t|.$$

Find the Fourier series for this function.

2 Fourier series for even and odd functions

In the last section we concentrated on finding the Fourier series for two particular even periodic functions with period $\tau = 2\pi$ and hence fundamental interval $[-\pi, \pi]$. In this section we extend the technique to periodic functions that are either even or odd and have any fixed period τ.

2.1 Fourier series for even functions with period τ

We shall now examine the function $w(t)$ described in Exercise 1.18. If its graph is repeated along the t-axis, then it looks like a saw-tooth function (see Figure 2.1).

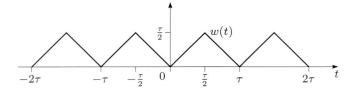

Figure 2.1

If the function is defined to have period τ (rather than 2π, as in Exercise 1.18), then a fundamental interval is $[-\frac{\tau}{2}, \frac{\tau}{2}]$. Restricting attention to this interval, the graph of the function is as shown in Figure 2.2.

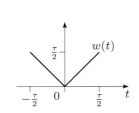

Figure 2.2

On this interval the function is given by $w(t) = |t|$ or

$$w(t) = \begin{cases} -t & \text{if } -\frac{\tau}{2} \leq t \leq 0, \\ t & \text{if } 0 < t \leq \frac{\tau}{2}. \end{cases} \tag{2.1}$$

You saw in Subsection 1.1 that, when we are trying to find a Fourier series for a function with period τ, we must also consider functions with the shorter periods

$$\frac{\tau}{2}, \frac{\tau}{3}, \frac{\tau}{4}, \frac{\tau}{5}, \ldots.$$

Corresponding to the fundamental period τ and to these shorter periods are the angular frequencies

$$\frac{2\pi}{\tau}, \frac{4\pi}{\tau}, \frac{6\pi}{\tau}, \frac{8\pi}{\tau}, \frac{10\pi}{\tau}, \ldots.$$

Hence we consider the family of even functions

$$C_r(t) = \cos\left(\frac{2r\pi t}{\tau}\right) \quad (r = 1, 2, 3, \ldots).$$

Since we are dealing with even functions, we also include the constant function

$$C_0(t) = 1.$$

As in Section 1, the argument used here is a general one. Thus, for the remainder of Subsection 2.1, we use the symbol $f(t)$ to refer to a general even periodic function with fundamental interval $\left[-\frac{\tau}{2}, \frac{\tau}{2}\right]$. As before, we assume that we can choose the coefficients in an infinite sum of these functions $C_r(t)$ in such a way that we can approximate the original function as accurately as required. We write this (as before) as

$$F(t) = A_0 + \sum_{r=1}^{\infty} A_r \cos\left(\frac{2r\pi t}{\tau}\right). \tag{2.2}$$

To find the coefficients in this sum, we need evaluated integrals of the cosine functions that generalize Equations (1.14)–(1.16) used in the last section. The integrals in which we are interested are for functions defined over the fundamental interval $\left[-\frac{\tau}{2}, \frac{\tau}{2}\right]$.

Trigonometric integrals over the interval $\left[-\frac{\tau}{2}, \frac{\tau}{2}\right]$

For any positive integers r and n,

$$\int_{-\tau/2}^{\tau/2} \cos\left(\frac{2n\pi t}{\tau}\right) dt = 0, \tag{2.3}$$

$$\int_{-\tau/2}^{\tau/2} \cos\left(\frac{2r\pi t}{\tau}\right) \cos\left(\frac{2n\pi t}{\tau}\right) dt = 0 \quad (r \neq n), \tag{2.4}$$

$$\int_{-\tau/2}^{\tau/2} \cos^2\left(\frac{2n\pi t}{\tau}\right) dt = \frac{\tau}{2}. \tag{2.5}$$

To find the coefficients in Fourier series (2.2), we proceed as before. We first multiply both sides of Equation (2.2) by a chosen cosine function. Then we integrate, and all but one of the coefficients become zero. We are left with a formula for that remaining coefficient.

First, to find the constant A_0, we integrate both sides of Equation (2.2) over the fundamental interval $[-\frac{\tau}{2}, \frac{\tau}{2}]$ to obtain

$$\int_{-\tau/2}^{\tau/2} F(t)\,dt = \int_{-\tau/2}^{\tau/2} A_0\,dt + \sum_{r=1}^{\infty} A_r \int_{-\tau/2}^{\tau/2} \cos\left(\frac{2r\pi t}{\tau}\right) dt.$$

Using formula (2.3), all the integrals in the infinite sum become zero, leaving

$$\int_{-\tau/2}^{\tau/2} F(t)\,dt = \int_{-\tau/2}^{\tau/2} A_0\,dt = \tau A_0,$$

so

$$A_0 = \tfrac{1}{\tau} \int_{-\tau/2}^{\tau/2} F(t)\,dt.$$

As in Section 1, we now use the fact that we wish to choose the coefficients so that $F(t) = f(t)$. Thus we put $F(t) = f(t)$ to give

$$A_0 = \tfrac{1}{\tau} \int_{-\tau/2}^{\tau/2} f(t)\,dt. \tag{2.6}$$

The constant A_0 can again be thought of as the average value of the function $f(t)$ on the fundamental interval.

Since the function $f(t)$ is even, the integral between $-\frac{\tau}{2}$ and 0 is the same as the integral between 0 and $\frac{\tau}{2}$. Hence

$$A_0 = \tfrac{2}{\tau} \int_{0}^{\tau/2} f(t)\,dt. \tag{2.7}$$

To find the remaining coefficients A_n in the Fourier series, we multiply each side of Equation (2.2) by the function $\cos(2n\pi t/\tau)$, and again integrate over the fundamental interval, to obtain

$$\int_{-\tau/2}^{\tau/2} F(t) \cos\left(\frac{2n\pi t}{\tau}\right) dt$$

$$= \int_{-\tau/2}^{\tau/2} A_0 \cos\left(\frac{2n\pi t}{\tau}\right) dt + \sum_{r=1}^{\infty} A_r \int_{-\tau/2}^{\tau/2} \cos\left(\frac{2r\pi t}{\tau}\right) \cos\left(\frac{2n\pi t}{\tau}\right) dt.$$

Using formulae (2.3) and (2.4), all the integrals on the right-hand side become zero except the one where $r = n$, and the equality reduces to

$$\int_{-\tau/2}^{\tau/2} F(t) \cos\left(\frac{2n\pi t}{\tau}\right) dt = A_n \int_{-\tau/2}^{\tau/2} \cos^2\left(\frac{2n\pi t}{\tau}\right) dt = \tfrac{\tau}{2} A_n,$$

where the last equality follows from formula (2.5).

Hence, in order to choose the coefficients to ensure that $F(t) = f(t)$, the coefficient A_n is given by

$$A_n = \tfrac{2}{\tau} \int_{-\tau/2}^{\tau/2} f(t) \cos\left(\frac{2n\pi t}{\tau}\right) dt. \tag{2.8}$$

Again, since the functions $f(t)$ and $\cos(2n\pi t/\tau)$ are both even, their product is even, so we can simplify this formula to

$$A_n = \tfrac{4}{\tau} \int_{0}^{\tau/2} f(t) \cos\left(\frac{2n\pi t}{\tau}\right) dt. \tag{2.9}$$

*Exercise 2.1 _____

For the saw-tooth function $w(t)$ defined by Equation (2.1), find the coefficients A_0 and A_n.

_____

Substituting the coefficients that you have found in Exercise 2.1 into Equation (2.2) gives the Fourier series $W(t)$ corresponding to the saw-tooth function $w(t)$:

$$
\begin{aligned}
W(t) &= \frac{\tau}{4} - \frac{2\tau}{\pi^2} \sum_{s=1}^{\infty} \frac{1}{(2s-1)^2} \cos\left(\frac{2(2s-1)\pi t}{\tau}\right) \\
&= \frac{\tau}{4} - \frac{2\tau}{\pi^2}\left(\cos\left(\frac{2\pi t}{\tau}\right) + \frac{1}{9}\cos\left(\frac{6\pi t}{\tau}\right)\right. \\
&\quad \left. + \frac{1}{25}\cos\left(\frac{10\pi t}{\tau}\right) + \cdots\right).
\end{aligned}
\tag{2.10}
$$

Since $w(t)$ is very similar in form to the saw-tooth function we investigated in Section 1, it should come as no surprise that the successive approximations to $w(t)$ generated by series (2.10) converge rapidly to $w(t)$. Figure 2.3 compares the graph of $w(t)$ with the graphs of the approximations $W_0(t) = \frac{\tau}{4}$ and $W_1(t) = \frac{\tau}{4} - \frac{2\tau}{\pi^2}\cos\left(\frac{2\pi t}{\tau}\right)$.

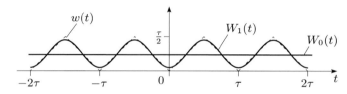

Figure 2.3

2.2   Fourier series for odd functions with period τ

We have so far concentrated on even periodic functions, but it is equally straightforward to deal with odd periodic functions. As an example of an odd periodic function, consider the function $v(t)$ whose graph is shown in Figure 2.4. You can think of $v(t)$ as representing another type of saw-tooth function, or as a broken surface made up of successive ramps and steps.

The definitions of even and odd periodic functions are given on page 13.

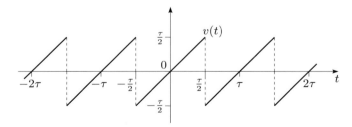

Figure 2.4

We have taken the function to have period τ, and hence it has a fundamental interval $[-\frac{\tau}{2}, \frac{\tau}{2}]$. Strictly speaking, the function $v(t)$ must specifically be defined to be 0 at the endpoints of the fundamental interval, as required for an odd periodic function (you verified this in Exercise 1.8). So, strictly speaking, we ought to define $v(t)$ on $[-\frac{\tau}{2}, \frac{\tau}{2}]$ as

$$
v(t) = \begin{cases} t & \text{if } -\frac{\tau}{2} < t < \frac{\tau}{2}, \\ 0 & \text{if } t = -\frac{\tau}{2} \text{ or } \frac{\tau}{2}. \end{cases}
\tag{2.11}
$$

However, when obtaining Fourier series for a discontinuous function, it is not necessary to define precisely the value the function takes at a discontinuity, since the value of a function at a single point will have no effect on the values of the integrals used to determine the coefficients in the Fourier series. As you saw for the square-wave function (in Section 1), at a discontinuity the Fourier series takes the average of the values either side of the discontinuity. This means that for our ramp function $v(t)$, we can simplify its specification on the fundamental interval $\left[-\frac{\tau}{2}, \frac{\tau}{2}\right]$ to

$$v(t) = t. \tag{2.12}$$

Its graph is shown in Figure 2.5.

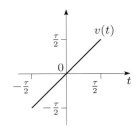

Figure 2.5

When dealing with even functions with period τ, you saw in the previous subsection that we could express their Fourier series in terms of the family of even functions

$$C_r(t) = \cos\left(\frac{2r\pi t}{\tau}\right) \quad (r = 1, 2, 3, \ldots).$$

In the case of odd functions, there is a similar family

$$S_r(t) = \sin\left(\frac{2r\pi t}{\tau}\right) \quad (r = 1, 2, 3, \ldots).$$

*Exercise 2.2

Show that the function

$$S_r(t) = \sin\left(\frac{2r\pi t}{\tau}\right)$$

is an odd function.

To approximate the ramp function $v(t)$ given by Equation (2.11), we need odd trigonometric functions with period τ. As usual, we must consider functions with periods

$$\tau, \quad \frac{\tau}{2}, \quad \frac{\tau}{3}, \quad \frac{\tau}{4}, \quad \frac{\tau}{5}, \quad \ldots.$$

Corresponding to these periods are the angular frequencies

$$\frac{2\pi}{\tau}, \quad \frac{4\pi}{\tau}, \quad \frac{6\pi}{\tau}, \quad \frac{8\pi}{\tau}, \quad \frac{10\pi}{\tau}, \quad \ldots.$$

So we must consider the family of sine functions

$$S_r(t) = \sin\left(\frac{2r\pi t}{\tau}\right) \quad (r = 1, 2, 3, \ldots),$$

which you have just verified (in Exercise 2.2) are all odd.

In contrast to Subsection 1.1 where we considered the cosine series, we do not bother with the function $S_0(t) = \sin 0 = 0$, since any multiple of this function is zero.

Example 2.1

Sketch the graphs of the functions $S_1(t)$, $S_2(t)$, $S_3(t)$ and $S_4(t)$ on the fundamental interval $\left[-\frac{\tau}{2}, \frac{\tau}{2}\right]$.

Solution

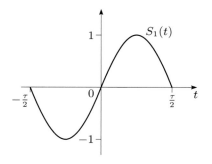
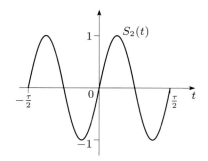
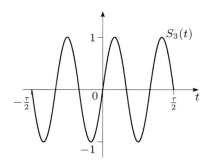
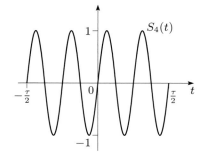

Figure 2.6

∎

As before, the argument used to find the coefficients in a Fourier series for an odd function is a general one. Thus, for the remainder of Subsection 2.2, we use the function $f(t)$ to refer to a general odd periodic function with fundamental interval $\left[-\frac{\tau}{2}, \frac{\tau}{2}\right]$. Then we assume that we can choose the coefficients in an infinite sum of these functions $S_r(t)$ in such a way that we can approximate the original function $f(t)$ as accurately as required. We write the sum as

$$F(t) = \sum_{r=1}^{\infty} B_n \sin\left(\frac{2r\pi t}{\tau}\right), \tag{2.13}$$

where the coefficients $B_1, B_2, B_3, \ldots$ are constants depending on the particular function $f(t)$. We shall refer to Equation (2.13) as the Fourier series for the odd function $f(t)$.

Now that we are dealing with odd functions, there is no constant term because $S_0(t) = 0$.

To find the coefficients B_n, we multiply both sides of Equation (2.13) by the function $\sin(2n\pi t/\tau)$ and integrate over the fundamental interval to give

$$\int_{-\tau/2}^{\tau/2} F(t) \sin\left(\frac{2n\pi t}{\tau}\right) dt$$

$$= \sum_{r=1}^{\infty} B_r \int_{-\tau/2}^{\tau/2} \sin\left(\frac{2r\pi t}{\tau}\right) \sin\left(\frac{2n\pi t}{\tau}\right) dt. \tag{2.14}$$

To simplify Equation (2.14), we need evaluated integrals of sine functions analogous to those for the cosine functions in Subsection 2.1.

Trigonometric integrals over the interval $\left[-\frac{\tau}{2}, \frac{\tau}{2}\right]$

For any positive integers r and n,

$$\int_{-\tau/2}^{\tau/2} \sin\left(\frac{2n\pi t}{\tau}\right) dt = 0, \tag{2.15}$$

$$\int_{-\tau/2}^{\tau/2} \sin\left(\frac{2r\pi t}{\tau}\right) \sin\left(\frac{2n\pi t}{\tau}\right) dt = 0 \quad (r \neq n), \tag{2.16}$$

$$\int_{-\tau/2}^{\tau/2} \sin^2\left(\frac{2n\pi t}{\tau}\right) dt = \frac{\tau}{2}. \tag{2.17}$$

Using formula (2.16), all the integrals on the right-hand side of Equation (2.14) become zero except when $r = n$. That is,

$$\int_{-\tau/2}^{\tau/2} F(t) \sin\left(\frac{2n\pi t}{\tau}\right) dt = B_n \int_{-\tau/2}^{\tau/2} \sin^2\left(\frac{2n\pi t}{\tau}\right) dt.$$

Using formula (2.17), this reduces to $\frac{\tau}{2} B_n$. Yet again, we are choosing the coefficients to make $F(t) = f(t)$, so B_n must be given by

$$B_n = \frac{2}{\tau} \int_{-\tau/2}^{\tau/2} f(t) \sin\left(\frac{2n\pi t}{\tau}\right) dt. \tag{2.18}$$

Since the functions $f(t)$ and $\sin(2n\pi t/\tau)$ are both odd, their product is even and therefore takes the same values on opposite sides of the origin. Hence we can simplify this formula to

$$B_n = \frac{4}{\tau} \int_{0}^{\tau/2} f(t) \sin\left(\frac{2n\pi t}{\tau}\right) dt. \tag{2.19}$$

Example 2.2

(a) Find the coefficients B_1, B_2 and B_3 for the function $v(t)$ defined in Equation (2.12).

(b) Sketch the graph of

$$V_3(t) = B_1 \sin\left(\frac{2\pi t}{\tau}\right) + B_2 \sin\left(\frac{4\pi t}{\tau}\right) + B_3 \sin\left(\frac{6\pi t}{\tau}\right)$$

on the interval $\left[-\frac{\tau}{2}, \frac{\tau}{2}\right]$, and compare it with the graph of $v(t)$.

Solution

(a) The coefficients B_n are given by formula (2.19) with $f(t) = t$.

For a general non-zero λ, the integral $\int_{0}^{\tau/2} t \sin \lambda t \, dt$ can be found by using integration by parts:

$$\int_{0}^{\tau/2} t \sin \lambda t \, dt = \left[t\left(-\frac{1}{\lambda} \cos \lambda t\right)\right]_{0}^{\tau/2} + \frac{1}{\lambda} \int_{0}^{\tau/2} \cos \lambda t \, dt$$

$$= -\frac{\tau}{2\lambda} \cos\left(\frac{\lambda\tau}{2}\right) + \frac{1}{\lambda^2} \sin\left(\frac{\lambda\tau}{2}\right).$$

Putting $\lambda = \frac{2\pi}{\tau}, \frac{4\pi}{\tau}, \frac{6\pi}{\tau}$, we note that the sine term is zero, so

$$B_1 = \tfrac{4}{\tau} \int_0^{\tau/2} t \sin\left(\frac{2\pi t}{\tau}\right) dt = \tfrac{4}{\tau}\left(-\frac{\tau^2}{4\pi}\cos\pi\right) = \tfrac{\tau}{\pi},$$

$$B_2 = \tfrac{4}{\tau} \int_0^{\tau/2} t \sin\left(\frac{4\pi t}{\tau}\right) dt = \tfrac{4}{\tau}\left(-\frac{\tau^2}{8\pi}\cos 2\pi\right) = -\tfrac{\tau}{2\pi},$$

$$B_3 = \tfrac{4}{\tau} \int_0^{\tau/2} t \sin\left(\frac{6\pi t}{\tau}\right) dt = \tfrac{4}{\tau}\left(-\frac{\tau^2}{12\pi}\cos 3\pi\right) = \tfrac{\tau}{3\pi}.$$

(b) The graphs of $v(t)$ and $V_3(t)$ on $\left[-\frac{\tau}{2}, \frac{\tau}{2}\right]$ are given in Figure 2.7.

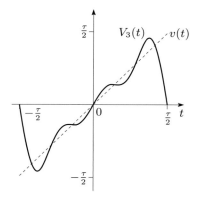

Figure 2.7   ■

The Fourier series for the ramp function $v(t)$ is thus

$$V(t) = \frac{\tau}{\pi} \sum_{r=1}^{\infty} \frac{(-1)^{r+1}}{r} \sin\left(\frac{2r\pi t}{\tau}\right)$$

$$= \frac{\tau}{\pi}\left(\sin\left(\frac{2\pi t}{\tau}\right) - \tfrac{1}{2}\sin\left(\frac{4\pi t}{\tau}\right) + \tfrac{1}{3}\sin\left(\frac{6\pi t}{\tau}\right) - \cdots\right).$$

Our sketch in Figure 2.7 of the sum of the first three terms gives an approximation to the function, but it is not as good as the corresponding approximation to the saw-tooth function that you met in the previous subsection. As in the case of the square-wave function studied in Subsection 1.5, this is due to the discontinuities in the original function. At these points, the Fourier series takes the average value in the middle of the jump. Here that value is 0. In the case of a continuous function, the sizes of the coefficients in the Fourier series decrease as $1/n^2$. By contrast, here and for the square-wave function, where there are discontinuities, the sizes of the coefficients decrease as $1/n$.

Procedure 2.1   Fourier series for even and odd periodic functions

For an even periodic function $f(t)$ with period τ and fundamental interval $\left[-\frac{\tau}{2}, \frac{\tau}{2}\right]$, the Fourier series

$$F(t) = A_0 + \sum_{r=1}^{\infty} A_r \cos\left(\frac{2r\pi t}{\tau}\right)$$

is found by using the formulae

$$A_0 = \frac{2}{\tau} \int_0^{\tau/2} f(t)\,dt,$$

$$A_n = \frac{4}{\tau} \int_0^{\tau/2} f(t) \cos\left(\frac{2n\pi t}{\tau}\right) dt \quad (n = 1, 2, \ldots).$$

For an odd periodic function $f(t)$ with period τ and fundamental interval $\left[-\frac{\tau}{2}, \frac{\tau}{2}\right]$, the Fourier series

$$F(t) = \sum_{r=1}^{\infty} B_r \sin\left(\frac{2r\pi t}{\tau}\right)$$

is found by using the formula

$$B_n = \frac{4}{\tau} \int_0^{\tau/2} f(t) \sin\left(\frac{2n\pi t}{\tau}\right) dt \quad (n = 1, 2, \ldots).$$

End-of-section Exercises

Exercise 2.3

The periodic function $f(t)$ with period τ is defined in the interval $\left[-\frac{\tau}{2}, \frac{\tau}{2}\right]$ by

$$f(t) = \begin{cases} -1 & \text{if } -\frac{\tau}{2} < t \le 0, \\ 1 & \text{if } 0 < t < \frac{\tau}{2}. \end{cases}$$

Find the Fourier series for this function.

Exercise 2.4

(a) Find a fundamental interval for, and hence the period of, the function $c(t)$ defined in the Introduction as

$$c(t) = |\cos t|.$$

(b) State whether $c(t)$ is even or odd and find the Fourier series for this function.

(*Hint*: Use the trigonometric identity

$$\cos t \cos 2nt = \tfrac{1}{2}\left(\cos(2n-1)t + \cos(2n+1)t\right),$$

which is based on a more general identity given in the Handbook.)

---

3 Fourier series for any periodic function

In the last section you saw how to find the Fourier series for even and odd periodic functions. Unfortunately, not all periodic functions are even or odd. However, any periodic function is a sum of an even and an odd function, so you would expect to be able to approximate it with a Fourier series involving both sine and cosine terms.

Exercise 3.1 _____

For any function $f(x)$, show the following.

(a) The function $g(x)$ defined by

$$g(x) = \frac{f(x) + f(-x)}{2}$$

is even.

(b) The function $h(x)$ defined by

$$h(x) = \frac{f(x) - f(-x)}{2}$$

is odd.

(c) The function $f(x)$ can be written as the sum

$$f(x) = g(x) + h(x),$$

where $g(x)$ and $h(x)$ are as defined above.

_____

Exercise 3.1 shows that one way of finding the Fourier series for a general function f is to find Fourier series for the functions g and h as defined in the exercise, and then add them. However, we can find the Fourier series for a general function more directly, as you will see in Subsection 3.1.

The modelling of a real problem may involve a function $f(t)$ that is defined only on some interval. We can choose the interval to be of the form $\left[0, \frac{\tau}{2}\right]$. Then we can extend the definition of the function to the interval $\left[-\frac{\tau}{2}, \frac{\tau}{2}\right]$ by choosing the function to be either even or odd on this interval. From there, we can extend the definition of the function to all the real numbers as a periodic function. You will see how to do this in Subsection 3.2.

It is this technique that will be used in *Unit 22* when we study vibrating strings. We extend the function modelling the initial displacement of a string to obtain an odd periodic function. Finding the Fourier series for this odd periodic function is a crucial step in the solution of problems of the type discussed in *Unit 22*, and a formula for obtaining such series is derived in Subsection 3.3.

3.1 Fourier series for general functions

Suppose that you have a periodic function $f(t)$ with period τ and fundamental interval $\left[-\frac{\tau}{2}, \frac{\tau}{2}\right]$. In general, the function will be neither odd nor even. However, it can always be written as a sum of an even function and an odd function, so it should have a Fourier series involving both cosine and sine terms. That is, we can try to represent $f(t)$ as the general Fourier series

$$F(t) = A_0 + \sum_{r=1}^{\infty} A_r \cos\left(\frac{2r\pi t}{\tau}\right) + \sum_{r=1}^{\infty} B_r \sin\left(\frac{2r\pi t}{\tau}\right).$$

As in Subsections 1.4, 2.1 and 2.2, the basic technique is to multiply by cosine or sine terms and integrate over the fundamental interval. We need an evaluated integral when a cosine and sine term are multiplied together.

Trigonometric integrals over the interval $\left[-\frac{\tau}{2}, \frac{\tau}{2}\right]$

For any pair of integers r and n,

$$\int_{-\tau/2}^{\tau/2} \sin\left(\frac{2r\pi t}{\tau}\right) \cos\left(\frac{2n\pi t}{\tau}\right) dt = 0. \tag{3.1}$$

Using this result, no new terms appear when we form our products, so we arrive at the same formulae as in the previous section. Formulae (2.6), (2.8) and (2.18) lead to the following result.

Procedure 3.1   Fourier series for periodic functions

For a periodic function $f(t)$, with period τ and fundamental interval $\left[-\frac{\tau}{2}, \frac{\tau}{2}\right]$, the Fourier series

$$F(t) = A_0 + \sum_{r=1}^{\infty} A_r \cos\left(\frac{2r\pi t}{\tau}\right) + \sum_{r=1}^{\infty} B_r \sin\left(\frac{2r\pi t}{\tau}\right)$$

is found by using the formulae

$$A_0 = \frac{1}{\tau} \int_{-\tau/2}^{\tau/2} f(t)\, dt,$$

$$A_n = \frac{2}{\tau} \int_{-\tau/2}^{\tau/2} f(t) \cos\left(\frac{2n\pi t}{\tau}\right) dt \quad (n = 1, 2, \ldots),$$

$$B_n = \frac{2}{\tau} \int_{-\tau/2}^{\tau/2} f(t) \sin\left(\frac{2n\pi t}{\tau}\right) dt \quad (n = 1, 2, \ldots).$$

The integrals here cannot be expressed as integrals from 0 to $\tau/2$, as the function is not necessarily even or odd.

Example 3.1

The periodic function $f(t)$ is defined by

$$f(t) = e^t \quad \text{for } -1 \le t \le 1,$$

on the fundamental interval $[-1, 1]$. Find its Fourier series.

Solution

The function $f(t)$ has the graph shown in Figure 3.1.

This function is clearly neither even nor odd. We use Procedure 3.1, with period $\tau = 2$, to find the Fourier series for this function. We obtain

$$A_0 = \frac{1}{2} \int_{-1}^{1} e^t\, dt = \frac{1}{2}(e - e^{-1}).$$

The other coefficients A_n and B_n $(n = 1, 2, 3, \ldots)$ can be obtained either by using symbolic integration in the computer algebra package for the course, or by hand using integration by parts. The software gives the formulae

$$A_n = \frac{(-1)^n (e - e^{-1})}{1 + n^2 \pi^2}, \qquad B_n = -\frac{n\pi(-1)^n (e - e^{-1})}{1 + n^2 \pi^2}.$$

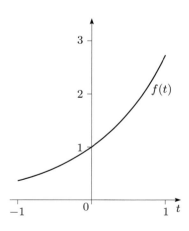

Figure 3.1

Every coefficient in the Fourier series involves the term $e - e^{-1}$. The series is therefore conveniently written as

$$F(t) = A_0 + \sum_{r=1}^{\infty} A_r \cos\left(\frac{2r\pi t}{\tau}\right) + \sum_{r=1}^{\infty} B_r \sin\left(\frac{2r\pi t}{\tau}\right)$$

$$= (e - e^{-1})\left(\tfrac{1}{2} + \sum_{r=1}^{\infty}\left(\frac{(-1)^r}{1 + r^2\pi^2}\right)(\cos r\pi t - r\pi \sin r\pi t)\right). \quad \blacksquare$$

The graph of the function $f(t)$ and the graph of $F_8(t)$, the sum of the constant and the first eight cosine and first eight sine terms in the Fourier series, are shown in Figure 3.2. There is a fairly good approximation to the function, except at the endpoints. At the endpoints, the Fourier series takes the average value, $\tfrac{1}{2}(e + e^{-1})$, of the function either side of the endpoints.

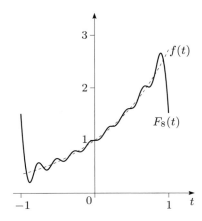

Figure 3.2

Exercise 3.2

Suppose that the periodic function $f(t)$ is defined on the fundamental interval $[-1, 1]$ by

$$f(t) = \begin{cases} 1 & \text{if } -1 \leq t < 0, \\ t & \text{if } 0 \leq t \leq 1. \end{cases}$$

Find the coefficients of its Fourier series.

3.2   Even and odd extensions

In the Introduction we noted that the Fourier series of a complicated forcing function can be used to find the steady-state solution of a differential equation.

In *Unit 22* you will meet *partial* differential equations where the initial condition is given by a function of x. For example, for a plucked violin string of length L, each point x along the string has an initial displacement $f(x)$ from its equilibrium position. Thus f is defined on an interval $[0, L]$.

If the function $f(x)$ is a sine function, then the solution of the equation can be found quite easily. By analogy with the discussion in the Introduction, we can solve the partial differential equation for a more complicated function f by finding the Fourier series for f.

Note the changes of notation, from a function of t to a function of x, and from τ to $2L$. This is because the context changes in *Unit 22* to one of position.

In these types of problem, the function is initially defined only on $[0, L]$ because that is the equilibrium position of the string. However, we can imagine that f is also defined on $[-L, 0]$ in such a way as to make f an odd function, which we denote by f_{odd}, defined on $[-L, L]$. In order to specify f_{odd} on this interval, we need to define $f_{\text{odd}}(x) = f(x)$ if $0 \leq x \leq L$, and $f_{\text{odd}}(x) = -f(-x)$ if $-L \leq x < 0$ (see Figure 3.3). Once f has been extended in this way to a function f_{odd} defined on $[-L, L]$, we can imagine that it repeats itself with period $2L$. That is, we regard f_{odd} as an odd periodic function with fundamental interval $[-L, L]$. This function is called the **odd extension** of the function f defined on $[0, L]$.

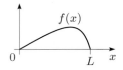

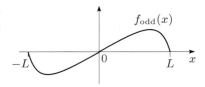

Example 3.2

Suppose that a violin string can vibrate in the (x, y)-plane, and is fixed at its ends which are at $(0, 0)$ and $(L, 0)$. A player grasps the string at the point $\left(\frac{1}{3}L, 0\right)$ and pulls it in the y-direction, displacing that point by a distance $\frac{1}{10}L$, as shown in Figure 3.4. We assume that the displacement of the string can be modelled as two straight line segments on $\left[0, \frac{1}{3}L\right]$ and on $\left(\frac{1}{3}L, L\right]$.

(a) Give a formula for $f(x)$, the function describing the transverse displacement of the string (i.e. the displacement in the y-direction, at right angles to the equilibrium position of the string) as a function of x.

(b) Construct the odd extension f_{odd} of f by defining f_{odd} on the fundamental interval $[-L, L]$. Sketch the graph of $f_{\text{odd}}(x)$ on this interval.

Figure 3.3

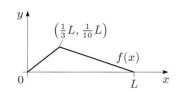

Figure 3.4

Solution

(a) The player displaces the point whose equilibrium position is $\left(\frac{1}{3}L, 0\right)$ to the point $\left(\frac{1}{3}L, \frac{1}{10}L\right)$. Thus the string is stretched along straight line segments from $(0, 0)$ to $\left(\frac{1}{3}L, \frac{1}{10}L\right)$ and from $\left(\frac{1}{3}L, \frac{1}{10}L\right)$ to $(L, 0)$. It follows that

$$f(x) = \begin{cases} \frac{3}{10}x & \text{if } 0 \leq x \leq \frac{1}{3}L, \\ \frac{3}{20}(L - x) & \text{if } \frac{1}{3}L < x \leq L. \end{cases}$$

(b) The odd extension coincides with f on $[0, L]$, and is defined on $[-L, 0]$ by

$$f_{\text{odd}}(x) = -f(-x)$$
$$= \begin{cases} -\frac{3}{20}(L - (-x)) = -\frac{3}{20}(L + x) & \text{if } -L \leq x < -\frac{1}{3}L, \\ -\frac{3}{10}(-x) = \frac{3}{10}x & \text{if } -\frac{1}{3}L \leq x \leq 0. \end{cases}$$

Thus, over the whole fundamental interval $[-L, L]$, we have

$$f_{\text{odd}}(x) = \begin{cases} -\frac{3}{20}(L + x) & \text{if } -L \leq x < -\frac{1}{3}L, \\ \frac{3}{10}x & \text{if } -\frac{1}{3}L \leq x \leq \frac{1}{3}L, \\ \frac{3}{20}(L - x) & \text{if } \frac{1}{3}L < x \leq L. \end{cases}$$

The graph of $f_{\text{odd}}(x)$ on the fundamental interval is given in Figure 3.5.

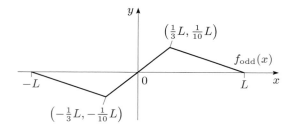

Figure 3.5

Exercise 3.3

Suppose now that the same player as in Example 3.2 displaces the point of the violin string, whose equilibrium position is $\left(\frac{2}{3}L, 0\right)$, so that it is displaced to $\left(\frac{2}{3}L, -\frac{1}{20}L\right)$.

(a) Give a formula for $f(x)$, the function describing the transverse displacement of the string.

(b) Construct the odd extension f_{odd} of f by defining f_{odd} on the fundamental interval $[-L, L]$. Sketch the graph of f_{odd} on this interval.

We can create even extensions just as easily as odd extensions. If $f(x)$ is defined on $[0, L]$, then we define f_{even} in $[-L, L]$ by stipulating that $f_{\text{even}}(x) = f(x)$ if $0 < x < L$ and $f_{\text{even}}(x) = f(-x)$ if $-L < x < 0$. This defines f_{even} in the fundamental interval $[-L, L]$ and hence on the whole real line. Defined in this way, f_{even} is called the **even extension** of the function f defined on $[0, L]$.

Exercise 3.4

Construct the even extension f_{even} of the function $f(x)$ found in Exercise 3.3(a), defined on $[0, L]$, by defining f_{even} on the fundamental interval $[-L, L]$. Sketch the graph of f_{even} on this fundamental interval.

3.3 Fourier series for odd extensions

In Subsection 3.2 you saw how to find the odd and even extensions of a function $f(x)$ defined on an interval $[0, L]$. Since these extensions are odd or even, their Fourier series will take a simple form. In *Unit 22* we shall be particularly interested in odd extensions, so we look now at the Fourier sine series corresponding to odd extensions.

Suppose that the function $f(x)$ is defined on the interval $[0, L]$ and extends to the odd periodic function $f_{\text{odd}}(x)$ as in Subsection 3.2. The fundamental interval is $[-L, L]$ and the period is $2L$. Thus, in finding the Fourier sine series for $f_{\text{odd}}(x)$, we must substitute $2L$ for τ (and x for t) in applying Equations (2.13) and (2.19). This gives us the following procedure.

Procedure 3.2   Fourier sine series

For an odd periodic extension $f_{\text{odd}}(x)$ of a function $f(x)$ defined on the interval $[0, L]$, the Fourier sine series for $f(x)$,

$$F_{\text{odd}}(x) = \sum_{r=1}^{\infty} B_r \sin\left(\frac{r\pi x}{L}\right),$$

is found by using the formula

$$B_n = \frac{2}{L} \int_0^L f(x) \sin\left(\frac{n\pi x}{L}\right) dx.$$

So the coefficients in the Fourier sine series can be found by using the function $f(x)$ as defined on $[0, L]$. We need to know only about odd extensions to understand the values given by the Fourier sine series at points other than those in the original interval $[0, L]$.

It is possible to obtain the Fourier cosine series for $f(x)$ by considering its even extension in a similar manner, as you will see in Activity 4.2.

End-of-section Exercises

Exercise 3.5

Find the coefficients of the Fourier series for the periodic function $f(t)$ defined on the fundamental interval $[-1, 1]$ by

$$f(t) = \begin{cases} t+1 & \text{if } -1 \le t \le 0, \\ 1 & \text{if } 0 < t \le 1. \end{cases}$$

Exercise 3.6

The function $f(x) = x(2 - x)$ is defined on the interval $[0, 2]$.

(a) Determine the odd extension of $f(x)$.

(b) Find the Fourier sine series for $f(x)$. You may use the formula

$$\int_0^\theta x(2 - x) \sin\left(\frac{n\pi x}{2}\right) dx$$
$$= -\frac{2}{n\pi}\left[x(2 - x)\cos\left(\frac{n\pi x}{2}\right)\right]_0^\theta + \frac{8}{n^2\pi^2}\left[(1 - x)\sin\left(\frac{n\pi x}{2}\right)\right]_0^\theta$$
$$- \frac{16}{n^3\pi^3}\left[\cos\left(\frac{n\pi x}{2}\right)\right]_0^\theta.$$

4 Fourier series on the computer

This section uses the computer algebra package for the course to revise the content of the unit. You are asked to examine a particular Fourier series, finding the coefficients by using both numerical and symbolic integration. The advantage of numerical methods is that they will work for a greater variety of functions. Though the symbolic method will work only for suitable functions, it has the advantage that when it does work, the form of the solution often throws some additional light on the problem.

Use your computer to complete the following activities.

PC

Activity 4.1

Consider the Fourier series approximation $F(t)$ for $f(t)$ when:

(a) $f(t) = \begin{cases} \frac{t}{\pi} + 1 & \text{if } -\pi \le t \le 0, \\ -\frac{t}{\pi} + 1 & \text{if } 0 < t \le \pi, \end{cases}$

defined on the fundamental interval $[-\pi, \pi]$;

(b) $f(t) = \begin{cases} 1 & \text{if } -\frac{\pi}{2} \le t \le \frac{\pi}{2}, \\ 0 & \text{otherwise}, \end{cases}$

defined on the fundamental interval $[-\pi, \pi]$;

(c) $f(t) = t$ defined on the fundamental interval $[-1, 1]$;

(d) $f(t) = t^2$ defined on the fundamental interval $[-1, 1]$;

(e) $f(t) = t^3$ defined on the fundamental interval $[-1, 1]$;

(f) $f(t) = t^2 + t^3$ defined on the fundamental interval $[-1, 1]$.

For each approximation $F(t)$ carry out the following.

(i) Comment on the numerical values obtained for the Fourier series coefficients.

(ii) Investigate how closely the Fourier series approximates f as the number N of terms in the series increases, and comment on any unusual behaviour.

(iii) Comment on the algebraic formulae obtained for the Fourier series coefficients.

Activity 4.2 _____

Consider the function

$$f(t) = \begin{cases} \frac{3}{10}t & \text{if } 0 \le t \le \frac{1}{3}, \\ \frac{3}{20}(1-t) & \text{if } \frac{1}{3} < t \le 1, \end{cases}$$

defined on the interval $[0, 1]$.

(a) Construct the even extension of $f(t)$ and obtain its Fourier cosine series $F_{\text{even}}(t)$. Show that, by using more and more terms in this Fourier series, better and better approximations to the even extension of $f(t)$ are obtained. Comment on the algebraic formulae obtained for the Fourier series coefficients.

(b) Repeat part (a) for the odd extension of $f(t)$ and its Fourier sine series $F_{\text{odd}}(t)$.

Outcomes

After studying this unit you should be able to:

- understand the ubiquity and importance of Fourier series;
- understand the terms frequency, period and fundamental interval, and be able to obtain them for a periodic function;
- understand the terms even and odd as applied to functions, and be able to test a function to see if it is either;
- find the Fourier series for an even and odd periodic function;
- compare the graph of a function with the graph of a sum of terms in the Fourier series, and comment on the closeness of the approximation to the function;
- find the Fourier series for a general periodic function;
- understand how to modify a function defined on an interval to give an even or odd extension;
- find the Fourier sine series for the odd extension of a function.

Solutions to the exercises

Section 1

1.1 We have

$G(t + 2\pi)$
$= \frac{1}{2} + \frac{4}{\pi^2} \left(\cos(t + 2\pi) + \frac{1}{9} \cos 3(t + 2\pi) \right.$
$\qquad \left. + \frac{1}{25} \cos 5(t + 2\pi) + \frac{1}{49} \cos 7(t + 2\pi) + \cdots \right)$
$= \frac{1}{2} + \frac{4}{\pi^2} \left(\cos(t + 2\pi) + \frac{1}{9} \cos(3t + 6\pi) \right.$
$\qquad \left. + \frac{1}{25} \cos(5t + 10\pi) + \frac{1}{49} \cos(7t + 14\pi) + \cdots \right)$
$= \frac{1}{2} + \frac{4}{\pi^2} \left(\cos t + \frac{1}{9} \cos 3t + \frac{1}{25} \cos 5t \right.$
$\qquad \left. + \frac{1}{49} \cos 7t + \cdots \right)$
$= G(t).$

Similarly, $G(t + 2n\pi) = G(t)$ where n is any integer. These results hold because adding 2π any number of times to a cosine argument does not change the value of the cosine.

1.2 The angular frequencies are

$\quad 1, \ 3, \ 5, \ 7, \ \ldots$

and the periods are

$\quad 2\pi, \ \frac{2\pi}{3}, \ \frac{2\pi}{5}, \ \frac{2\pi}{7}, \ \ldots .$

1.3 The angular frequencies of the component functions are

$\quad \pi, \ \frac{3\pi}{2}, \ 2\pi$

and the corresponding periods are

$\quad 2, \ \frac{4}{3}, \ 1.$

The least common multiple of these periods is 4, so the period of the function $f(t)$ is $\tau = 4$.

1.4 The graphs are as follows.

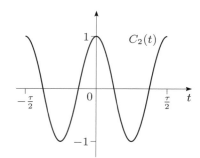

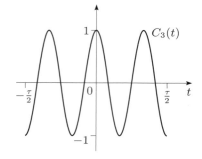

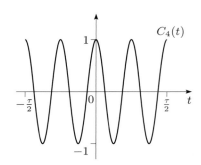

When $n = 0$, formula (1.3) gives

$$C_0(t) = \cos \left(\frac{2 \times 0 \pi t}{\tau} \right) = \cos 0 = 1.$$

This is a constant function, which is periodic.

1.5 Since $g(-t) = (-t)^3 = -t^3 = -g(t)$ for all t, the function is odd.

1.6 (a) The function $C_0(t)$ has the following graph.

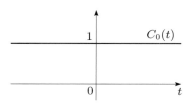

Since the graph is reflected in the vertical axis, the function must be even.

(b) Here $h(-t) = (-t)^2 + (-t)^3 = t^2 - t^3$.

In general, this is equal neither to $h(t)$ nor $-h(t)$, so the function is neither even nor odd.

1.7 All the powers of t in the product $f(t)g(t)$ are odd, so $h(t)$ is an odd function.

Alternatively, since $f(t)$ and $g(t)$ are odd and even functions, respectively, we know by definition that

$$f(-t) = -f(t), \quad g(-t) = g(t).$$

Hence

$$h(-t) = f(-t)g(-t) = -f(t)g(t) = -h(t),$$

so $h(t)$ is an odd function.

1.8 Since $f(t)$ has period τ, it must be true that $f\left(-\frac{\tau}{2}\right) = f\left(\frac{\tau}{2}\right)$. Also, as $f(t)$ is odd, it must be true that $f\left(-\frac{\tau}{2}\right) = -f\left(\frac{\tau}{2}\right)$. Thus $f\left(-\frac{\tau}{2}\right) = f\left(\frac{\tau}{2}\right) = 0$.

The fact that $f(t)$ is odd also gives

$$f(0) = -f(-0) = -f(0),$$

so $f(0) = 0$.

1.9 From the graph, the values of the function repeat after an interval of length 2π. Hence the period is $\tau = 2\pi$. The angular frequency Ω satisfies $\tau = \frac{2\pi}{\Omega}$, so here $\Omega = 1$.

1.10 For $r = 1, 2, 3, \ldots$,
$$\int_{-\pi}^{\pi} \cos rt \, dt = \left[\frac{\sin rt}{r} \right]_{-\pi}^{\pi} = 0,$$
since $\sin r\pi = 0$ and $\sin(-r\pi) = 0$.

1.11 (a) Here the function takes the value 1 between 0 and $\frac{\pi}{2}$, and 0 between $\frac{\pi}{2}$ and π, giving
$$A_0 = \frac{1}{\pi} \int_0^{\pi/2} 1 \, dt + \frac{1}{\pi} \int_{\pi/2}^{\pi} 0 \, dt = \frac{1}{2}.$$

(b) This time, between $\frac{\pi}{2}$ and π the function takes the value $-\frac{1}{2}$, giving
$$A_0 = \frac{1}{\pi} \int_0^{\pi/2} 1 \, dt + \frac{1}{\pi} \int_{\pi/2}^{\pi} \left(-\frac{1}{2}\right) dt = \frac{1}{2} - \frac{1}{4} = \frac{1}{4}.$$

1.12 (a) Using the given trigonometric identity with $r = 2$, we have
$$\int_{-\pi}^{\pi} \cos 2t \cos t \, dt = \int_{-\pi}^{\pi} \frac{1}{2}(\cos 3t + \cos t) \, dt$$
$$= \left[\frac{1}{6} \sin 3t + \frac{1}{2} \sin t \right]_{-\pi}^{\pi}$$
$$= 0.$$

(b) Again using the trigonometric identity, this time with general $r > 1$, we obtain
$$\int_{-\pi}^{\pi} \cos rt \cos t \, dt$$
$$= \int_{-\pi}^{\pi} \frac{1}{2} \left(\cos(r+1)t + \cos(r-1)t \right) \, dt$$
$$= \left[\frac{\sin(r+1)t}{2(r+1)} + \frac{\sin(r-1)t}{2(r-1)} \right]_{-\pi}^{\pi}$$
$$= 0.$$

(c) Using the given trigonometric identity, we have
$$\int_{-\pi}^{\pi} \cos^2 t \, dt = \int_{-\pi}^{\pi} \frac{1}{2}(\cos 2t + 1) \, dt$$
$$= \left[\frac{1}{4} \sin 2t + \frac{1}{2} t \right]_{-\pi}^{\pi}$$
$$= \pi.$$

(Alternatively, these integrals can all be evaluated symbolically using the computer algebra package for the course.)

1.13 Substitute the definition of $h(t)$ from Exercise 1.11(a) into Equation (1.13), and use integration by parts. The function $h(t)$ takes the value 1 between 0 and $\frac{\pi}{2}$, and 0 between $\frac{\pi}{2}$ and π, giving Equation (1.13) as
$$A_1 = \frac{2}{\pi} \int_0^{\pi/2} 1 \times \cos t \, dt + \frac{2}{\pi} \int_{\pi/2}^{\pi} 0 \times \cos t \, dt$$
$$= \frac{2}{\pi} [\sin t]_0^{\pi/2} + 0 = \frac{2}{\pi}.$$

1.14 Substitute the definition of $h(t)$ from Exercise 1.11(a) into formula (1.17). We could obtain a general formula for A_n, as in Example 1.6, and then substitute $n = 2$ and $n = 3$ into that. Alternatively, put $n = 2$ and $n = 3$ into formula (1.17) and obtain
$$A_2 = \frac{2}{\pi} \int_0^{\pi/2} 1 \times \cos 2t \, dt + \frac{2}{\pi} \int_{\pi/2}^{\pi} 0 \times \cos 2t \, dt$$
$$= \frac{1}{\pi} [\sin 2t]_0^{\pi/2} + 0 = 0,$$
$$A_3 = \frac{2}{\pi} \int_0^{\pi/2} 1 \times \cos 3t \, dt + \frac{2}{\pi} \int_{\pi/2}^{\pi} 0 \times \cos 3t \, dt$$
$$= \frac{2}{3\pi} [\sin 3t]_0^{\pi/2} + 0 = -\frac{2}{3\pi}.$$

1.15 The closed form is
$$H(t) = \frac{1}{2} + \frac{2}{\pi} \sum_{s=1}^{\infty} \frac{-(-1)^s}{2s-1} \cos(2s-1)t.$$

1.16 Since $f(t)$ and $g(t)$ are both odd functions,
$$f(-t) = -f(t), \quad g(-t) = -g(t).$$
Hence
$$k(-t) = f(-t) + g(-t)$$
$$= -f(t) + (-g(t))$$
$$= -(f(t) + g(t)) = -k(t),$$
so $k(t)$ is an odd function.

1.17 We have (using the hint)
$$A_0 = \frac{1}{\pi} \int_0^{\pi} f(t) \, dt = \frac{1}{\pi} \int_0^{\pi} t^2 \, dt = \frac{\pi^2}{3},$$
and, for $n = 1, 2, 3, \ldots$,
$$A_n = \frac{2}{\pi} \int_0^{\pi} t^2 \cos nt \, dt$$
$$= \frac{2}{\pi} \times \frac{1}{n^3} \left((n^2\pi^2 - 2) \sin n\pi + 2n\pi \cos n\pi \right).$$
Since n is an integer, $\sin n\pi = 0$ and $\cos n\pi = (-1)^n$, giving
$$A_n = \frac{4(-1)^n}{n^2} \quad (n = 1, 2, 3, \ldots).$$
The Fourier series is therefore
$$F(t) = \frac{\pi^2}{3} + 4 \sum_{r=1}^{\infty} \frac{(-1)^r}{r^2} \cos rt$$
$$= \frac{\pi^2}{3} - 4 \cos t + \cos 2t - \frac{4}{9} \cos 3t$$
$$+ \frac{1}{4} \cos 4t + \cdots.$$

(The graph of $F(t)$ matches the expected graph, which consists of a parabola on the fundamental interval repeated indefinitely to both the left and the right (see below).)

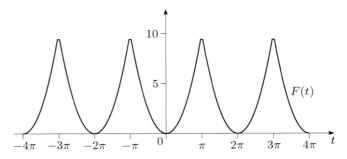

1.18 The function $w(t)$ is even, and $w(t) = t$ on the interval $[0, \pi]$. Therefore

$$A_0 = \tfrac{1}{\pi} \int_0^\pi w(t)\, dt = \tfrac{1}{\pi} \int_0^\pi t\, dt = \tfrac{1}{\pi} \left[\tfrac{1}{2}t^2\right]_0^\pi = \tfrac{\pi}{2},$$

and, for $n = 1, 2, 3, \ldots$,

$$A_n = \tfrac{2}{\pi} \int_0^\pi t \cos nt\, dt$$

$$= \tfrac{2}{\pi} \left[\tfrac{t}{n} \sin nt\right]_0^\pi - \tfrac{2}{\pi} \int_0^\pi \tfrac{1}{n} \sin nt\, dt$$

$$= \tfrac{2}{n^2\pi} \left[\cos nt\right]_0^\pi$$

$$= \frac{2((-1)^n - 1)}{n^2\pi}$$

$$= \begin{cases} 0 & \text{if } n \text{ is even,} \\ -\dfrac{4}{n^2\pi} & \text{if } n \text{ is odd.} \end{cases}$$

Thus the Fourier series is

$$W(t) = \tfrac{\pi}{2} - \tfrac{4}{\pi} \sum_{s=1}^{\infty} \frac{1}{(2s-1)^2} \cos(2s-1)t$$

$$= \tfrac{\pi}{2} - \tfrac{4}{\pi} \cos t - \tfrac{4}{9\pi} \cos 3t - \tfrac{4}{25\pi} \cos 5t - \cdots.$$

Section 2

2.1 The function $w(t)$ takes the value t between 0 and $\tfrac{\tau}{2}$, so, using Equation (2.7),

$$A_0 = \tfrac{2}{\tau} \int_0^{\tau/2} w(t)\, dt = \tfrac{2}{\tau} \int_0^{\tau/2} t\, dt = \tfrac{2}{\tau} \left[\tfrac{1}{2}t^2\right]_0^{\tau/2} = \tfrac{\tau}{4}.$$

Using formula (2.9), we also have

$$A_n = \tfrac{4}{\tau} \int_0^{\tau/2} w(t) \cos\left(\frac{2n\pi t}{\tau}\right) dt$$

$$= \tfrac{4}{\tau} \int_0^{\tau/2} t \cos\left(\frac{2n\pi t}{\tau}\right) dt$$

$$= \frac{2}{n\pi} \left[t \sin\left(\frac{2n\pi t}{\tau}\right)\right]_0^{\tau/2} - \frac{2}{n\pi} \int_0^{\tau/2} \sin\left(\frac{2n\pi t}{\tau}\right) dt$$

$$= 0 + \frac{\tau}{n^2\pi^2} \left[\cos\left(\frac{2n\pi t}{\tau}\right)\right]_0^{\tau/2}$$

$$= \frac{\tau((-1)^n - 1)}{n^2\pi^2}$$

$$= \begin{cases} 0 & \text{if } n \text{ is even,} \\ -\dfrac{2\tau}{n^2\pi^2} & \text{if } n \text{ is odd.} \end{cases}$$

(So we have

$$A_0 = \tfrac{\tau}{4}, \quad A_1 = -\tfrac{2\tau}{\pi^2}, \quad A_2 = 0, \quad A_3 = -\tfrac{2\tau}{9\pi^2},$$

$$A_4 = 0, \quad A_5 = -\tfrac{2\tau}{25\pi^2}, \quad A_6 = 0, \quad A_7 = -\tfrac{2\tau}{49\pi^2},$$

$$A_8 = 0, \quad \ldots.)$$

2.2 $S_n(-t) = \sin\left(-\dfrac{2n\pi t}{\tau}\right)$

$$= -\sin\left(\frac{2n\pi t}{\tau}\right) = -S_n(t),$$

so $S_n(t)$ is an odd function.

2.3 The function is odd, so its Fourier series involves only sine terms (see Procedure 2.1):

$$F(t) = \sum_{r=1}^{\infty} B_r \sin\left(\frac{2r\pi t}{\tau}\right),$$

where the coefficients are given by

$$B_n = \tfrac{4}{\tau} \int_0^{\tau/2} f(t) \sin\left(\frac{2n\pi t}{\tau}\right) dt$$

$$= \tfrac{4}{\tau} \int_0^{\tau/2} \sin\left(\frac{2n\pi t}{\tau}\right) dt$$

$$= \tfrac{4}{\tau} \left[-\frac{\tau}{2n\pi} \cos\left(\frac{2n\pi t}{\tau}\right)\right]_0^{\tau/2}$$

$$= \frac{2((-1)^{n+1} + 1)}{n\pi}.$$

Evaluating each coefficient in turn yields

$$\tfrac{4}{\pi}, \ 0, \ \tfrac{4}{3\pi}, \ 0, \ \tfrac{4}{5\pi}, \ 0, \ \ldots,$$

so the Fourier series is

$$F(t) = \tfrac{4}{\pi} \sum_{s=1}^{\infty} \frac{1}{2s-1} \sin\left(\frac{2(2s-1)\pi t}{\tau}\right)$$

$$= \tfrac{4}{\pi} \left(\sin\left(\frac{2\pi t}{\tau}\right) + \tfrac{1}{3} \sin\left(\frac{6\pi t}{\tau}\right)\right.$$

$$\left. + \tfrac{1}{5} \sin\left(\frac{10\pi t}{\tau}\right) + \cdots\right).$$

2.4 (a) It is clear from the graph of $c(t)$ (Figure 0.2) that $\left[-\tfrac{\pi}{2}, \tfrac{\pi}{2}\right]$ is a fundamental interval, so $c(t)$ has period π.

(b) The function $c(t)$ is even, so its Fourier series involves only the constant and cosine terms (see Procedure 2.1). Moreover, $c(t) = \cos t$ on the interval $\left[0, \tfrac{\pi}{2}\right]$. Therefore

$$A_0 = \tfrac{2}{\pi} \int_0^{\pi/2} \cos t\, dt = \tfrac{2}{\pi},$$

$$A_n = \tfrac{4}{\pi} \int_0^{\pi/2} \cos t \cos 2nt\, dt$$

$$= \tfrac{4}{\pi} \int_0^{\pi/2} \tfrac{1}{2} \left(\cos(2n-1)t + \cos(2n+1)t\right) dt$$

$$= \tfrac{2}{\pi} \left[\frac{\sin(2n-1)t}{2n-1} + \frac{\sin(2n+1)t}{2n+1}\right]_0^{\pi/2}$$

$$= \begin{cases} \tfrac{2}{\pi} \left(\tfrac{1}{2n-1} - \tfrac{1}{2n+1}\right) & \text{if } n \text{ is odd,} \\ \tfrac{2}{\pi} \left(-\tfrac{1}{2n-1} + \tfrac{1}{2n+1}\right) & \text{if } n \text{ is even.} \end{cases}$$

Now

$$\frac{1}{2n-1} - \frac{1}{2n+1} = \frac{2}{(2n-1)(2n+1)},$$

so the Fourier series is

$$C(t) = \tfrac{2}{\pi} + \tfrac{4}{\pi} \sum_{n=1}^{\infty} \frac{(-1)^{n+1}}{(2n-1)(2n+1)} \cos 2nt$$

$$= \tfrac{2}{\pi} \left(1 + \tfrac{2}{1\times 3} \cos 2t - \tfrac{2}{3\times 5} \cos 4t\right.$$

$$\left. + \tfrac{2}{5\times 7} \cos 6t - \tfrac{2}{7\times 9} \cos 8t + \cdots\right).$$

Section 3

3.1 (a) Using the definition of $g(x)$, we have

$$g(-x) = \frac{f(-x) + f(-(-x))}{2}$$
$$= \frac{f(x) + f(-x)}{2} = g(x).$$

Hence $g(x)$ is an even function.

(b) Using the definition of $h(x)$, we have

$$h(-x) = \frac{f(-x) - f(-(-x))}{2}$$
$$= -\frac{f(x) - f(-x)}{2} = -h(x).$$

Hence $h(x)$ is an odd function.

(c) Using the definitions of $g(x)$ and $h(x)$, we have

$$g(x) + h(x) = \frac{f(x) + f(-x)}{2} + \frac{f(x) - f(-x)}{2}$$
$$= f(x).$$

3.2 Using Procedure 3.1, we obtain

$$A_0 = \frac{1}{2} \int_{-1}^{0} 1 \, dt + \frac{1}{2} \int_{0}^{1} t \, dt = \frac{1}{2} + \frac{1}{4} = \frac{3}{4},$$

$$A_n = \int_{-1}^{0} \cos n\pi t \, dt + \int_{0}^{1} t \cos n\pi t \, dt$$
$$= \frac{1}{n\pi} [\sin n\pi t]_{-1}^{0} + \frac{1}{n\pi} [t \sin n\pi t]_{0}^{1}$$
$$\quad - \frac{1}{n\pi} \int_{0}^{1} \sin n\pi t \, dt$$
$$= 0 + 0 + \frac{1}{n^2\pi^2} [\cos n\pi t]_{0}^{1}$$
$$= \begin{cases} 0 & \text{if } n \text{ is even,} \\ -\dfrac{2}{n^2\pi^2} & \text{if } n \text{ is odd,} \end{cases}$$

$$B_n = \int_{-1}^{0} \sin n\pi t \, dt + \int_{0}^{1} t \sin n\pi t \, dt$$
$$= -\frac{1}{n\pi} [\cos n\pi t]_{-1}^{0} - \frac{1}{n\pi} [t \cos n\pi t]_{0}^{1}$$
$$\quad + \frac{1}{n\pi} \int_{0}^{1} \cos n\pi t \, dt$$
$$= -\frac{1}{n\pi} [\cos n\pi t]_{-1}^{0} - \frac{1}{n\pi} [t \cos n\pi t]_{0}^{1}$$
$$\quad + \frac{1}{n^2\pi^2} [\sin n\pi t]_{0}^{1}$$
$$= \begin{cases} 0 - \frac{1}{n\pi} + 0 & \text{if } n \text{ is even,} \\ -\frac{2}{n\pi} + \frac{1}{n\pi} + 0 & \text{if } n \text{ is odd,} \end{cases}$$
$$= -\frac{1}{n\pi}.$$

3.3 (a) The string is stretched in straight lines from $(0,0)$ to $\left(\frac{2}{3}L, -\frac{1}{20}L\right)$ and from $\left(\frac{2}{3}L, -\frac{1}{20}L\right)$ to $(L,0)$, so

$$f(x) = \begin{cases} -\frac{3}{40}x & \text{if } 0 \le x \le \frac{2}{3}L, \\ \frac{3}{20}(x - L) & \text{if } \frac{2}{3}L < x \le L. \end{cases}$$

(b) The odd extension coincides with f on $[0, L]$, and is defined on $[-L, 0]$ as

$$f_{\text{odd}}(x) =$$
$$\begin{cases} -\frac{3}{20}(-x - L) = \frac{3}{20}(x + L) & \text{if } -L \le x < -\frac{2}{3}L, \\ \frac{3}{40}(-x) = -\frac{3}{40}x & \text{if } -\frac{2}{3}L \le x \le 0. \end{cases}$$

Thus, over the fundamental interval $[-L, L]$,

$$f_{\text{odd}}(x) = \begin{cases} \frac{3}{20}(x + L) & \text{if } -L \le x < -\frac{2}{3}L, \\ -\frac{3}{40}x & \text{if } -\frac{2}{3}L \le x \le \frac{2}{3}L, \\ \frac{3}{20}(x - L) & \text{if } \frac{2}{3}L < x \le L. \end{cases}$$

The graph of $f_{\text{odd}}(x)$ on the fundamental interval is shown below.

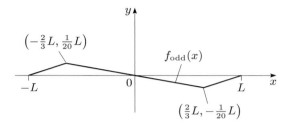

3.4 The definition of f_{even} on the interval $[-L, 0]$ is the negative of that in Solution 3.3. Thus

$$f_{\text{even}}(x) = \begin{cases} -\frac{3}{20}(x + L) & \text{if } -L \le x < -\frac{2}{3}L, \\ \frac{3}{40}x & \text{if } -\frac{2}{3}L \le x \le 0, \\ -\frac{3}{40}x & \text{if } 0 < x \le \frac{2}{3}L, \\ \frac{3}{20}(x - L) & \text{if } \frac{2}{3}L < x \le L. \end{cases}$$

The graph of f_{even} on the fundamental interval is shown below.

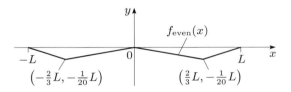

3.5 Using Procedure 3.1, we obtain

$$A_0 = \frac{1}{2} \int_{-1}^{0} (t + 1) \, dt + \frac{1}{2} \int_{0}^{1} 1 \, dt$$
$$= \frac{1}{2} \left[\frac{1}{2}t^2 + t \right]_{-1}^{0} + \frac{1}{2} = \frac{1}{4} + \frac{1}{2} = \frac{3}{4},$$

$$A_n = \int_{-1}^{0} (t + 1) \cos n\pi t \, dt + \int_{0}^{1} \cos n\pi t \, dt$$
$$= \int_{-1}^{0} t \cos n\pi t \, dt + \int_{-1}^{1} \cos n\pi t \, dt$$
$$= \frac{1}{n\pi} [t \sin n\pi t]_{-1}^{0} - \frac{1}{n\pi} \int_{-1}^{0} \sin n\pi t \, dt$$
$$\quad + \int_{-1}^{1} \cos n\pi t \, dt$$
$$= 0 + \frac{1}{n^2\pi^2} [\cos n\pi t]_{-1}^{0} + \frac{1}{n\pi} [\sin n\pi t]_{-1}^{1}$$
$$= \frac{1 - (-1)^n}{n^2\pi^2},$$

$$B_n = \int_{-1}^{0} (t+1) \sin n\pi t \, dt + \int_{0}^{1} \sin n\pi t \, dt$$

$$= \int_{-1}^{0} t \sin n\pi t \, dt + \int_{-1}^{1} \sin n\pi t \, dt$$

$$= -\frac{1}{n\pi} \left[t \cos n\pi t \right]_{-1}^{0} + \frac{1}{n\pi} \int_{-1}^{0} \cos n\pi t \, dt$$

$$+ \int_{-1}^{1} \sin n\pi t \, dt$$

$$= -\frac{1}{n\pi} \cos(-n\pi) + \frac{1}{n^2\pi^2} \left[\sin n\pi t \right]_{-1}^{0}$$

$$- \frac{1}{n\pi} \left[\cos n\pi t \right]_{-1}^{1}$$

$$= -\frac{1}{n\pi} \cos n\pi$$

$$= -\frac{(-1)^n}{n\pi}.$$

3.6 (a) Following the method in Example 1.3, the odd extension is

$$f_{\text{odd}}(x) = \begin{cases} x(2+x) & \text{if } -2 \leq x < 0, \\ x(2-x) & \text{if } 0 \leq x \leq 2. \end{cases}$$

(b) Using Procedure 3.2, the Fourier sine series is

$$F_{\text{odd}}(x) = \sum_{r=1}^{\infty} B_r \sin\left(\frac{r\pi x}{2}\right),$$

where the coefficients are given by

$$B_n = \int_{0}^{2} x(2-x) \sin\left(\frac{n\pi x}{2}\right) dx$$

$$= -\frac{2}{n\pi} \left[x(2-x) \cos\left(\frac{n\pi x}{2}\right) \right]_{0}^{2}$$

$$+ \frac{8}{n^2\pi^2} \left[(1-x) \sin\left(\frac{n\pi x}{2}\right) \right]_{0}^{2}$$

$$- \frac{16}{n^3\pi^3} \left[\cos\left(\frac{n\pi x}{2}\right) \right]_{0}^{2}$$

$$= -\frac{2}{n\pi}(0-0) + \frac{8}{n^2\pi^2}(-\sin n\pi - \sin 0)$$

$$- \frac{16}{n^3\pi^3}((-1)^n - 1)$$

$$= \frac{16}{n^3\pi^3}(1 - (-1)^n).$$

Thus

$$F_{\text{odd}}(x) = \frac{16}{\pi^3} \sum_{r=1}^{\infty} \frac{(1-(-1)^r)}{r^3} \sin\left(\frac{r\pi x}{2}\right).$$

UNIT 22   Partial differential equations

Study guide for Unit 22

The recommended study pattern is to study the sections in numerical order over five study sessions. However, the models developed in Section 1 are solved in Section 3, and the models developed in Section 2 are solved in Section 4, so you may prefer to study Section 3 straight after Section 1, and Section 4 straight after Section 2. Section 3 contains the main technique of the unit and is rather longer than the other sections.

You will need your computer for Section 5, which involves using the computer algebra package for the course as a tool for solving and interpreting the results from the problems developed earlier in the unit.

Partial differentiation was introduced in *Unit 12*, and the techniques in Sections 3 and 4 are based on ideas from *Units 3* and *21*. The discussion of diffusion in Sections 2 and 4 uses ideas from *Unit 15*.

Introduction

A **partial differential equation** is an equation relating a dependent variable and two or more independent variables through the *partial* derivatives of the dependent variable. Differential equations have played a very important role in the course so far. But until now, all the differential equations you have met have involved just one independent variable, and have been equations containing one or more dependent variables and their *ordinary* derivatives with respect to that independent variable. Such equations are often called *ordinary* differential equations when it is necessary to distinguish them from partial differential equations. For many systems that we want to be able to model, ordinary differential equations are inadequate because the states of the system can be specified only in terms of two — or even more — independent variables. When we are trying to model the way in which such a system changes, we are inevitably led to consider partial differential equations.

Partial derivatives were introduced in *Unit 12*.

Ordinary differential equations are the subject of *Units 2, 3, 11* and *13*.

One example of such a system is a plucked guitar string. One of the main topics of this unit is the derivation and analysis of a mathematical model for a taut string, such as a guitar string, plucked at some point along its length. A partial differential equation is required because the state of the string — by which is meant its shape at any given time after it has been plucked — requires a function $u(x, t)$ of two independent variables, x and t, where x is the distance along the straight line joining the two points at which the string is anchored (which we can consider as an axis with origin at one end of the string), and t is the time since the string was plucked. The dependent variable $u = u(x, t)$ is the sideways displacement of the string from the point on the axis determined by x, at time t. For fixed $t = t_1$ and varying x, $u(x, t_1)$ specifies the shape of the string at time t_1; for fixed $x = x_1$ and varying t, on the other hand, $u(x_1, t)$ tells how the sideways displacement of the string from the fixed point $x = x_1$ on the axis varies with time (see Figure 0.1).

The straight line joining the two points at which the string is anchored is the equilibrium position of the string.

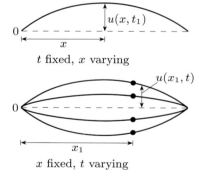

t fixed, *x* varying

x fixed, *t* varying

The model of the motion of the string that we shall develop will be a differential equation for the variable u. Since u depends on both x and t, an equation that models the motion of the string will involve partial derivatives of u with respect to both x and t. One such equation is

$$\frac{\partial^2 u}{\partial x^2} = \frac{1}{c^2} \frac{\partial^2 u}{\partial t^2}, \qquad (0.1)$$

where c is a constant whose value depends on various physical characteristics of the string. This partial differential equation is called the *wave equation*. It is a very important equation of mathematical physics, in part because it occurs in many situations that involve vibrations of extended flexible objects like strings and springs.

Figure 0.1

The name *wave* equation is used because it models wave-like motions such as that of a plucked guitar string.

The wave equation is derived in Section 1, in the context of modelling the vibrations of a taut string (such as a guitar string). Another partial differential equation, the *diffusion equation*, is developed in Section 2. Both are examples of second-order partial differential equations, in that the highest-order derivative that occurs is second order. Just as is the case for ordinary differential equations, the **order** of a partial differential equation is the order of the highest derivative that occurs in it. In this unit we deal only with second-order partial differential equations. Furthermore, all the equations that we deal with are **linear**, in that they contain no products of terms involving the dependent variable and its partial derivatives.

Sections 3, 4 and 5 are concerned with solving examples of the wave equation and the diffusion equation. We shall not be able to obtain general solutions to these equations, but we shall be able to obtain a whole host of particular solutions, based on the imposition of appropriate initial conditions and/or boundary conditions. The techniques that we use to solve these two specific types of partial differential equation illustrate some of the techniques that can be applied to partial differential equations in general. However, here we shall not attempt to generalize beyond solutions to the wave equation and the diffusion equation. Section 5 shows how problems involving these equations can readily be solved with the aid of the computer.

Checking whether or not a given function is a solution of a given partial differential equation is simply a matter of substituting the given function into the given equation, and seeing whether it is satisfied. The only difference from the case of an ordinary differential equation is that you have to calculate all the relevant partial derivatives. For example, let us check that

$$u(x, t) = \sin(kx) \cos(kct)$$

is a solution of the wave equation (0.1) for any constant k. We have

$$\frac{\partial u}{\partial x} = k \cos(kx) \cos(kct), \quad \frac{\partial^2 u}{\partial x^2} = -k^2 \sin(kx) \cos(kct),$$

$$\frac{\partial u}{\partial t} = -kc \sin(kx) \sin(kct), \quad \frac{\partial^2 u}{\partial t^2} = -k^2 c^2 \sin(kx) \cos(kct);$$

so, when $u(x, t) = \sin(kx) \cos(kct)$,

$$\frac{\partial^2 u}{\partial x^2} = \frac{1}{c^2} \frac{\partial^2 u}{\partial t^2}$$

and this function is indeed a solution of the wave equation.

The initial conditions and/or boundary conditions appropriate to obtaining a particular solution of the wave equation or the diffusion equation depend on the context. For example, for the wave equation as a model of the vibrations of a guitar string, we can use *two* boundary conditions and *two* initial conditions. If L is the equilibrium length of the string, then the boundary conditions are

$$u(0, t) = u(L, t) = 0, \quad t \geq 0; \tag{0.2}$$

these conditions correspond to the string being fixed at its ends. The initial conditions model the action of plucking the string, which sets it in motion. Plucking consists of holding the string in a certain shape, at rest, and then releasing it. If the initial shape of the string is given by a function $f(x)$, the initial conditions may be specified in the form

$$u(x, 0) = f(x), \quad 0 < x < L,$$
$$\frac{\partial u}{\partial t}(x, 0) = 0, \quad 0 \leq x \leq L.$$

The first initial condition models the initial shape of the string, while the second corresponds to it being at rest initially.

In order to obtain particular solutions, we shall need to make use of Fourier series, introduced in *Unit 21*, and of some ideas from *Unit 3*. In particular, we shall need to apply the *principle of superposition*, which applies to linear second-order partial differential equations in the same way as to linear second-order ordinary differential equations. The equations studied in this unit are all **homogeneous**, in that each additive term involves the dependent variable or its derivatives — there are no constant terms or terms involving solely the independent variables. However, the boundary

The *boundary* conditions are conditions where the spatial variable x is fixed.

The *initial* conditions are conditions where the time variable t is fixed (usually at zero).

We use the range $0 < x < L$ for the initial condition $u(x, 0) = f(x)$ because the values of $u(x, 0)$ when $x = 0$ and $x = L$ are specified by boundary conditions (0.2) when $t = 0$.

and initial conditions may be homogeneous (e.g. $u(0,t) = u(L,t) = 0$ and $(\partial u/\partial t)(x,0) = 0$) or inhomogeneous (e.g. $u(x,0) = f(x)$, where f is not the zero function). The **principle of superposition** says that if u_1 and u_2 are both solutions of a homogeneous linear partial differential equation, then so is any linear combination of u_1 and u_2. Furthermore, if u_1 and u_2 both satisfy a homogeneous boundary or initial condition, then so does any linear combination of u_1 and u_2.

You will be asked to verify that this version of the principle of superposition applies to the wave equation at the end of Section 3.

1 Modelling using the wave equation

In this section we shall look at two situations that can be modelled by the wave equation. In Subsection 1.1 we shall see how the wave equation arises as a model of the transverse vibrations of a taut string. Then, in Subsection 1.2, we shall see how damping can be incorporated into the model.

1.1   The taut string

In this subsection you will see how a continuous model of a guitar string — or indeed of any taut string — leads to a model of the transverse vibrations of the string as a second-order partial differential equation.

You saw a **discrete** model of a guitar string in Subsection 4.2 of *Unit 18*.

We need to make some assumptions in order to develop this model. We assume that:

- the string is uniform, with total mass M and equilibrium length L;
- the string is taut, so that in equilibrium it lies in a straight line, which we shall take to be horizontal and label as the x-axis, with origin at the left-hand end;
- each point of the string is subject only to a small, smoothly varying transverse displacement u, as shown in Figure 1.1, and the effect of such a displacement on the horizontal component of the tension force in the string is negligible;
- the string is sufficiently light for the transverse displacement, though small, to produce a tension force much greater than the weight of the string, so that the weight of the string can be neglected;
- all external forces, such as friction and air resistance, are negligible.

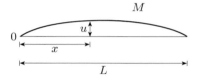

Figure 1.1

Consider a small segment of string, as shown in Figure 1.2, that in its equilibrium position (no displacement) would occupy the interval $[x, x + \delta x]$ on the x-axis.

Since the string is uniform, the mass of this segment is $M\delta x/L$. As we are considering only transverse displacements, at some point in the motion the two ends of this segment occupy positions $u(x,t)$ and $u(x + \delta x, t)$, respectively.

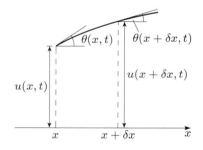

Figure 1.2

Since the segment is small we may model it as a particle of mass $M\delta x/L$ located at the midpoint $u(x + \frac{1}{2}\delta x, t)$ of the segment.

Since we are assuming that the tension in the string is much greater than the weight of the string, the only forces that we need to model are the tension forces on the segment, as shown in Figure 1.3. So the total force on the segment is $\mathbf{T}_1 + \mathbf{T}_2$, and Newton's second law gives

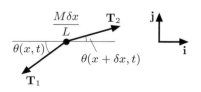

Figure 1.3

$$\frac{M\delta x}{L}\frac{\partial^2 u}{\partial t^2}(x + \tfrac{1}{2}\delta x, t)\mathbf{j} \simeq \mathbf{T}_1 + \mathbf{T}_2. \tag{1.1}$$

(The left-hand term is just mass × acceleration.)

We now need expressions for $\mathbf{T}_1$ and $\mathbf{T}_2$. If we write $\mathbf{T}_1 = H_1\mathbf{i} + V_1\mathbf{j}$, where $\mathbf{i}$ and $\mathbf{j}$ are Cartesian unit vectors as shown in Figure 1.3, then we have $H_1 = -|\mathbf{T}_1|\cos(\theta(x,t))$ and $V_1 = -|\mathbf{T}_1|\sin(\theta(x,t))$, so $V_1 = H_1\tan(\theta(x,t))$. One of our assumptions is that the horizontal component of the tension force in the string has constant magnitude, T say. So here $H_1 = -T$. Also (see Figure 1.4), $\tan(\theta(x,t))$ is the slope of the segment at x, which is also given by the first derivative of the displacement with respect to x, so that we can write $\tan(\theta(x,t)) = (\partial u/\partial x)(x,t)$. Hence we have

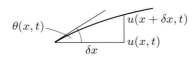

Figure 1.4

$$\mathbf{T}_1 = -T\mathbf{i} - T\frac{\partial u}{\partial x}(x,t)\mathbf{j}.$$

Similarly, for $\mathbf{T}_2$, which acts at $x + \delta x$ where the slope is $\tan(\theta(x+\delta x, t))$, we have $H_2 = -H_1 = T$, so that

$$\mathbf{T}_2 = T\mathbf{i} + T\frac{\partial u}{\partial x}(x + \delta x, t)\mathbf{j}.$$

Substituting into approximation (1.1) and resolving in the $\mathbf{j}$-direction gives

$$\frac{M\delta x}{L}\frac{\partial^2 u}{\partial t^2}(x + \tfrac{1}{2}\delta x, t) \simeq T\left(\frac{\partial u}{\partial x}(x + \delta x, t) - \frac{\partial u}{\partial x}(x,t)\right).$$

Expanding the left-hand side as a linear Taylor approximation gives

$$\frac{M\delta x}{L}\left(\frac{\partial^2 u}{\partial t^2}(x,t) + \tfrac{1}{2}\delta x\frac{\partial}{\partial x}\frac{\partial^2 u}{\partial t^2}(x,t)\right) \simeq T\left(\frac{\partial u}{\partial x}(x + \delta x, t) - \frac{\partial u}{\partial x}(x,t)\right),$$

and rearranging gives

$$\frac{M}{TL}\frac{\partial^2 u}{\partial t^2}(x,t) \simeq \frac{\frac{\partial u}{\partial x}(x + \delta x, t) - \frac{\partial u}{\partial x}(x,t)}{\delta x} - \frac{1}{2}\frac{M}{TL}\delta x\frac{\partial}{\partial x}\frac{\partial^2 u}{\partial t^2}(x,t).$$

Taking the limit as $\delta x \to 0$, the last term on the right-hand side vanishes, and the approximation becomes an equality. We then obtain

Recall from *Unit 12* that

$$\lim_{\delta x \to 0}\frac{f(x+\delta x, t) - f(x,t)}{\delta x} = \frac{\partial f}{\partial x}(x,t).$$

Here $f = \partial u/\partial x$.

$$\frac{M}{TL}\frac{\partial^2 u}{\partial t^2}(x,t) = \frac{\partial^2 u}{\partial x^2}(x,t),$$

which, on rearranging and writing $c^2 = TL/M$, becomes

$$\frac{\partial^2 u}{\partial x^2}(x,t) = \frac{1}{c^2}\frac{\partial^2 u}{\partial t^2}(x,t). \tag{1.2}$$

This is the **wave equation** for transverse vibrations of a taut string.

Example 1.1

Use Equation (1.2) to determine the dimensions of the constant c.

Solution

$$[\partial^2 u/\partial x^2] = \mathrm{L}\,\mathrm{L}^{-2} = \mathrm{L}^{-1}, \quad [\partial^2 u/\partial t^2] = \mathrm{L}\,\mathrm{T}^{-2}.$$

The dimensions of a derivative were dealt with in Exercise 2.3 of *Unit 16*.

Therefore

$$[c^2] = \frac{[\partial^2 u/\partial t^2]}{[\partial^2 u/\partial x^2]} = \frac{\mathrm{L}\,\mathrm{T}^{-2}}{\mathrm{L}^{-1}} = \mathrm{L}^2\mathrm{T}^{-2},$$

so $[c] = \mathrm{L}\,\mathrm{T}^{-1}$.   ■

So c has the dimensions of velocity, and Equation (1.2) will be dimensionally consistent provided that $\sqrt{TL/M}$ has the same dimensions.

Exercise 1.1

Show that $\sqrt{TL/M}$ has the dimensions of velocity.

To obtain a particular solution to Equation (1.2), we need some initial conditions. Suitable initial conditions are values for the displacement and the velocity of the string at time $t = 0$ for all points x along the string. These initial conditions will generally need to be expressed as functions of x, say $f(x)$ and $g(x)$. Therefore we can write the initial conditions as

The transverse component of the velocity of the string is given by the first derivative of u with respect to t.

$$u(x, 0) = f(x), \quad \frac{\partial u}{\partial t}(x, 0) = g(x).$$

Example 1.2

A taut string of equilibrium length L is plucked at its midpoint, which is given an initial displacement d, as shown in Figure 1.5. It is then released from rest. Write down the initial conditions for the wave equation for the transverse vibrations of this string.

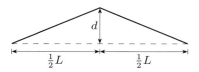

Solution

The displacement shown in Figure 1.5 has two linear sections. These have slopes $\pm d/(\frac{1}{2}L) = \pm 2d/L$. Hence the initial displacement is given by

Figure 1.5

$$u(x, 0) = \begin{cases} \dfrac{2d}{L}x, & 0 < x \le \frac{1}{2}L, \\ \dfrac{2d}{L}(L - x), & \frac{1}{2}L < x < L. \end{cases}$$

As the string is released from rest, the transverse component of the initial velocity is given by

$$\frac{\partial u}{\partial t}(x, 0) = 0, \quad 0 \le x \le L. \quad \blacksquare$$

*Exercise 1.2

A taut string of equilibrium length L is plucked one third of the way along its length, which is given an initial displacement d, as shown in Figure 1.6. What is the corresponding initial condition, for this displacement, for the wave equation for the transverse vibrations of this string?

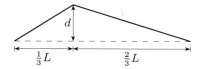

Figure 1.6

To obtain a particular solution of Equation (1.2), we also need boundary conditions that correspond to the ends of the string being fixed. The displacements of the ends at time t are given by $u(0, t)$ and $u(L, t)$. Hence the required boundary conditions are

$$u(0, t) = 0, \quad u(L, t) = 0, \quad t \ge 0.$$

Once you have tightened the string, fixed its ends, plucked it and gently let it go, its subsequent behaviour is determined. So the two initial conditions and two boundary conditions are sufficient to be able to determine a unique solution to the wave equation for transverse vibrations of a taut string, as you will see in Section 3.

Wave equation for transverse vibrations of a taut string

A uniform taut string of mass M, equilibrium length L and constant horizontal tension T, fixed at both ends, is given a displacement d at its midpoint and then released from rest. The function $u(x,t)$ represents the transverse displacement at the point x along the equilibrium position of the string, measured from one fixed end, at time t.

The behaviour of u is modelled by the wave equation

$$\frac{\partial^2 u}{\partial x^2} = \frac{1}{c^2}\frac{\partial^2 u}{\partial t^2}, \quad \text{where } c^2 = \frac{TL}{M},$$

subject to boundary conditions

$$u(0,t) = u(L,t) = 0, \quad t \geq 0,$$

and initial conditions

$$u(x,0) = \begin{cases} \dfrac{2d}{L}x, & 0 < x \leq \tfrac{1}{2}L, \\[2mm] \dfrac{2d}{L}(L-x), & \tfrac{1}{2}L < x < L, \end{cases}$$

$$\frac{\partial u}{\partial t}(x,0) = 0, \quad 0 \leq x \leq L.$$

If the string is not plucked at its midpoint, then a different formula for the initial displacement will need to be used.

In the Introduction it was shown that any function of the form $u(x,t) = \sin(kx)\cos(kct)$ is a solution of the wave equation, for any constant k. In particular, therefore,

$$u(x,t) = \sin\left(\frac{\pi x}{L}\right)\cos\left(\frac{\pi ct}{L}\right) \tag{1.3}$$

is a solution of the wave equation for transverse vibrations of a taut string, where L is the equilibrium length of the string. This solution also satisfies the boundary conditions and the second initial condition for the model.

Exercise 1.3

Show that the solution given by Equation (1.3) satisfies the boundary conditions

$$u(0,t) = u(L,t) = 0, \quad t \geq 0,$$

and the initial condition

$$\frac{\partial u}{\partial t}(x,0) = 0, \quad 0 \leq x \leq L.$$

We shall see in Section 3 how to find a solution that also satisfies the other initial condition.

1.2 Adding damping

When we modelled the transverse vibrations of a taut string, we applied
Newton's second law to a segment of string and obtained the approximation

$$\frac{M\delta x}{L}\frac{\partial^2 u}{\partial t^2}(x + \tfrac{1}{2}\delta x, t) \simeq T\left(\frac{\partial u}{\partial x}(x + \delta x, t) - \frac{\partial u}{\partial x}(x, t)\right). \tag{1.4}$$

This model assumes that the only forces on the segment of string are the
tension forces due to the string. In practice, it is likely that there will be
forces damping the motion. A first model of the damping force assumes
that its magnitude is proportional to the length of the segment δx and to
the transverse component of the segment's velocity $(\partial u/\partial t)(x, t)$, and that
it acts in the direction opposite to the velocity. Approximation (1.4) then
becomes

$$\frac{M\delta x}{L}\frac{\partial^2 u}{\partial t^2}(x + \tfrac{1}{2}\delta x, t) \simeq T\left(\frac{\partial u}{\partial x}(x + \delta x, t) - \frac{\partial u}{\partial x}(x, t)\right)$$

$$- \alpha\,\delta x\,\frac{\partial u}{\partial t}(x + \tfrac{1}{2}\delta x, t),$$

where α is a constant to be determined experimentally. Dividing through
by δx and taking the limit as $\delta x \to 0$, we obtain

$$\frac{M}{L}\frac{\partial^2 u}{\partial t^2}(x, t) = T\frac{\partial^2 u}{\partial x^2}(x, t) - \alpha\frac{\partial u}{\partial t}(x, t).$$

Rearranging gives

$$\frac{\partial^2 u}{\partial x^2} = \frac{1}{c^2}\left(\frac{\partial^2 u}{\partial t^2} + 2\varepsilon\frac{\partial u}{\partial t}\right), \quad \text{where } c^2 = \frac{TL}{M} \text{ and } \varepsilon = \frac{\alpha L}{2M}. \tag{1.5}$$

For obvious reasons, we call this the **damped wave equation**. The boundary and initial conditions are as before.

End-of-section Exercises

Exercise 1.4

How would the wave equation have to be modified to deal with a damping
force with a magnitude proportional to the square of the magnitude of the
velocity? Would the resulting equation be linear?

Exercise 1.5

Suppose that the initial conditions for the transverse vibrations of a taut
string are

$$u(x, 0) = \begin{cases} -\dfrac{3d}{L}x, & 0 < x \leq \tfrac{1}{3}L, \\[2mm] -\dfrac{3d}{2L}(L - x), & \tfrac{1}{3}L < x < L, \end{cases}$$

$$\frac{\partial u}{\partial t}(x, 0) = 0, \quad 0 \leq x \leq L.$$

Describe how the string has been set in motion.

*Exercise 1.6

A taut string is initially in its equilibrium position. At time $t = 0$, it is
struck in such a way as to impart, instantaneously, a transverse velocity
v (in the positive direction) to the middle third of the string. Modify the
initial conditions for the wave equation for transverse vibrations of the string
to model this situation.

2 Modelling using the diffusion equation

In this section we shall look at a situation that can be modelled using a different second-order partial differential equation, known as the diffusion equation. In Subsection 2.1 we shall see how the diffusion equation arises as a model of heat transfer by conduction through an insulated metal rod. In Subsection 2.2 we shall see how, for an uninsulated metal rod, heat transfer by convection can be incorporated into the model.

Heat flow was the subject of Unit 15.

2.1   The insulated rod

In this subsection we shall model the cooling of a hot metal rod, both of whose ends are kept at a fixed temperature Θ_0. We assume that the rod is insulated along its length, so that the only significant heat loss is through its ends. This means that the situation is effectively one-dimensional, so that the temperature of a point of the rod *at a given time* varies only according to the distance x of the point along the rod, which we shall measure from one of its ends, as shown in Figure 2.1. As the rod is cooling down, the temperature also varies with time t. Thus the temperature is a function of the two variables x and t, and will be denoted by $\Theta(x, t)$. We shall also assume that the rod is uniform, of mass M, length L and cross-sectional area A, with specific heat c and thermal conductivity κ.

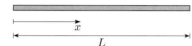

Figure 2.1

To see how the temperature changes with time, we model the flow of heat. As we did when modelling the motion of a taut string, we shall look at a small segment of rod occupying the interval $[x, x + \delta x]$. As the rod is uniform, this segment has mass $M \delta x / L$. We then consider the flow of heat into and out of this segment. We shall measure the heat flow from left to right in Figure 2.2, to match the positive x-direction.

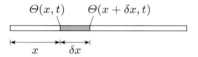

Figure 2.2

For a sufficiently small segment, we may assume that $\Theta(x, t) \simeq \Theta(x + \delta x, t)$. So the change in heat energy of the segment over a small time interval $[t, t + \delta t]$ is given approximately by

$$E(t + \delta t) - E(t) \simeq \frac{M \delta x}{L} c (\Theta(x, t + \delta t) - \Theta(x, t)),$$

where $E(t)$ is the heat energy of the segment at time t. Dividing both sides by δt and taking the limit as $\delta t \to 0$, we obtain

$$\frac{dE}{dt} \simeq \frac{M c \delta x}{L} \frac{\partial \Theta}{\partial t}(x, t), \tag{2.1}$$

which is the approximate rate of change of heat energy in the segment at time t.

We can now use Fourier's law to obtain another expression for the rate of change of heat energy in the segment. We shall apply Fourier's law to the cross-sectional surface of area A at each end of the segment, noting that the temperature gradient normal to each surface is given by $\partial \Theta / \partial x$. So, at time t, the rate of heat transfer by conduction into the left-hand end of the segment is

$$-\kappa A \frac{\partial \Theta}{\partial x}(x, t),$$

As temperature is a function of two variables here, the temperature gradient is a partial derivative.

and the rate of heat transfer by conduction out of the right-hand end of the segment is

$$-\kappa A \frac{\partial \Theta}{\partial x}(x + \delta x, t).$$

Therefore, since there is no source of heat transfer into or out of the segment other than by conduction along the rod, the rate of change of heat energy in the segment at time t is

We assume that the segment is not at either end of the rod.

$$-\kappa A \frac{\partial \Theta}{\partial x}(x,t) - \left(-\kappa A \frac{\partial \Theta}{\partial x}(x+\delta x, t)\right)$$

$$= \kappa A \left(\frac{\partial \Theta}{\partial x}(x+\delta x, t) - \frac{\partial \Theta}{\partial x}(x,t)\right). \qquad (2.2)$$

Hence, using Equation (2.1), we have

$$\kappa A \left(\frac{\partial \Theta}{\partial x}(x+\delta x, t) - \frac{\partial \Theta}{\partial x}(x,t)\right) \simeq \frac{Mc\,\delta x}{L}\frac{\partial \Theta}{\partial t}(x,t).$$

Dividing both sides by δx and taking the limit as $\delta x \to 0$, we obtain

$$\kappa A \frac{\partial^2 \Theta}{\partial x^2}(x,t) = \frac{Mc}{L}\frac{\partial \Theta}{\partial t}(x,t),$$

which, on rearranging and writing $\alpha = \kappa A L/(Mc)$, becomes

$$\frac{\partial^2 \Theta}{\partial x^2}(x,t) = \frac{1}{\alpha}\frac{\partial \Theta}{\partial t}(x,t). \qquad (2.3)$$

This is known as the **diffusion equation**, or sometimes as the **heat equation**, for the variation of temperature along an insulated rod.

Since the ends of the rod are kept at a steady temperature Θ_0, the boundary conditions are

$$\Theta(0,t) = \Theta(L,t) = \Theta_0, \quad t \geq 0. \qquad (2.4)$$

Further, if the initial distribution of temperature along the rod is given by a function $f(x)$, then we have the initial condition

$$\Theta(x,0) = f(x), \quad 0 < x < L. \qquad (2.5)$$

Note that we need only one initial condition because the equation is first order in time.

These conditions are sufficient for us to be able to obtain a unique solution to the diffusion equation for the variation of temperature in an insulated rod, as you will see in Section 4.

Exercise 2.1 _____

Suppose that the uniform rod in the above model has density ρ. Simplify the formula for the constant α.

_____

We have found that the constant in the diffusion equation is $\alpha = \kappa/(c\rho)$, which depends only on the intrinsic properties of the material, and not on its shape. The length L does, however, enter the problem through the boundary conditions, and implicitly in the initial condition.

Diffusion equation for temperature variation along a rod

A uniform rod of mass M, length L, density ρ, thermal conductivity κ, specific heat c and cross-sectional area A, completely insulated apart from its ends, which are both at the same fixed temperature Θ_0, has an initial temperature distribution given by a function $f(x)$, where x is the distance from one end of the rod. The function $\Theta(x,t)$ represents the temperature at the point x along the rod at time t.

The behaviour of Θ is modelled by the diffusion equation

$$\frac{\partial^2 \Theta}{\partial x^2} = \frac{1}{\alpha}\frac{\partial \Theta}{\partial t}, \quad \text{where } \alpha = \frac{\kappa A L}{Mc} = \frac{\kappa}{c\rho},$$

subject to boundary conditions

$$\Theta(0,t) = \Theta(L,t) = \Theta_0, \quad t \geq 0,$$

and initial condition

$$\Theta(x,0) = f(x), \quad 0 < x < L.$$

The model still applies if the ends of the rod are at different temperatures, in which case the two boundary conditions would have different right-hand sides.

Exercise 2.2

Show that the function

$$\Theta(x,t) = e^{-\frac{\alpha\pi^2 t}{L^2}} \sin\left(\frac{\pi x}{L}\right)$$

satisfies the diffusion equation (2.3) and the boundary conditions (2.4) if $\Theta_0 = 0$.

Exercise 2.3

Suppose that, initially, the temperature of the rod rises linearly towards a peak in the centre, d above the end temperature Θ_0, as shown in Figure 2.3. Write down a formula describing the initial temperature function $f(x)$.

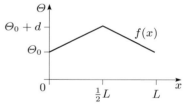

Figure 2.3

2.2   The convecting rod

Suppose that the rod in Subsection 2.1 is not insulated. In this case, heat is not only being conducted along the rod, but is also being convected from its surface, of area S. Let us suppose that the ambient temperature of the fluid surrounding the rod is Θ_0, the same as the temperature at its ends, and that the convective heat transfer coefficient is h. To add the effects of convection to our model, we again look at a small segment of the rod of length δx. The rate of change of heat energy in the segment by conduction is given still by the right-hand side of Equation (2.2). We now need to subtract from this the rate of loss of heat energy by convection. Since the surface area of the segment is $S\delta x/L$, this rate of loss of heat energy is given by Equation (3.1) of *Unit 15* as approximately

$$h\frac{S\delta x}{L}(\Theta(x,t) - \Theta_0), \tag{2.6}$$

where again we assume that the temperature of the whole segment at time t is approximately $\Theta(x,t)$.

Exercise 2.4 _____

Use formulae (2.1), (2.2) and (2.6) to obtain a second-order partial differential equation modelling the temperature variation in the convecting rod.

_____

So, for the convecting rod, the model of the temperature variation is

$$\frac{\partial^2 \Theta}{\partial x^2} = \frac{1}{\alpha}\frac{\partial \Theta}{\partial t} + \gamma(\Theta - \Theta_0), \quad \text{where } \alpha = \frac{\kappa AL}{Mc} \text{ and } \gamma = \frac{hS}{\kappa AL}.$$

The boundary and initial conditions are as before.

Exercise 2.5 _____

Suppose that the convecting rod has uniform density ρ and circular cross-section of radius r. Find expressions for the constants α and γ that do not involve M, L, A or S.

_____

End-of-section Exercise

*Exercise 2.6 _____

Write down the initial condition describing the temperature distribution if the central third of the rod is initially heated to a temperature Θ_1 while the remainder of the rod stays at the background temperature Θ_0.

_____

3 Separating the variables

In the first two sections you have seen several physical situations modelled using partial differential equations. The next step is to find solutions to these models. We shall find solutions in this and the next section, but detailed interpretation of these solutions will be left until Section 5, where you will be able to explore the solutions on your computer.

In this section we shall solve the wave equation and the damped wave equation from Section 1. We shall do so in the context of the taut string, though the method of solution is independent of the physical context and can be applied to any model involving the wave equation. We begin in Subsection 3.1 by solving the wave equation for the taut string subject to its homogeneous boundary conditions and to the homogeneous initial condition specifying a zero initial velocity. Then, in Subsection 3.2, we go on to examine how to amend this solution to satisfy the inhomogeneous initial condition, specifying the initial displacement of the string. Finally, in Subsection 3.3, we extend our solutions to the damped wave equation. The goal, which is presented at the end of the section, is a systematic procedure, which will enable us to solve a wide variety of partial differential equations.

Indeed, the method of solution can be applied to models involving the diffusion equation too, as you will see in Section 4.

3.1 Normal modes

In this subsection we shall solve the wave equation for vibrations of a taut string,

$$\frac{\partial^2 u}{\partial x^2} = \frac{1}{c^2}\frac{\partial^2 u}{\partial t^2}, \tag{3.1}$$

subject to the boundary conditions

$$u(0,t) = u(L,t) = 0, \quad t \geq 0, \tag{3.2}$$

and the initial condition

$$\frac{\partial u}{\partial t}(x,0) = 0, \quad 0 \leq x \leq L. \tag{3.3}$$

The method that we shall use, known as **separating the variables**, is applicable to a variety of homogeneous linear partial differential equations, including the wave equation and the diffusion equation. Essentially, it involves looking for solutions of the form $u(x,t) = X(x)T(t)$, where $X(x)$ is a function of x alone and $T(t)$ is a function of t alone, so that the variables x and t occur in two separate functions that make up the solution.

> Note that the function T here has no connection with the (constant) tension T used in Section 1.

It turns out that in this particular problem $T(t)$ has the form

$$T(t) = \cos(\omega t),$$

where ω is the angular frequency of the vibrations.

We shall see why in Subsection 3.3.

In fact there are an infinite number of such solutions, corresponding to different values of ω. Each solution of the form $X(x)\cos(\omega t)$ is known as a **normal mode** of the continuous model. Let us now proceed to determine the form that $X(x)$ and ω must take if a function of the form $X(x)\cos(\omega t)$ is to be a normal mode of the model. In other words, we are going to look for solutions of the form $u(x,t) = X(x)T(t)$, where $T(t) = \cos(\omega t)$. (As we shall see later, this form of the function $T(t)$ ensures that initial condition (3.3) is satisfied.)

> These normal modes are analogous to the normal modes studied in *Unit 18*.
>
> We shall see later how the method can be generalized to any function $T(t)$.

Exercise 3.1

Determine the partial derivatives $\partial^2 u/\partial x^2$ and $\partial^2 u/\partial t^2$ of the function

$$u(x,t) = X(x)\cos(\omega t).$$

Substituting the values found for the partial derivatives in Exercise 3.1 into the wave equation (3.1) gives

$$X''(x)\cos(\omega t) = -\frac{\omega^2}{c^2}X(x)\cos(\omega t),$$

which on rearranging gives

$$\left(X''(x) + \frac{\omega^2}{c^2}X(x)\right)\cos(\omega t) = 0.$$

Since the time-dependent function $\cos(\omega t)$ is not always zero, the other factor must be zero. So we must have

$$X''(x) + \frac{\omega^2}{c^2}X(x) = 0. \tag{3.4}$$

We have reduced a partial differential equation to an ordinary differential equation, involving functions and derivatives depending on x alone, which we can solve immediately.

Exercise 3.2 _____

What is the general solution of the differential equation (3.4)?

_____

So the wave equation (3.1) has normal mode solutions of the form

$$u(x,t) = X(x)\cos(\omega t),$$

where $X(x)$, the initial displacement, is given by

$$X(x) = A\cos\left(\frac{\omega x}{c}\right) + B\sin\left(\frac{\omega x}{c}\right), \tag{3.5}$$

where A and B are arbitrary constants.

> Note that $u(x,0) = X(x)$, so that $X(x)$ is the initial displacement.

These solutions do not restrict the angular frequency ω in any way. However, for the taut string, there are very severe restrictions placed on ω by the boundary conditions.

Exercise 3.3 _____

What do the boundary conditions (3.2) tell you about the initial displacement function $X(x)$?

_____

The boundary conditions tell us that

$$X(0) = 0 \quad \text{and} \quad X(L) = 0.$$

Using Equation (3.5), these conditions reduce to

$$A = 0 \quad \text{and} \quad B\sin\left(\frac{\omega L}{c}\right) = 0.$$

From this second condition we have $B = 0$ or $\sin(\omega L/c) = 0$. The case where $B = 0$ gives $X(x) = 0$ for all x, the zero function, which corresponds to no initial displacement. More interesting is the case where $\sin(\omega L/c) = 0$, which gives $\omega L/c = r\pi$ for any integer r, so that the only possible values for ω are

$$\omega = \frac{cr\pi}{L}, \quad r = 0, \pm 1, \pm 2, \pm 3, \ldots .$$

So the conditions on A and ω give

$$X(x) = B\sin\left(\frac{r\pi x}{L}\right), \quad r = 0, \pm 1, \pm 2, \pm 3, \ldots, \tag{3.6}$$

> The case where $X(x)$ is the zero function is covered by the case where $r = 0$.

where B is an arbitrary constant. Since B is an arbitrary constant and $\sin(-y) = -\sin y$, the cases where $r = -1, -2, -3, \ldots$ can be absorbed into B. Also, the case $r = 0$ is covered by taking $B = 0$. So we can write Equations (3.6) more succinctly as

$$X(x) = B\sin\left(\frac{r\pi x}{L}\right), \quad r = 1, 2, 3, \ldots .$$

> Hence the allowed values for ω are now restricted to $\omega = cr\pi/L, \quad r = 1, 2, 3, \ldots .$

We have found a range of values of ω and the form of the function $X(x)$ in the normal mode. Now it is time to concentrate on the function $T(t) = \cos(\omega t)$. For our allowed values for ω, the cosine term in the normal mode solution $u(x,t) = X(x)\cos(\omega t)$ must take the form

$$\cos\left(\frac{cr\pi t}{L}\right), \quad r = 1, 2, 3, \ldots .$$

Hence normal mode solutions of the wave equation (3.1) that also satisfy the boundary conditions (3.2) are

$$u(x,t) = X(x)T(t) = B \sin\left(\frac{r\pi x}{L}\right) \cos\left(\frac{cr\pi t}{L}\right), \quad r = 1, 2, 3, \ldots, \quad (3.7)$$

where B is an arbitrary constant.

Now, there is a version of the *principle of superposition* that applies to linear partial differential equations. As you saw in the Introduction, in the case of homogeneous equations of this type (such as the wave equation), the principle of superposition says that any linear combination of solutions of the equation is also a solution. So all linear combinations of solutions (3.7) are also solutions of the wave equation (3.1). Furthermore, the principle of superposition says that any linear combination of solutions that satisfy a homogeneous boundary condition is also a solution satisfying that boundary condition. Hence, since each of solutions (3.7) satisfies the homogeneous boundary conditions (3.2), so does any linear combination of them. So every linear combination of Equations (3.7) satisfies the wave equation (3.1) subject to boundary conditions (3.2).

In the light of all this, consider the family of solutions

$$u_r(x,t) = \sin\left(\frac{r\pi x}{L}\right) \cos\left(\frac{cr\pi t}{L}\right), \quad r = 1, 2, 3, \ldots. \quad (3.8)$$

The set of linear combinations of these functions is the same as the set of linear combinations of solutions (3.7), and so also forms a set of solutions of the wave equation (3.1) subject to boundary conditions (3.2). We shall take the family of solutions (3.8) to be our standard set of normal mode solutions from which every solution of the wave equation (3.1) subject to boundary conditions (3.2) and initial condition (3.3) can be obtained by taking an appropriate linear combination.

Exercise 3.4

Interpret solutions (3.8) for $r = 1$, 2 and 3 in terms of the transverse vibrations of a taut string.

The first three solutions in family (3.8) have initial displacements given by the graphs in Figure 3.1. Clearly the larger the value of r, the higher the frequency (and the higher the pitch of the note).

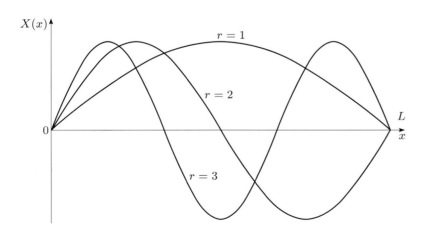

Figure 3.1

So far, we have found a family of solutions (3.8) satisfying the wave equation (3.1) and the boundary conditions (3.2). In fact, these solutions also satisfy the initial condition (3.3).

Exercise 3.5

Check that the solutions (3.8) satisfy the initial condition (3.3).

The principle of superposition tells us that if solutions (3.8) satisfy the homogeneous initial condition (3.3), then so must any linear combination of solutions (3.8). Thus we have found a family of solutions (3.8), the linear combinations of which comprise a set of solutions to the wave equation (3.1) subject to the homogeneous boundary conditions (3.2) and the homogeneous initial condition (3.3). Moreover, though we do not prove it here, the set of linear combinations of solutions (3.8) is the *complete* set of solutions with these properties. It remains to determine what restrictions we need to place on our family of solutions to satisfy the other, inhomogeneous, initial condition of our model of the transverse vibrations of a taut string.

3.2   The initial displacement

In this subsection we shall see how we need to restrict the solutions we obtained in Subsection 3.1 to the wave equation (3.1), subject to boundary conditions (3.2) and initial condition (3.3), so as to satisfy the condition for the initial displacement. We shall look in detail at just one initial displacement, given by

$$u(x,0) = f(x), \quad 0 < x < L, \tag{3.9}$$

where

$$f(x) = \begin{cases} \dfrac{2d}{L}x, & 0 < x \leq \tfrac{1}{2}L, \\ \dfrac{2d}{L}(L-x), & \tfrac{1}{2}L < x < L, \end{cases} \tag{3.10}$$

which is the initial displacement of a taut string plucked at its centre. The technique can be applied to other initial displacements, in an obvious way, as we shall indicate later.

Unfortunately, none of the individual members of the family (3.8) of functions $u_r(x,t)$ satisfies condition (3.9), since

$$u_r(x,0) = \sin\left(\frac{r\pi x}{L}\right) \neq f(x).$$

However, we can find a linear combination of the family (3.8) of functions that does satisfy condition (3.9). You will recall from *Unit 21* that a function such as $f(x)$ can be approximated by a Fourier series, i.e. by an infinite sum of sinusoidal terms. So it should come as no surprise that what we need to satisfy condition (3.9) is an infinite linear combination of the family (3.8) of solutions, i.e. a solution of the form

$$u(x,t) = \sum_{r=1}^{\infty} B_r u_r(x,t) = \sum_{r=1}^{\infty} B_r \sin\left(\frac{r\pi x}{L}\right) \cos\left(\frac{cr\pi t}{L}\right). \tag{3.11}$$

The principle of superposition extends to such infinite sums, so that they satisfy not only the wave equation (3.1), but also the homogeneous boundary conditions (3.2) and the homogeneous initial condition (3.3). So all that remains is to determine when Equation (3.11) satisfies the inhomogeneous initial condition (3.9).

When $t = 0$, Equation (3.11) becomes

$$u(x, 0) = \sum_{r=1}^{\infty} B_r \sin\left(\frac{r\pi x}{L}\right).$$

So if Equation (3.11) is to satisfy condition (3.9), then we must have

$$f(x) = \sum_{r=1}^{\infty} B_r \sin\left(\frac{r\pi x}{L}\right).$$

Hence all we need to do is to express the function $f(x)$, describing the initial displacement, as a Fourier sine series. You saw in *Unit 21* how to deal with such functions that are not naturally periodic. The function $f(x)$ in Equation (3.10) is defined on the interval $[0, L]$. We want it described as a sine series, in which the sine functions are periodic on the fundamental interval $[-L, L]$.

This technique can be applied to any initial displacement function for which we can obtain a Fourier sine series.

You saw in *Unit 21* that the coefficients B_r are given by the integrals

$$B_r = \frac{2}{L} \int_0^L f(x) \sin\left(\frac{r\pi x}{L}\right) dx.$$

For the function $f(x)$ in Equation (3.10), these integrals evaluate to

$$B_r = \frac{8d}{r^2\pi^2} \sin\left(\frac{r\pi}{2}\right),$$

so the values for the coefficients B_r, for $r = 1, 2, 3, 4, 5, 6, \ldots$, are given by

This can easily be checked using the computer algebra package (cf. Activity 4.2 in *Unit 21*).

$$\frac{8d}{\pi^2},\ 0,\ -\frac{8d}{9\pi^2},\ 0,\ \frac{8d}{25\pi^2},\ 0,\ \ldots.$$

Substituting into Equation (3.11) gives the solution for our plucked string problem as

$$u(x, t) = \frac{8d}{\pi^2}\left[\sin\left(\frac{\pi x}{L}\right)\cos\left(\frac{\pi ct}{L}\right) - \frac{1}{9}\sin\left(\frac{3\pi x}{L}\right)\cos\left(\frac{3\pi ct}{L}\right)\right.$$
$$\left. + \frac{1}{25}\sin\left(\frac{5\pi x}{L}\right)\cos\left(\frac{5\pi ct}{L}\right) - \cdots\right].$$

This may seem a very complicated solution, and you may not be able to see immediately how this combination of terms behaves. However, in Section 5 you will be able to plot the solution graphically, using your computer. The method used to obtain this solution, known as separating the variables, can be applied to a variety of homogeneous linear partial differential equations, not just the wave equation.

3.3   The damped plucked string

In Subsections 3.1 and 3.2 we solved the wave equation model for vibrations of a taut string initially plucked at its midpoint. In this subsection we shall generalize the method in order to solve the damped wave equation model for vibrations of a damped taut string plucked at its midpoint. The model developed in Subsection 1.2 is

We shall label each step, and at the end of the subsection the method will be summarized as Procedure 3.1.

$$\frac{\partial^2 u}{\partial x^2} = \frac{1}{c^2}\left(\frac{\partial^2 u}{\partial t^2} + 2\varepsilon\frac{\partial u}{\partial t}\right), \tag{3.12}$$

subject to boundary conditions

$$u(0,t) = u(L,t) = 0, \quad t \geq 0, \tag{3.13}$$

and initial conditions

$$u(x,0) = \begin{cases} \dfrac{2d}{L}x, & 0 < x \leq \tfrac{1}{2}L, \\[2mm] \dfrac{2d}{L}(L-x), & \tfrac{1}{2}L < x < L, \end{cases} \tag{3.14}$$

$$\frac{\partial u}{\partial t}(x,0) = 0, \quad 0 \leq x \leq L. \tag{3.15}$$

We shall assume that the damping is very weak, so that ε is small, as this makes the solution process easier.

Step (a)

In Subsection 3.1 we wrote the unknown function as

$$u(x,t) = X(x)T(t) = X(x)\cos(\omega t).$$

Such solutions, with $T(t) = \cos(\omega t)$, represent a system that vibrates indefinitely. At a point a distance x along the string, the amplitude of the vibration is $X(x)$ for all times t. Clearly, this will not do for the damped taut string, as we expect the vibrations to fade away. So here we just look for solutions of the form

$$u(x,t) = X(x)T(t),$$

without giving any specific form to $T(t)$.

We now have to find the relevant partial derivatives of the function $u(x,t)$ in terms of the functions $X(x)$ and $T(t)$.

*Exercise 3.6

If the function u is defined as a product

$$u(x,t) = X(x)T(t),$$

find formulae for the partial derivatives $\partial u/\partial t$, $\partial^2 u/\partial t^2$ and $\partial^2 u/\partial x^2$ in terms of the functions X and T and their ordinary derivatives.

Step (b)

Substituting the results of Exercise 3.6 into Equation (3.12) gives

$$X''(x)T(t) = \frac{1}{c^2}\left(X(x)T''(t) + 2\varepsilon X(x)T'(t)\right).$$

We now want to separate the variables, i.e. to make each side of the equation a function of a single variable. We do this by dividing through by $X(x)T(t)$ to obtain

$$\frac{X''(x)}{X(x)} = \frac{1}{c^2}\left(\frac{T''(t)}{T(t)} + 2\varepsilon\frac{T'(t)}{T(t)}\right). \tag{3.16}$$

On the left-hand side there is a function of the variable x only, and on the right-hand side there is a function of the variable t only. Whatever the value of x and whatever the value of t, the two sides of the equation must always be equal. The only way that this can occur for *all* x and *all* t is for both sides of the equation to be *constant*. Let us call this constant μ. Then

$$\frac{X''(x)}{X(x)} = \frac{1}{c^2}\left(\frac{T''(t)}{T(t)} + 2\varepsilon\frac{T'(t)}{T(t)}\right) = \mu.$$

The single equation (3.16) then becomes a pair of equations. The first of these is

$$\frac{X''(x)}{X(x)} = \mu,$$

which on rearranging becomes

$$X'' - \mu X = 0. \tag{3.17}$$

*Exercise 3.7

Find the corresponding differential equation satisfied by the function T.

The second equation reduces to

$$T'' + 2\varepsilon T' - c^2\mu T = 0. \tag{3.18}$$

Now we have completed the process of separating the single partial differential equation into two ordinary differential equations, but we still have to find boundary conditions for the function X. To do this, we substitute $u(x,t) = X(x)T(t)$ into the boundary conditions (3.13).

The boundary condition $u(0,t) = 0$ becomes $X(0)T(t) = 0$ for all t. It is possible that the function T always takes the value zero, i.e. is the zero function, but that gives us the uninteresting solution $u = 0$, where the system remains undisturbed. If the system is in motion, then the function T cannot be the zero function, and hence the boundary condition reduces to $X(0) = 0$. Similarly, the boundary condition $u(L,t) = 0$ gives $X(L)T(t) = 0$ for all t, and hence by a similar argument $X(L) = 0$. So the boundary conditions become

$$X(0) = 0 \quad \text{and} \quad X(L) = 0, \tag{3.19}$$

which are boundary conditions for the ordinary differential equation (3.17).

Step (c)

We solve the differential equations for X and T so that the boundary conditions (3.19) are satisfied.

For the function X, we have Equation (3.17) and boundary conditions (3.19). If μ is positive, then we can write $\mu = k^2$, for some non-zero number k, and the general solution to Equation (3.17) is

$$X(x) = Ae^{kx} + Be^{-kx}.$$

The only way to satisfy the boundary conditions is for A and B both to be zero, which leads to the trivial solution $u = 0$.

The boundary conditions reduce to $A + B = 0$ and $Ae^{kL} + Be^{-kL} = 0$. Substituting $B = -A$ into the second equation gives $A(e^{kL} - e^{-kL}) = 0$. Since $L \neq 0$ and $k \neq 0$ we have $e^{kL} - e^{-kL} \neq 0$, so that $A = B = 0$.

Exercise 3.8

What is the solution when $\mu = 0$?

Hence, to obtain interesting answers, we assume that μ is negative and write $\mu = -k^2$, for some non-zero number k. Equation (3.17) becomes

$$X'' + k^2 X = 0,$$

with general solution

$$X(x) = A\cos(kx) + B\sin(kx).$$

As in Subsection 3.1, the boundary conditions (3.19) tell us that $A = 0$ and $B\sin(kL) = 0$, so that $B = 0$ or $\sin(kL) = 0$. The case $B = 0$ gives the trivial solution again, whereas the case $\sin(kL) = 0$ restricts k to take one of the values $r\pi/L$, where r is an integer. Hence, as in Subsection 3.1, we find again a family of solutions to the boundary-value problem for X of the form

$$X_r(x) = B\sin\left(\frac{r\pi x}{L}\right), \quad r = 1, 2, 3, \ldots, \tag{3.20}$$

where B is an arbitrary constant.

Now we must deal with the equation for T. We know from our discussion of the function X that to have a non-trivial solution u, we must have $\mu = -k^2$ and $k = r\pi/L$ (for positive integers r), so that the differential equation (3.18) for T becomes

$$T'' + 2\varepsilon T' + \omega^2 T = 0, \quad \text{where } \omega = ck. \tag{3.21}$$

To solve Equation (3.21) for T, we first solve the auxiliary equation

$$\lambda^2 + 2\varepsilon\lambda + \omega^2 = 0,$$

which gives

$$\lambda = -\varepsilon \pm \sqrt{\varepsilon^2 - \omega^2}.$$

Using the assumption that $\varepsilon \ll \omega$, i.e. ε is much smaller than ω, which corresponds to very weak damping, this reduces to

$$\lambda \simeq -\varepsilon \pm i\omega.$$

The corresponding general solution is

$$T(t) \simeq e^{-\varepsilon t}(\alpha\cos(\omega t) + \beta\sin(\omega t)),$$

where α and β are arbitrary constants.

Using the allowed values for k (i.e. $r\pi/L$, for positive integers r), where $\omega = ck$, this gives the approximate solutions

$$T_r(t) \simeq e^{-\varepsilon t}\left(\alpha \cos\left(\frac{cr\pi t}{L}\right) + \beta \sin\left(\frac{cr\pi t}{L}\right)\right), \quad r = 1, 2, 3, \ldots, \quad (3.22)$$

where α and β are arbitrary constants.

Thus, we can combine the two families of solutions (3.20) and (3.22) to obtain the family of approximate solutions

$$u_r(x,t) = X_r(x)T_r(t)$$
$$\simeq e^{-\varepsilon t}\sin\left(\frac{r\pi x}{L}\right)\left(\alpha \cos\left(\frac{cr\pi t}{L}\right) + \beta \sin\left(\frac{cr\pi t}{L}\right)\right),$$
$$r = 1, 2, 3, \ldots, \quad (3.23)$$

where α and β are arbitrary constants. By the principle of superposition, any linear combination of members of this family of solutions is (approximately) a solution to the original partial differential equation (3.12) and satisfies the boundary conditions (3.13).

The fact that we allow all linear combinations of members of the family (3.23) allows us to omit the arbitrary constants from family (3.20), but we cannot omit the arbitrary constants α and β.

Step (d)

Now we try to satisfy the initial conditions. We begin with the homogeneous initial condition (3.15). This was automatically satisfied for the undamped problem, but it is not automatically satisfied here. We know, from the principle of superposition, that if each member of family (3.23) satisfies the homogeneous initial condition (3.15), then so will any linear combination of members of the family. So we just need to consider $u_r(x,t)$ for an arbitrary r (in the range $r = 1, 2, 3, \ldots$). Differentiating (3.23) with respect to t, we obtain

$$\frac{\partial u_r}{\partial t}(x,t) \simeq e^{-\varepsilon t}\sin\left(\frac{r\pi x}{L}\right)\left(-\alpha\frac{cr\pi}{L}\sin\left(\frac{cr\pi t}{L}\right) + \beta\frac{cr\pi}{L}\cos\left(\frac{cr\pi t}{L}\right)\right)$$
$$- \varepsilon e^{-\varepsilon t}\sin\left(\frac{r\pi x}{L}\right)\left(\alpha\cos\left(\frac{cr\pi t}{L}\right) + \beta\sin\left(\frac{cr\pi t}{L}\right)\right).$$

When $t = 0$, and writing $\omega = ck = cr\pi/L$ as earlier, we obtain

$$\frac{\partial u_r}{\partial t}(x,0) \simeq \left(\beta\frac{cr\pi}{L} - \varepsilon\alpha\right)\sin\left(\frac{r\pi x}{L}\right) = (\omega\beta - \varepsilon\alpha)\sin\left(\frac{r\pi x}{L}\right).$$

For initial condition (3.15) to be satisfied, for $0 \le x \le L$, we must have $\omega\beta - \varepsilon\alpha \simeq 0$. For very weak damping, as we noted earlier, we have $\varepsilon \ll \omega$. This means that to satisfy $\omega\beta - \varepsilon\alpha \simeq 0$, we must have $\beta \simeq 0$. Thus, to satisfy the initial condition (3.15), approximately, we need to restrict family (3.23) to

$$u_r(x,t) \simeq \alpha e^{-\varepsilon t}\sin\left(\frac{r\pi x}{L}\right)\cos\left(\frac{cr\pi t}{L}\right), \quad r = 1, 2, 3, \ldots,$$

where α is an arbitrary constant. As before, since our solutions are linear combinations of these functions $u_r(x,t)$, we can ignore the arbitrary constants α and obtain the family of approximate solutions

$$u_r(x,t) \simeq e^{-\varepsilon t}\sin\left(\frac{r\pi x}{L}\right)\cos\left(\frac{cr\pi t}{L}\right), \quad r = 1, 2, 3, \ldots. \quad (3.24)$$

By the principle of superposition, any linear combination of members of this family of solutions is (approximately) a solution to the damped wave equation (3.12) and satisfies the homogeneous boundary conditions (3.13) and (approximately) the homogeneous initial condition (3.15).

We now need to satisfy the inhomogeneous initial condition (3.14). As in Subsection 3.2, we look for an approximate solution of the form

$$u(x,t) = \sum_{r=1}^{\infty} B_r u_r(x,t) \simeq e^{-\varepsilon t} \sum_{r=1}^{\infty} B_r \sin\left(\frac{r\pi x}{L}\right) \cos\left(\frac{cr\pi t}{L}\right), \qquad (3.25)$$

where the B_r are constants.

Setting $t = 0$ in approximation (3.25) gives

$$u(x,0) \simeq \sum_{r=1}^{\infty} B_r \sin\left(\frac{r\pi x}{L}\right), \qquad (3.26)$$

while the given initial condition (3.14) is

$$u(x,0) = \begin{cases} \dfrac{2d}{L}x, & 0 < x \le \tfrac{1}{2}L, \\[2mm] \dfrac{2d}{L}(L-x), & \tfrac{1}{2}L < x < L. \end{cases}$$

The situation is exactly the same as in Subsection 3.2, so we obtain the same Fourier coefficients B_r as there. Substituting these into approximation (3.25) gives the final form of the approximate solution as

$$u(x,t) \simeq \frac{8d}{\pi^2} e^{-\varepsilon t} \left[\sin\left(\frac{\pi x}{L}\right) \cos\left(\frac{\pi ct}{L}\right) - \frac{1}{9} \sin\left(\frac{3\pi x}{L}\right) \cos\left(\frac{3\pi ct}{L}\right) \right.$$
$$\left. + \frac{1}{25} \sin\left(\frac{5\pi x}{L}\right) \cos\left(\frac{5\pi ct}{L}\right) - \cdots \right].$$

Remember that this is an approximate solution, under the assumption of very weak damping, where ε is very small.

This is the same as the solution to the undamped problem except for the factor $e^{-\varepsilon t}$, which describes exponential decay. Hence the shape of the string is roughly the same as before, apart from the amplitude becoming progressively smaller by the factor $e^{-\varepsilon t}$. The shape determines the sound, so the sound stays the same, only now it gets progressively quieter, since the volume is determined by the amplitude. You will be able to investigate the predicted behaviour more fully by use of your computer in Section 5.

As promised, we now summarize the method of separating the variables in the form of a procedure.

Procedure 3.1   Separating the variables

Given a homogeneous linear partial differential equation with dependent variable u and independent variables x and t, subject to appropriate homogeneous boundary and initial conditions, a solution can often be found by means of the following steps.

(a) Write the unknown function as a product of functions of one variable, i.e. write

$$u(x,t) = X(x)T(t).$$

Find the required partial derivatives of u in terms of the ordinary derivatives of the functions X and T.

(b) Substitute the partial derivatives found in (a) into the partial differential equation. Rearrange the equation so that each side consists of a function of a single independent variable. Each side of the rearranged equation must equal a constant, giving separate ordinary differential equations for X and T. Use the boundary conditions for u to find boundary conditions for X.

(c) Solve the differential equations for X and T found in (b). Use the boundary conditions for X to find families of solutions $X_r(x)$ and $T_r(t)$ that combine to give a family of solutions

$$u_r(x,t) = X_r(x)T_r(t), \quad r = 0, 1, 2, 3, \ldots,$$

of the original partial differential equation.

The non-zero members of the family of solutions $u_r(x,t) = X_r(x)T_r(t)$ are known as **normal mode solutions** of the problem.

(d) Use the initial conditions and results about Fourier series to determine (when possible) an infinite linear combination of the family of solutions found in (c), i.e.

$$u(x,t) = \sum_{r=0}^{\infty} B_r u_r(x,t),$$

that solves the original problem.

End-of-section Exercises

*Exercise 3.9

This exercise asks you to verify that the principle of superposition applies to the wave equation subject to certain homogeneous conditions, to justify its use in this section. Suppose that the functions u_1 and u_2 satisfy the wave equation

$$\frac{\partial^2 u}{\partial x^2} = \frac{1}{c^2}\frac{\partial^2 u}{\partial t^2}$$

and the homogeneous conditions

$$u(0,t) = u(L,t) = 0 \quad \text{and} \quad \frac{\partial u}{\partial t}(x,0) = 0.$$

Show that the linear combination $u = a_1 u_1 + a_2 u_2$, where a_1 and a_2 are constants, is a function that satisfies the same equation and conditions.

Exercise 3.10 _____

Use Steps (a) to (c) of Procedure 3.1 to find an infinite family of solutions for the following model:

$$\frac{\partial^2 u}{\partial x^2} + \frac{\partial^2 u}{\partial t^2} = 0,$$

subject to boundary conditions

$$u(0,t) = u(1,t) = 0, \quad t \geq 0.$$

This equation is known as *Laplace's equation.*

4 Solving the heat transfer problems

In this short section we shall see how the method of separating the variables, in Procedure 3.1, can be used to solve the diffusion equation subject to appropriate boundary and initial conditions. We shall do this in Subsection 4.1 in the context of the insulated rod problem of Subsection 2.1, and in Subsection 4.2 in the context of the convecting rod problem of Subsection 2.2.

If you feel confident about the method of Procedure 3.1, then you might like to try and solve the models for these problems yourself before working through this section — in this way you might consider this section as an extended End-of-section Exercise for Section 3.

4.1 The insulated rod problem solved

In this subsection we shall use Procedure 3.1 to solve a particular model for the insulated rod problem discussed in Subsection 2.1. In this model, the temperatures at the ends of the rod are zero ($\Theta_0 = 0\,°\mathrm{C}$), and the initial temperature of the rod is given by a function $f(x)$ identical to the initial displacement function for the taut string problem considered in Section 3. The model is

$$\frac{\partial^2 \Theta}{\partial x^2} = \frac{1}{\alpha}\frac{\partial \Theta}{\partial t}, \tag{4.1}$$

subject to boundary conditions

$$\Theta(0,t) = \Theta(L,t) = 0, \quad t \geq 0, \tag{4.2}$$

and initial condition

$$\Theta(x,0) = f(x) = \begin{cases} \dfrac{2d}{L}x, & 0 < x \leq \tfrac{1}{2}L, \\[2mm] \dfrac{2d}{L}(L-x), & \tfrac{1}{2}L < x < L. \end{cases} \tag{4.3}$$

Later in this subsection we shall see how our solution can be adapted to cover any fixed temperature Θ_0 at the ends of the rod.

Step (a)

We begin separating the variables by setting

$$\Theta(x,t) = X(x)T(t), \tag{4.4}$$

and finding the relevant partial derivatives:

$$\frac{\partial^2 \Theta}{\partial x^2} = X''T, \tag{4.5}$$

$$\frac{\partial \Theta}{\partial t} = XT'. \tag{4.6}$$

Step (b)

To find separate ordinary differential equations for X and T, we substitute the formulae for the partial derivatives into the partial differential equation, and rearrange. Here, substituting (4.5) and (4.6) into Equation (4.1) gives

$$X''T = \frac{1}{\alpha}XT'.$$

Dividing by XT, to separate the variables, results in

$$\frac{X''}{X} = \frac{1}{\alpha}\frac{T'}{T}. \tag{4.7}$$

Here the left-hand side is a function of the variable x alone and the right-hand side is a function of the variable t alone, so both are equal to a constant μ. The single equation (4.7) then becomes a pair of equations

$$\frac{X''}{X} = \mu, \quad \frac{1}{\alpha}\frac{T'}{T} = \mu,$$

which on rearranging give

$$X'' - \mu X = 0, \tag{4.8}$$
$$T' - \alpha\mu T = 0. \tag{4.9}$$

To find boundary conditions for X, we put $x = 0$ and $x = L$ in Equation (4.4) and substitute into the boundary conditions (4.2), which gives

$$X(0)T(t) = X(L)T(t) = 0, \quad t \geq 0,$$

and hence

$$X(0) = X(L) = 0. \tag{4.10}$$

Step (c)

Next we solve the differential equations for X and T, and combine the families of solutions.

The differential equation (4.8) for X, and its boundary conditions (4.10), are the same as in Section 3. You have seen that a non-trivial solution occurs only if the constant μ is negative. Hence, as before, we replace μ by $-k^2$ and find the same family of solutions

$$X_r(x) = B\sin\left(\frac{r\pi x}{L}\right), \quad r = 1, 2, 3, \ldots, \tag{4.11}$$

As before, k takes one of the values $r\pi/L$.

where B is an arbitrary constant.

Our next task is to solve Equation (4.9) for the function T when the constant μ is replaced by $-k^2$ and k takes the value $r\pi/L$ for some positive integer r.

Under these circumstances, Equation (4.9) is the equation for exponential decay.

*Exercise 4.1

Solve the differential equation

$$T' + \alpha k^2 T = 0.$$

Putting $k = r\pi/L$ in the solution to Exercise 4.1 gives the family of solutions

$$T_r(t) = Ae^{-\frac{\alpha r^2\pi^2 t}{L^2}}, \quad r = 1, 2, 3, \ldots, \tag{4.12}$$

where A is an arbitrary constant.

Combining families (4.11) and (4.12), we obtain the following family of solutions to the diffusion equation (4.1) subject to boundary conditions (4.2):

$$\Theta_r(x,t) = e^{-\frac{\alpha r^2 \pi^2 t}{L^2}} \sin\left(\frac{r\pi x}{L}\right), \quad r = 1, 2, 3, \ldots . \tag{4.13}$$

As before, any linear combination of members of this family is a solution to (4.1) subject to (4.2).

Step (d)

Finally, we form the infinite linear combination

$$\Theta(x,t) = \sum_{r=1}^{\infty} B_r e^{-\frac{\alpha r^2 \pi^2 t}{L^2}} \sin\left(\frac{r\pi x}{L}\right), \tag{4.14}$$

and use the initial condition (4.3) and results on Fourier series to determine the coefficients B_r. Setting $t = 0$ in Equation (4.14) gives

$$\Theta(x,0) = \sum_{r=1}^{\infty} B_r \sin\left(\frac{r\pi x}{L}\right).$$

The function $f(x)$ used in initial condition (4.3) is the same as that used in Section 3, hence we arrive at the same values for the coefficients B_r, and the solution is therefore

$$\Theta(x,t) = \frac{8d}{\pi^2}\left[e^{-\frac{\alpha\pi^2 t}{L^2}} \sin\left(\frac{\pi x}{L}\right) - \frac{1}{9} e^{-\frac{9\alpha\pi^2 t}{L^2}} \sin\left(\frac{3\pi x}{L}\right) \right.$$
$$\left. + \frac{1}{25} e^{-\frac{25\alpha\pi^2 t}{L^2}} \sin\left(\frac{5\pi x}{L}\right) - \cdots \right].$$

Now, as promised earlier, let us see how to amend our solution to cover the case where $\Theta_0 \neq 0$, i.e. where the boundary conditions are

$$\Theta(0,t) = \Theta(L,t) = \Theta_0, \quad t \geq 0.$$

Exercise 4.2

Consider the diffusion equation

$$\frac{\partial^2 \Theta}{\partial x^2} = \frac{1}{\alpha}\frac{\partial \Theta}{\partial t},$$

subject to boundary conditions

$$\Theta(0,t) = \Theta(L,t) = \Theta_0, \quad t \geq 0,$$

where $\Theta_0 \neq 0$, and initial condition

$$\Theta(x,0) = f(x), \quad 0 < x < L,$$

for some function $f(x)$.

(a) Show that the function $\Theta(x,t) = \Theta_0$ satisfies the differential equation.

(b) Use the principle of superposition, Equations (4.13) and the result from part (a) to obtain a family of solutions to the differential equation subject to the boundary conditions.

(c) Explain how you would go on to obtain a solution that also satisfies the initial condition.

4.2   The convecting rod problem solved

In this subsection we shall look briefly at how Procedure 3.1 can be used to solve the following model for the convecting rod:

$$\frac{\partial^2 \Theta}{\partial x^2} = \frac{1}{\alpha}\frac{\partial \Theta}{\partial t} + \gamma\Theta, \tag{4.15}$$

subject to boundary conditions

This is the equation obtained in Exercise 2.4, with $\Theta_0 = 0$.

$$\Theta(0,t) = \Theta(L,t) = 0, \quad t \geq 0, \tag{4.16}$$

and initial condition

$$\Theta(x,0) = \begin{cases} \dfrac{2d}{L}x, & 0 < x \leq \tfrac{1}{2}L, \\[2mm] \dfrac{2d}{L}(L-x), & \tfrac{1}{2}L < x < L. \end{cases} \tag{4.17}$$

Exercise 4.3

Perform Steps (a) and (b) of Procedure 3.1 to begin the process of solving the above model for a convecting rod.

Exercise 4.3 shows that the function X satisfies the equation

$$X'' + k^2 X = 0, \quad \text{with } X(0) = X(L) = 0,$$

while T satisfies the equation

$$T' + \alpha(k^2 + \gamma)T = 0.$$

Step (c) of Procedure 3.1 leads again to $k = r\pi/L$, for any integer r, and then to the family of solutions for X given by

$$X_r(x) = B\sin\left(\frac{r\pi x}{L}\right), \quad r = 1, 2, 3, \ldots, \tag{4.18}$$

where B is an arbitrary constant.

Exercise 4.4

Solve the differential equation

$$T' + \alpha(k^2 + \gamma)T = 0.$$

Putting $k = r\pi/L$, for any positive integer r, into the solution to Exercise 4.4 gives the family of solutions

$$T_r(t) = Ae^{-\alpha\left(\frac{r^2\pi^2}{L^2} + \gamma\right)t}, \quad r = 1, 2, 3, \ldots, \tag{4.19}$$

where A is an arbitrary constant.

Combining families (4.18) and (4.19), we obtain the following family of solutions to Equation (4.15) subject to boundary conditions (4.16):

$$\Theta_r(x,t) = e^{-\alpha\left(\frac{r^2\pi^2}{L^2} + \gamma\right)t}\sin\left(\frac{r\pi x}{L}\right), \quad r = 1, 2, 3, \ldots.$$

As before, any linear combination of members of this family is a solution to (4.15) subject to (4.16).

In Step (d) of Procedure 3.1 we write

$$\Theta(x,t) = \sum_{r=1}^{\infty} B_r e^{-\alpha\left(\frac{r^2\pi^2}{L^2}+\gamma\right)t} \sin\left(\frac{r\pi x}{L}\right),$$

and setting $t = 0$ gives

$$\Theta(x,0) = \sum_{r=1}^{\infty} B_r \sin\left(\frac{r\pi x}{L}\right).$$

This is exactly the same as in the three previous cases, so we arrive at the same values for the coefficients. Therefore the solution is

$$\begin{aligned}
\Theta(x,t) &= \frac{8d}{\pi^2}\left[e^{-\alpha\left(\frac{\pi^2}{L^2}+\gamma\right)t} \sin\left(\frac{\pi x}{L}\right) - \frac{1}{9} e^{-\alpha\left(\frac{9\pi^2}{L^2}+\gamma\right)t} \sin\left(\frac{3\pi x}{L}\right) \right. \\
&\qquad \left. + \frac{1}{25} e^{-\alpha\left(\frac{25\pi^2}{L^2}+\gamma\right)t} \sin\left(\frac{5\pi x}{L}\right) - \cdots \right] \\
&= \frac{8d}{\pi^2} e^{-\alpha\gamma t}\left[e^{-\frac{\alpha\pi^2 t}{L^2}} \sin\left(\frac{\pi x}{L}\right) - \frac{1}{9} e^{-\frac{9\alpha\pi^2 t}{L^2}} \sin\left(\frac{3\pi x}{L}\right) \right. \\
&\qquad \left. + \frac{1}{25} e^{-\frac{25\alpha\pi^2 t}{L^2}} \sin\left(\frac{5\pi x}{L}\right) - \cdots \right].
\end{aligned}$$

This is the same as the solution for the insulated rod except for the $e^{-\alpha\gamma t}$ factor, so the convecting rod cools more quickly than the insulated rod by a factor of $e^{-\alpha\gamma t}$.

End-of-section Exercises

Exercise 4.5

Apply Steps (a) to (c) of Procedure 3.1 to the diffusion equation

$$\frac{\partial^2 \Theta}{\partial x^2} = \frac{1}{\alpha}\frac{\partial \Theta}{\partial t},$$

subject to boundary conditions

$$\frac{\partial \Theta}{\partial x}(0,t) = \frac{\partial \Theta}{\partial x}(L,t) = 0, \quad t \geq 0,$$

and initial condition

$$\Theta(x,0) = \begin{cases} \dfrac{2d}{L}x, & 0 < x \leq \tfrac{1}{2}L, \\[2mm] \dfrac{2d}{L}(L-x), & \tfrac{1}{2}L < x < L. \end{cases}$$

These boundary conditions model the situation where the ends of a hot rod are insulated.

Explain how you would go about applying Step (d) of the procedure, but do not attempt to find the Fourier coefficients needed for the solution that satisfies the initial condition.

Exercise 4.6 _____

Consider the diffusion equation

$$\frac{\partial^2 \Theta}{\partial x^2} = \frac{1}{\alpha}\frac{\partial \Theta}{\partial t},$$

subject to boundary conditions

$$\Theta(0,t) = \Theta_0, \quad \Theta(L,t) = \Theta_L, \quad t \geq 0,$$

These boundary conditions model the situation where the ends of the rod are kept at fixed temperatures.

where Θ_0 and Θ_L are non-zero constants, and initial condition

$$\Theta(x,0) = f(x), \quad 0 < x < L,$$

for some function $f(x)$.

(a) Show that the function

$$\Theta(x,t) = \frac{L-x}{L}\Theta_0 + \frac{x}{L}\Theta_L$$

satisfies the differential equation and the boundary conditions.

(b) Obtain a family of solutions to the differential equation subject to the boundary conditions.

(c) Explain how you would go on to obtain a solution that also satisfies the initial condition.

5 *Interpreting solutions*

This computer section revises some of the ideas in the previous four sections, and allows you to observe and interpret the solutions to problems modelled using the wave equation and the diffusion equation.

You are asked to use the computer algebra package to solve problems of the type considered in Sections 1–4, and to explore the solutions graphically. You will be able to see how changes to boundary and/or initial conditions affect the solutions, and you will be asked to interpret what you see.

Use your computer to complete the following activities.

Activity 5.1

This activity concerns the damped wave equation model for transverse vibrations of a taut string, of mass $M = 0.000\,25\,\text{kg}$, equilibrium length $L = 1\,\text{m}$, horizontal tension $T = 100\,\text{N}$ and damping coefficient $\varepsilon = 0.01$, given by

$$\frac{\partial^2 u}{\partial x^2} = \frac{1}{c^2}\left(\frac{\partial^2 u}{\partial t^2} + 2\varepsilon\frac{\partial u}{\partial t}\right), \quad \text{where } c^2 = \frac{TL}{M},$$

This is Equation (1.5).

subject to the boundary conditions

$$u(0,t) = u(L,t) = 0, \quad t \geq 0,$$

and the initial conditions

$$u(x,0) = f(x), \quad 0 < x < L,$$
$$\frac{\partial u}{\partial t}(x,0) = 0, \quad 0 \leq x \leq L,$$

where

$$f(x) = \begin{cases} \dfrac{3d}{L}x, & 0 < x \leq \tfrac{1}{3}L, \\[2mm] \dfrac{3d}{2L}(L-x), & \tfrac{1}{3}L < x < L. \end{cases}$$

Take the maximum displacement $d = 0.1\,\text{m}$.

(a) Solve the problem, and determine the angular frequency ω, period τ and frequency $1/\tau$ of the vibrations.

(b) Obtain a plot of $u(x,t)$ against x for a number of values of t in the range $0 \leq t \leq 2\tau$ and for $t = 10\tau,\ 100\tau,\ 1000\tau,\ 10\,000\tau,\ 100\,000\tau$. Interpret what you see in terms of the vibrations of the string.

(c) Obtain a contour plot of $u(x,t)$ for $0 \leq x \leq L$ and $0 \leq t \leq 2\tau$. Interpret what you see in terms of the vibrations of the string.

Activity 5.2

This activity concerns the diffusion model for a uniform cylindrical steel rod of mass $M = 2.5\,\text{kg}$, length $L = 1\,\text{m}$, radius $R = 0.01\,\text{m}$, cross-sectional area $A = \pi(0.01)^2 \simeq 3.142 \times 10^{-4}\,\text{m}^2$, density $\rho = M/(AL) \simeq 7.958 \times 10^3\,\text{kg m}^{-3}$, thermal conductivity $\kappa = 63\,\text{W m}^{-1}\,\text{K}^{-1}$ and specific heat $c = 420\,\text{J kg}^{-1}\,\text{K}^{-1}$.

The rod is subject to convection from its surface so that the model is given by

$$\frac{\partial^2 \Theta}{\partial x^2} = \frac{1}{\alpha}\frac{\partial \Theta}{\partial t} + \gamma\Theta,$$

This is Equation (4.15).

where $\alpha = \kappa AL/(Mc) = \kappa/(c\rho)$, and $\gamma = hS/(\kappa AL)$, where $h = 10\,\text{W m}^{-2}\,\text{K}^{-1}$ is the convective heat transfer coefficient and S is the surface area of the rod (in m^2). The rod is subject to the boundary conditions

$$\Theta(0,t) = \Theta(L,t) = 0, \quad t \geq 0,$$

and the initial condition

$$\Theta(x,0) = \begin{cases} \dfrac{2d}{L}x, & 0 < x \leq \tfrac{1}{2}L, \\[2mm] \dfrac{2d}{L}(L-x), & \tfrac{1}{2}L < x < L. \end{cases}$$

Take the maximum temperature difference $d = 50\,^\circ\text{C}$.

(a) Solve the problem.

(b) Obtain a plot of $\Theta(x,t)$ against x for a number of values of t in the range $0 \leq t \leq 10\,000$, including $t = 0$, 10, 100, 1000, 3600, 5000, 10\,000. Interpret what you see in terms of the change in temperature of the rod.

(c) Obtain a contour plot of $\Theta(x,t)$ for $0 \leq x \leq L$ and $0 \leq t \leq 3600$. Interpret what you see in terms of the change in temperature of the rod.

Outcomes

After studying this unit you should be able to:
- understand how the wave and diffusion partial differential equations can be used to model certain systems;
- determine appropriate simple boundary and initial conditions for such models;
- find families of solutions for the wave equation, damped wave equation, diffusion equation and similar homogeneous linear second-order partial differential equations, subject to simple boundary conditions, using the method of separating the variables;
- combine solutions of partial differential equations to satisfy given initial conditions by finding the coefficients of a Fourier series.

Solutions to the exercises

Section 1

1.1 T is the magnitude of a force, so $[T] = \mathrm{MLT^{-2}}$. Also, $[M] = \mathrm{M}$ and $[L] = \mathrm{L}$. Hence
$$[TL/M] = \mathrm{M\,L\,T^{-2}} \times \mathrm{L/M} = \mathrm{L^2\,T^{-2}},$$
so $[\sqrt{TL/M}] = \mathrm{L\,T^{-1}}$, as required.

1.2 The initial displacement has two linear sections, with slopes
$$\frac{d}{\frac{1}{3}L} = \frac{3d}{L} \quad \text{and} \quad -\frac{d}{\frac{2}{3}L} = -\frac{3d}{2L},$$
respectively. Hence the required initial condition is
$$u(x,0) = \begin{cases} \dfrac{3d}{L}x, & 0 < x \le \tfrac{1}{3}L, \\[2mm] \dfrac{3d}{2L}(L-x), & \tfrac{1}{3}L < x < L. \end{cases}$$

1.3 The boundary conditions are satisfied since
$$u(0,t) = \sin 0 \cos\left(\frac{\pi ct}{L}\right) = 0,$$
$$u(L,t) = \sin \pi \cos\left(\frac{\pi ct}{L}\right) = 0.$$
The initial condition is satisfied since
$$\frac{\partial u}{\partial t}(x,0) = -\frac{\pi c}{L}\sin\left(\frac{\pi x}{L}\right)\sin 0 = 0.$$

1.4 To deal with damping that varies with the square of the magnitude of the velocity, the equation needs to be modified to take the form
$$\frac{\partial^2 u}{\partial x^2} = \frac{1}{c^2}\left(\frac{\partial^2 u}{\partial t^2} + 2\varepsilon \frac{\partial u}{\partial t}\left|\frac{\partial u}{\partial t}\right|\right).$$
The modulus sign is essential to ensure that the added force is always damping. (If we had written $(\partial u/\partial t)^2$ instead, then the last term would always be positive, but we need it to take positive and negative values in accordance with $\partial u/\partial t$.)

The product of velocities in the last term means that the equation is not linear.

1.5 The initial velocity is zero, so the string is released from rest. When $x = \tfrac{1}{3}L$, $u(x,0) = -d$, so the point one third of the way along the string has been displaced downward by a distance d.

1.6 Initially there is no displacement, so
$$u(x,0) = 0, \quad 0 < x < L.$$
Since only the middle third is set in motion, the initial velocity is given by
$$\frac{\partial u}{\partial t}(x,0) = \begin{cases} v, & \tfrac{1}{3}L \le x \le \tfrac{2}{3}L, \\ 0, & \text{otherwise.} \end{cases}$$

Section 2

2.1 Since the rod is uniform with length L and cross-sectional area A, it has volume AL. Hence the density is given by $M/(AL)$. Replacing this expression by ρ gives
$$\alpha = \frac{\kappa AL}{Mc} = \frac{\kappa}{c\rho}.$$

2.2 $\dfrac{\partial \Theta}{\partial x} = e^{-\frac{\alpha\pi^2 t}{L^2}}\frac{\pi}{L}\cos\left(\frac{\pi x}{L}\right),$

so $\dfrac{\partial^2 \Theta}{\partial x^2} = -e^{-\frac{\alpha\pi^2 t}{L^2}}\frac{\pi^2}{L^2}\sin\left(\frac{\pi x}{L}\right) = -\frac{\pi^2}{L^2}\Theta(x,t),$

and $\dfrac{\partial \Theta}{\partial t} = -\frac{\alpha\pi^2}{L^2}e^{\frac{-\alpha\pi^2 t}{L^2}}\sin\left(\frac{\pi x}{L}\right) = -\frac{\alpha\pi^2}{L^2}\Theta(x,t),$

thus $\dfrac{1}{\alpha}\dfrac{\partial \Theta}{\partial t} = -\frac{\pi^2}{L^2}\Theta(x,t) = \dfrac{\partial^2 \Theta}{\partial x^2}.$

Hence Equation (2.3) is satisfied.

The boundary conditions are
$$\Theta(0,t) = e^{-\frac{\alpha\pi^2 t}{L^2}}\sin 0 = 0,$$
$$\Theta(L,t) = e^{-\frac{\alpha\pi^2 t}{L^2}}\sin \pi = 0,$$
so these are satisfied for a temperature at the rod ends of $\Theta_0 = 0$.

2.3 The graph in Figure 2.3 looks just like the picture of the plucked string in Figure 1.5, so the required formula is
$$f(x) = \begin{cases} \Theta_0 + \dfrac{2d}{L}x, & 0 \le x \le \tfrac{1}{2}L, \\[2mm] \Theta_0 + \dfrac{2d}{L}(L-x), & \tfrac{1}{2}L < x \le L. \end{cases}$$
As required, this function takes the value Θ_0 when x is 0 or L, and takes the value $\Theta_0 + d$ when x is $\tfrac{1}{2}L$.

2.4 The rate of change of heat energy given by (2.1) must be equated with the rate of change due to conduction minus the rate of loss due to convection, given by (2.2) and (2.6), so we have
$$\kappa A\left(\frac{\partial \Theta}{\partial x}(x+\delta x,t) - \frac{\partial \Theta}{\partial x}(x,t)\right) - \frac{hS\delta x}{L}(\Theta(x,t)-\Theta_0)$$
$$\simeq \frac{Mc\,\delta x}{L}\frac{\partial \Theta}{\partial t}(x,t).$$
Dividing by δx, taking the limit as $\delta x \to 0$ and rearranging, we obtain
$$\frac{\partial^2 \Theta}{\partial x^2}(x,t) = \frac{1}{\alpha}\frac{\partial \Theta}{\partial t}(x,t) + \gamma(\Theta(x,t)-\Theta_0),$$
where $\alpha = \kappa AL/(Mc)$ and $\gamma = hS/(\kappa AL)$.

2.5 As before, $\alpha = \kappa/(c\rho)$. In this case, $A = \pi r^2$ and $S = 2\pi r L$, so
$$\gamma = \frac{hS}{\kappa AL} = \frac{2\pi r Lh}{\kappa \pi r^2 L} = \frac{2h}{\kappa r}.$$

2.6 $\Theta(x,0) = \begin{cases} \Theta_0, & 0 < x < \frac{1}{3}L, \\ \Theta_1, & \frac{1}{3}L \le x \le \frac{2}{3}L, \\ \Theta_0, & \frac{2}{3}L < x < L. \end{cases}$

Section 3

3.1 $\dfrac{\partial u}{\partial x} = X'(x)\cos(\omega t), \qquad \dfrac{\partial^2 u}{\partial x^2} = X''(x)\cos(\omega t).$

$\dfrac{\partial u}{\partial t} = -\omega X(x)\sin(\omega t), \qquad \dfrac{\partial^2 u}{\partial t^2} = -\omega^2 X(x)\cos(\omega t).$

3.2 The equation defines simple harmonic motion, with general solution
$$X(x) = A\cos\left(\frac{\omega x}{c}\right) + B\sin\left(\frac{\omega x}{c}\right),$$
where A and B are arbitrary constants.

3.3 The boundary conditions are
$$u(0,t) = X(0)\cos(\omega t) = 0,$$
$$u(L,t) = X(L)\cos(\omega t) = 0,$$
both of which hold for all t. The only way that this can happen is if
$$X(0) = X(L) = 0.$$

3.4 The solutions model the transverse vibrations about the equilibrium position of a taut string released from rest. They have initial displacements given by the graphs of the functions $u_1(x,0)$, $u_2(x,0)$ and $u_3(x,0)$, which are the sine curves shown in Figure 3.1.

3.5 For the solution
$$u_r(x,t) = \sin\left(\frac{r\pi x}{L}\right)\cos\left(\frac{cr\pi t}{L}\right),$$
we have
$$\frac{\partial u_r}{\partial t}(x,t) = -\frac{cr\pi}{L}\sin\left(\frac{r\pi x}{L}\right)\sin\left(\frac{cr\pi t}{L}\right),$$
so
$$\frac{\partial u_r}{\partial t}(x,0) = 0.$$
Thus the initial condition (3.3) is satisfied, for each r.

3.6 $\dfrac{\partial u}{\partial t} = X(x)T'(t),$

$\dfrac{\partial^2 u}{\partial t^2} = X(x)T''(t),$

$\dfrac{\partial^2 u}{\partial x^2} = X''(x)T(t).$

3.7 The second equation is
$$\frac{1}{c^2}\left(\frac{T''(t)}{T(t)} + 2\varepsilon\frac{T'(t)}{T(t)}\right) = \mu,$$
which on rearranging becomes
$$T'' + 2\varepsilon T' - c^2\mu T = 0.$$

3.8 When $\mu = 0$, the differential equation becomes $X'' = 0$, with solution
$$X(x) = A + Bx,$$
for constants A and B. The boundary conditions $X(0) = 0$ and $X(L) = 0$ become
$$A = 0 \quad \text{and} \quad A + BL = 0.$$
It follows that $A = B = 0$, and again the only solution is the trivial solution $u = 0$.

3.9 When $u(x,t) = a_1 u_1(x,t) + a_2 u_2(x,t)$,
$$\begin{aligned}\frac{\partial^2 u}{\partial x^2} &= \frac{\partial^2}{\partial x^2}(a_1 u_1 + a_2 u_2) \\ &= a_1\frac{\partial^2 u_1}{\partial x^2} + a_2\frac{\partial^2 u_2}{\partial x^2} \\ &= a_1\frac{1}{c^2}\frac{\partial^2 u_1}{\partial t^2} + a_2\frac{1}{c^2}\frac{\partial^2 u_2}{\partial t^2} \\ &= \frac{1}{c^2}\frac{\partial^2}{\partial t^2}(a_1 u_1 + a_2 u_2) = \frac{1}{c^2}\frac{\partial^2 u}{\partial t^2},\end{aligned}$$
so the linear combination also satisfies the differential equation. Similarly, the given conditions lead to
$$u(0,t) = a_1 u_1(0,t) + a_2 u_2(0,t) = 0,$$
$$u(L,t) = a_1 u_1(L,t) + a_2 u_2(L,t) = 0$$
and
$$\frac{\partial u}{\partial t}(x,0) = a_1\frac{\partial u_1}{\partial t}(x,0) + a_2\frac{\partial u_2}{\partial t}(x,0) = 0,$$
showing that the linear combination $u = a_1 u_1 + a_2 u_2$ satisfies the same conditions.

3.10 Step (a) Setting $u(x,t) = X(x)T(t)$, the required partial derivatives are
$$\frac{\partial^2 u}{\partial x^2} = X''T \quad \text{and} \quad \frac{\partial^2 u}{\partial t^2} = XT''.$$
Step (b) Substituting into the partial differential equation and dividing by XT gives
$$\frac{X''}{X} + \frac{T''}{T} = 0,$$
from which it follows that
$$\frac{X''}{X} = -\frac{T''}{T}.$$
Both sides of the equation must be a constant, say μ, giving
$$\frac{X''}{X} = \mu \quad \text{and} \quad -\frac{T''}{T} = \mu$$
or, equivalently,
$$X'' - \mu X = 0 \quad \text{and} \quad T'' + \mu T = 0.$$
The boundary conditions become $X(0) = X(1) = 0$.

Arguing as in the text, only negative μ gives a non-trivial solution for X. Hence we can write $\mu = -k^2$, and the two equations become
$$X'' + k^2 X = 0 \quad \text{and} \quad T'' - k^2 T = 0.$$

Step (c)   The equation for X has general solution

$$X(x) = A\cos(kx) + B\sin(kx).$$

In order to satisfy the boundary conditions, we must have $A = 0$ and $k = r\pi$ for some integer r. So there is a family of solutions

$$X_r(x) = B\sin(r\pi x), \quad r = 1, 2, 3, \ldots.$$

The equation for T has general solution

$$T(t) = \alpha e^{kt} + \beta e^{-kt}.$$

Using the allowed values for k, we have the solutions

$$T_r(t) = \alpha e^{r\pi t} + \beta e^{-r\pi t}, \quad r = 1, 2, 3, \ldots.$$

Thus the required family of solutions is

$$u_r(x, t) = \sin(r\pi x)(\alpha e^{r\pi t} + \beta e^{-r\pi t}), \quad r = 1, 2, 3, \ldots.$$

Section 4

4.1 If you write the equation as

$$T' = -\alpha k^2 T,$$

then you can see that the general solution is a negative exponential of the form

$$T(t) = Ae^{-\alpha k^2 t},$$

where A is an arbitrary constant.

4.2 (a) Since the function $\Theta(x, t) = \Theta_0$ is constant, all its derivatives are zero, and the differential equation reduces to $0 = 0$ and so is satisfied.

(b) We know that $\Theta(x, t) = \Theta_0$ and

$$\Theta_r(x, t) = e^{-\frac{\alpha r^2 \pi^2 t}{L^2}} \sin\left(\frac{r\pi x}{L}\right), \quad r = 1, 2, 3, \ldots,$$

are solutions to the diffusion equation (4.1). Therefore, by the principle of superposition, so are

$$\Theta_r(x, t) = \Theta_0 + e^{-\frac{\alpha r^2 \pi^2 t}{L^2}} \sin\left(\frac{r\pi x}{L}\right),$$

$$r = 1, 2, 3, \ldots. \tag{S.1}$$

Furthermore, each of these also satisfies the boundary conditions $\Theta(0, t) = \Theta(L, t) = \Theta_0$, since the second term in each is zero when $x = 0$ or $x = L$. Therefore Equations (S.1) comprise the required family of solutions.

(c) To find a solution that satisfies the initial condition, we consider a solution of the form

$$\Theta(x, t) = \Theta_0 + \sum_{r=1}^{\infty} B_r e^{-\frac{\alpha r^2 \pi^2 t}{L^2}} \sin\left(\frac{r\pi x}{L}\right), \tag{S.2}$$

where we include Θ_0 only once, to ensure that the boundary conditions are satisfied. Setting $t = 0$, we obtain

$$\Theta(x, 0) = \Theta_0 + \sum_{r=1}^{\infty} B_r \sin\left(\frac{r\pi x}{L}\right).$$

So to satisfy $\Theta(x, 0) = f(x)$, we need to obtain the Fourier sine series coefficients B_r for the function $f(x) - \Theta_0$. Substituting these coefficients in Equation (S.2) then gives the required solution.

4.3 Step (a)   Set $\Theta(x, t) = X(x)T(t)$. Then

$$\frac{\partial^2 \Theta}{\partial x^2} = X''T \quad \text{and} \quad \frac{\partial \Theta}{\partial t} = XT'.$$

Step (b)   Equation (4.15) becomes

$$X''T = \frac{1}{\alpha}XT' + \gamma XT,$$

and dividing by XT gives

$$\frac{X''}{X} = \frac{1}{\alpha}\frac{T'}{T} + \gamma.$$

Again, a function of x is equal to a function of t, so both must be constant. Choosing the constant to be $\mu = -k^2$, as before, the equations become

$$X'' + k^2 X = 0,$$
$$T' + \alpha(k^2 + \gamma)T = 0.$$

The boundary conditions reduce to

$$X(0) = 0 \quad \text{and} \quad X(L) = 0.$$

4.4 The general solution of the differential equation is

$$T(t) = Ae^{-\alpha(k^2 + \gamma)t},$$

where A is an arbitrary constant.

4.5 Step (a)   We write $\Theta(x, t) = X(x)T(t)$, so

$$\frac{\partial \Theta}{\partial x} = X'T, \quad \frac{\partial^2 \Theta}{\partial x^2} = X''T \quad \text{and} \quad \frac{\partial \Theta}{\partial t} = XT'.$$

Step (b)   As in Subsection 4.1, we obtain the differential equations

$$X'' - \mu X = 0 \quad \text{and} \quad T' - \alpha\mu T = 0.$$

We have $\partial\Theta/\partial x = X'T$, so the boundary conditions become

$$X'(0)T(t) = X'(L)T(t) = 0, \quad t \geq 0,$$

and hence

$$X'(0) = X'(L) = 0.$$

Step (c)   Consider the three cases $\mu = k^2 > 0$, $\mu = 0$ and $\mu = -k^2 < 0$. The former gives no non-trivial solutions. The second yields $X'' = 0$ so that $X(x) = Ax + B$. Then $X'(0) = 0$ implies that $A = 0$, and $X'(L) = 0$ gives nothing new, so that only a constant solution is possible. Finally for $\mu = -k^2$ the general solution to the equation for X is

$$X(x) = A\cos(kx) + B\sin(kx),$$

so that

$$X'(x) = -Ak\sin(kx) + Bk\cos(kx).$$

Using the boundary conditions, we find that $B = 0$, and $A = 0$ or $k = r\pi/L$ for any non-zero integer r. This leads to the family of solutions

$$X_r(x) = A\cos\left(\frac{r\pi x}{L}\right), \quad r = 1, 2, 3, \ldots,$$

where A is an arbitrary constant. Combining results we may write

$$X_r(x) = A\cos\left(\frac{r\pi x}{L}\right), \quad r = 0, 1, 2, 3, \ldots.$$

As in Subsection 4.1, solving the differential equation for T leads to the family of solutions

$$T_r(t) = Be^{-\frac{\alpha r^2 \pi^2 t}{L^2}}, \quad r = 0, 1, 2, 3, \ldots,$$

where B is an arbitrary constant.

The family of solutions obtained by combining the families for X and T is

$$\Theta_r(x,t) = e^{-\frac{\alpha r^2 \pi^2 t}{L^2}} \cos\left(\frac{r\pi x}{L}\right), \quad r = 0, 1, 2, 3, \ldots.$$

(Notice that we need to include $r = 0$, for the member of the family that is a constant function.)

The solutions to the partial differential equation subject to the boundary conditions are all the linear combinations of the members of this family.

Step (d) To find the solution that satisfies the initial condition, we would write

$$\Theta(x,t) = \sum_{r=0}^{\infty} A_r e^{-\frac{\alpha r^2 \pi^2 t}{L^2}} \cos\left(\frac{r\pi x}{L}\right), \tag{S.3}$$

and set $t = 0$ to give

$$\Theta(x,0) = \sum_{r=0}^{\infty} A_r \cos\left(\frac{r\pi x}{L}\right)$$

$$= A_0 + \sum_{r=1}^{\infty} A_r \cos\left(\frac{r\pi x}{L}\right). \tag{S.4}$$

Then we would use the results on Fourier cosine series from *Unit 21* to find the coefficients A_r that ensure that $\Theta(x,0)$, as specified in Equation (S.4), matches the initial condition for the problem. The solution is then given by Equation (S.3) using the coefficients A_r so obtained.

4.6 (a) For

$$\Theta(x,t) = \frac{L-x}{L}\Theta_0 + \frac{x}{L}\Theta_L,$$

we have

$$\frac{\partial^2 \Theta}{\partial x^2} = 0 \quad \text{and} \quad \frac{\partial \Theta}{\partial t} = 0,$$

so that the differential equation reduces to $0 = 0$ and so is satisfied.

When $x = 0$, we have

$$\Theta(0,t) = \frac{L-0}{L}\Theta_0 + 0 = \Theta_0,$$

and when $x = L$, we have

$$\Theta(L,t) = \frac{L-L}{L}\Theta_0 + \frac{L}{L}\Theta_L = \Theta_L,$$

so the boundary conditions are satisfied.

(b) Since $\Theta(x,t) = (L-x)\Theta_0/L + x\Theta_L/L$ and Equations (4.13) satisfy the diffusion equation (4.1), by the principle of superposition so must each of

$$\Theta_r(x,t) = \frac{L-x}{L}\Theta_0 + \frac{x}{L}\Theta_L + e^{-\frac{\alpha r^2 \pi^2 t}{L^2}} \sin\left(\frac{r\pi x}{L}\right),$$

$$r = 1, 2, 3, \ldots. \tag{S.5}$$

Furthermore, each of these also satisfies the boundary conditions, since the third term in each is zero when $x = 0$ or $x = L$. Therefore Equations (S.5) comprise the required family of solutions.

(c) To find a solution that satisfies the initial condition, we consider a solution of the form

$$\Theta(x,t) = \frac{L-x}{L}\Theta_0 + \frac{x}{L}\Theta_L + \sum_{r=1}^{\infty} B_r e^{-\frac{\alpha r^2 \pi^2 t}{L^2}} \sin\left(\frac{r\pi x}{L}\right). \tag{S.6}$$

Setting $t = 0$, we obtain

$$\Theta(x,0) = \frac{L-x}{L}\Theta_0 + \frac{x}{L}\Theta_L + \sum_{r=1}^{\infty} B_r \sin\left(\frac{r\pi x}{L}\right),$$

and to satisfy $\Theta(x,0) = f(x)$, we need to obtain the Fourier sine series coefficients B_r for the function $f(x) - (L-x)\Theta_0/L - x\Theta_L/L$. Substituting these into Equation (S.6) gives the required result.

UNIT 23 Scalar and vector fields

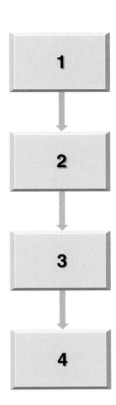

Study guide for Unit 23

The material in this unit relies rather heavily on *Units 4* and *12*. In particular, you will need to know how to calculate the partial derivatives of functions of two and three variables. The Chain Rule for differentiating such functions plays a significant role. You may also find it useful to review the gradient function **grad** *f* in *Unit 12* and the use of polar coordinates for representing vectors in *Unit 20*. Other ideas developed in this unit include heat transfer, especially Fourier's law (introduced in *Unit 15*), and vector fields (introduced in *Unit 13*).

The sections are best studied in order. Sections 2, 3 and 4 are the most important, and conceptually demanding, sections.

Vector calculus will be developed further in *Unit 24*, where many of the topics introduced in this unit will be applied, especially the vector operator 'del' and the use of three-dimensional polar coordinate systems.

Introduction

In *Unit 4* you saw how a physical quantity can be categorized as either a scalar or a vector, and we spent some time adding, scaling and multiplying vectors. In this unit we shall consider scalars and vectors that have different values at different points in a region of space. For instance, you know from practical experience that the temperature in a bowl of hot soup varies quite significantly from the middle to the edge of the bowl. The temperature depends on where in the soup it is measured. Temperature is a scalar quantity and the temperature distribution is an example of a *scalar field*. Similarly, the force of the Earth's gravity on a body in space depends on where the body is in relation to the Earth. The direction of the force is always towards the Earth's centre and the magnitude of the force depends on the distance of the body from the Earth's centre. This dependence of force on position is an example of a *vector field*.

For bodies close to the Earth's surface, we assume that the magnitude of the acceleration due to gravity is constant.

The main focus of this unit, and the next, is the differential calculus of scalar and vector fields, i.e. the study of how scalar and vector fields vary from one point to another. Many physical laws are expressed in terms of the spatial variations of fields. One important example is the flow of heat by conduction. You will see that we can describe the spatial pattern of heat flow in a conducting material as a vector field. The rate of heat flow at any point is proportional to the negative of the temperature *gradient*. You will see in Section 3 that we can express this relationship as a vector form of Fourier's law.

You saw some simple examples of Fourier's law expressed rather differently in *Unit 15*.

Section 1 is a brief introduction to the properties of orthogonal matrices that we need in Sections 3 and 4.

Section 2 introduces pictorial representations of scalar and vector fields, such as contour curves and vector field lines, and describes how we use functions of two or three spatial variables to represent, or model, scalar and vector fields mathematically. In Section 3 we extend the discussion of the *gradient function* of a scalar field from *Unit 12*.

While most of the calculations are carried out using Cartesian coordinates, it is often easier to use other coordinate systems more suited to the symmetry of the problem. Section 4 introduces *cylindrical* and *spherical polar coordinate systems* for specifying points in three dimensions. We find expressions for the gradient function in each of these systems.

These polar coordinate systems are generalizations of the plane polar coordinate system that you have used many times in this course.

The *gradient function*, and the associated vector operator 'del', are fundamental tools of vector calculus: they are used to solve a range of physical and engineering problems, especially problems involving heat flow, fluid flow, dynamics and electromagnetism.

You will meet the gradient function again in *Unit 24*, in connection with 'conservative' forces.

1 Orthogonal matrices

Later in the unit we shall study some very useful coordinate systems in three dimensions. However utility comes at a price, and some of the calculations involved in using these systems can be quite complicated. Fortunately, much of the complication can be removed by judicious use of matrix algebra, so in this short first section we study the properties of a particular type of matrix.

One way of defining a set of coordinates is by specifying three unit vectors to form a right-handed set. The set of Cartesian unit vectors **i**, **j** and **k** is one example, but there are other possibilities. In two dimensions you have already seen that plane polar coordinates correspond to the pair of unit vectors $\mathbf{e}_r$, $\mathbf{e}_\theta$. In order to relate the coordinates of a point in one system to those in another, it will be useful to have a systematic way of transforming the corresponding sets of unit vectors.

In two dimensions we know from *Unit 20* that

$$\mathbf{e}_r = \cos\theta\,\mathbf{i} + \sin\theta\,\mathbf{j},$$
$$\mathbf{e}_\theta = -\sin\theta\,\mathbf{i} + \cos\theta\,\mathbf{j}.$$

These equations can be written in matrix form as

$$\begin{bmatrix} \mathbf{e}_r \\ \mathbf{e}_\theta \end{bmatrix} = \begin{bmatrix} \cos\theta & \sin\theta \\ -\sin\theta & \cos\theta \end{bmatrix} \begin{bmatrix} \mathbf{i} \\ \mathbf{j} \end{bmatrix}$$

and doing so enables us to see quickly how to express **i** and **j** in terms of $\mathbf{e}_r$ and $\mathbf{e}_\theta$:

$$\begin{bmatrix} \mathbf{i} \\ \mathbf{j} \end{bmatrix} = \begin{bmatrix} \cos\theta & \sin\theta \\ -\sin\theta & \cos\theta \end{bmatrix}^{-1} \begin{bmatrix} \mathbf{e}_r \\ \mathbf{e}_\theta \end{bmatrix}$$
$$= \begin{bmatrix} \cos\theta & -\sin\theta \\ \sin\theta & \cos\theta \end{bmatrix} \begin{bmatrix} \mathbf{e}_r \\ \mathbf{e}_\theta \end{bmatrix}.$$

> This is a new use of vectors in which the components of vectors are vector quantities.

It is an interesting fact that the inverse of the matrix is the same as its transpose.

Of course, matrices can be thought of in another context, as you saw in *Unit 9*: any 3×3 matrix represents a linear transformation of space. However, the type of transformation we are concerned with here is rather special. A general linear transformation will alter lengths and angles, so the images of a right-handed set of unit vectors will usually be neither of unit length nor mutually perpendicular. In changing coordinates we wish to ensure that a right-handed set of unit vectors remains as such (which, incidentally, rules out reflections). It may help to think of the two sets of unit vectors as having arrowheads that lie on the surface of a unit sphere (of radius 1). It is not hard to see (though we shall not prove it) that any transformation taking one set to the other is simply a rotation of three-dimensional space about the origin.

> That is, a linear transformation fixes the origin and transforms lines into lines.

> This means that the distance between any two points is preserved.

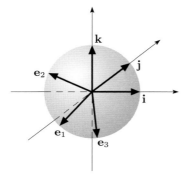

Figure 1.1

> Here **i**, **j** and **k** form a right-handed set of unit vectors, and $\mathbf{e}_1$, $\mathbf{e}_2$ and $\mathbf{e}_3$ form another.

So we concentrate on rotations. Consider a pair of points P_1 and P_2, and their rotated images P_1' and P_2'. A rotation does not change the distance between two points, so the distance between P_1 and P_2 is the same as the distance between P_1' and P_2'.

A similar remark applies to the angle between two lines — think of the angle between two straight lines l_1 and l_2. After a rotation, the images l_1' and l_2' will be inclined at the same angle. In summary, a rotation preserves distance and angle. One consequence of this observation is that a rotation preserves the dot product. Since

$$\mathbf{a} \cdot \mathbf{b} = |\mathbf{a}|\,|\mathbf{b}|\cos\theta,$$

where θ is the angle between $\mathbf{a}$ and $\mathbf{b}$, and since a rotation preserves each term on the right, a rotation must also preserve the dot product.

Suppose the rotation is represented by the matrix $\mathbf{A}$. Now take any two vectors $\mathbf{v}$ and $\mathbf{w}$ and form their dot product $\mathbf{v} \cdot \mathbf{w}$. Since this is preserved by the rotation, we have $\mathbf{v} \cdot \mathbf{w} = (\mathbf{Av}) \cdot (\mathbf{Aw})$. Therefore

$$\begin{aligned} \mathbf{v} \cdot \mathbf{w} &= \mathbf{Av} \cdot \mathbf{Aw} \\ &= (\mathbf{Av})^T(\mathbf{Aw}) \\ &= \mathbf{v}^T(\mathbf{A}^T\mathbf{A})\mathbf{w} \\ &= \mathbf{v} \cdot (\mathbf{A}^T\mathbf{Aw}). \end{aligned}$$

Because this is true for any vector $\mathbf{v}$, it must hold when $\mathbf{v}$ is, in turn, $\mathbf{i}$, $\mathbf{j}$ and $\mathbf{k}$. Thus the components of $\mathbf{A}^T\mathbf{Aw}$ are the same as those of $\mathbf{w}$, so $\mathbf{A}^T\mathbf{Aw} = \mathbf{w}$. This is true for any vector $\mathbf{w}$, so we are forced to conclude that $\mathbf{A}^T\mathbf{A} = \mathbf{I}$, the identity matrix. This confirms what we saw above in one case, namely that the inverse of the transformation matrix is its transpose.

A matrix with the property $\mathbf{A}^T\mathbf{A} = \mathbf{I}$ is called *orthogonal*. Any orthogonal matrix must preserve lengths and angles, since (according to the above argument in reverse) it preserves the dot product.

Exercise 1.1

What is the determinant of an orthogonal matrix?

*Exercise 1.2

Which of the following matrices are orthogonal?

(a) $\begin{bmatrix} 1 & 1 \\ 0 & 1 \end{bmatrix}$ (b) $\begin{bmatrix} \frac{1}{\sqrt{2}} & -\frac{1}{\sqrt{2}} \\ \frac{1}{\sqrt{2}} & \frac{1}{\sqrt{2}} \end{bmatrix}$ (c) $\begin{bmatrix} 2 & 0 \\ 0 & 1 \end{bmatrix}$

(d) $\begin{bmatrix} \frac{1}{2} & -\frac{1}{2}\sqrt{3} \\ \frac{1}{2}\sqrt{3} & \frac{1}{2} \end{bmatrix}$ (e) $\begin{bmatrix} \frac{1}{2} & 0 & -\frac{1}{2}\sqrt{3} \\ 0 & 1 & 0 \\ \frac{1}{2}\sqrt{3} & 0 & \frac{1}{2} \end{bmatrix}$

In Exercise 1.1 you saw that the determinant of an orthogonal matrix is ± 1. However, the converse is not true: a matrix with determinant 1 may not be orthogonal, as you saw in Exercise 1.2(a).

If the determinant of an orthogonal matrix is -1, then the matrix represents a rotated reflection, though we shall not prove this.

Exercise 1.3

Construct a 3×3 matrix $\mathbf{A}$ which is not orthogonal, but such that

$$\det(\mathbf{A}) = 1.$$

2   Scalar and vector fields

In this section we introduce scalar and vector fields, and use ideas from *Unit 12* to show how they can be described mathematically.

2.1   Scalar fields

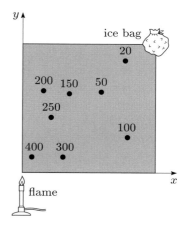

Figure 2.1

The function $\Theta = \Theta(x, y)$ is an example of a function of more than one variable, as introduced in *Unit 12*.

Figure 2.1 shows the steady-state temperature, in degrees Celsius, at different points of a square plate. Temperature is a scalar quantity and its value depends on where on the plate it is measured. The distribution of temperatures on the plate is an example of a scalar field. If we define Cartesian coordinate x- and y-axes as shown, then the variable Θ, representing the temperature, will be a function of x and y, i.e. $\Theta = \Theta(x, y)$. Another example of a scalar field is the atmospheric pressure distribution, in millibars, at ground level over the UK at midday on a certain day, as shown in Figure 2.2. Atmospheric pressure is a scalar quantity and its value depends on where in the UK it is measured. The curves in Figure 2.2 are *isobars* and join up places where the atmospheric pressure at ground level is the same. Each isobar is labelled with the value of the atmospheric pressure in millibars. The isobars in Figure 2.2 give an overall picture of the atmospheric pressure across the country.

On weather maps, the pressure is usually given in millibars. The SI unit of pressure is the pascal (Pa). (1 bar = 10^3 millibars = 10^5 Pa = 10^5 N m^{-2}.)

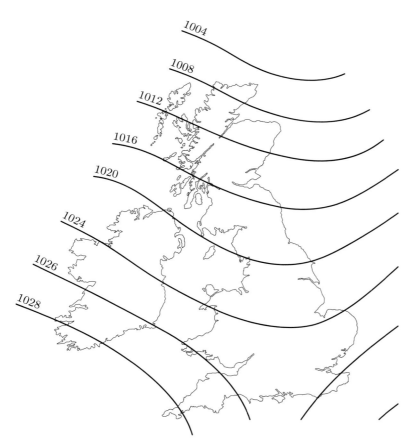

Figure 2.2

If we choose London as an origin and set up a Cartesian coordinate system with the x-axis pointing East and the y-axis pointing North, then each place in the UK can be represented by its coordinates (x, y). The atmospheric pressure distribution can then be represented by a function of two variables $P = P(x, y)$. Of course, atmospheric pressure varies over time. In this unit we shall consider only the spatial variations of scalar fields, not the time variations.

In each of the above cases, the variable representing the scalar quantity Θ or P is a function of the two coordinates x and y. These scalar distributions are examples of *two-dimensional scalar fields*, i.e. they are scalar fields on a two-dimensional domain. The steady-state temperature distribution in a room is an example of a *three-dimensional scalar field*. (The atmospheric pressure at a particular point in time is a three-dimensional scalar field, since it varies with altitude as well as with position. In Figure 2.2 only the ground-level pressures at midday are shown and so this is effectively a two-dimensional scalar field.)

Each point in the room, which can be located by three coordinates, has a temperature.

In any scalar field we have:

- some scalar quantity (e.g. temperature);
- a region of a plane or a region of space, i.e. a domain, over which the scalar is defined (e.g. a flat plate or the interior of a room);
- the values of the scalar quantity at all points of the region.

The mathematical model of a two-dimensional scalar field is a function $f(x, y)$ of two spatial variables. For a three-dimensional field, a function $f(x, y, z)$ of three spatial variables is required.

Functions of two and three variables were introduced, and discussed extensively, in *Unit 12*.

Definition

A **scalar field** is a distribution of scalar values on a two- or three-dimensional region and is represented mathematically by a function of two or three spatial variables, respectively.

The domain of the field is the given two-dimensional or three-dimensional region in which the field exists. We shall use the terms *scalar field* and *function of two (or three) variables* interchangeably, according to whether we want to emphasize the physical or the mathematical properties.

The domain of the atmospheric pressure field is the map of the UK.

Example 2.1

The light intensity I in the region outside a spherical lamp of radius a, such as a light bulb, is inversely proportional to the square of the distance r from the centre of the lamp. The intensity 1 metre away from the centre is I_0. Specify a scalar field, as a function of three Cartesian variables, which models the light intensity in the space outside the lamp, and state the domain of the function.

Solution

The light intensity at a point a distance $r > a$ from the centre of the lamp is $I \propto 1/r^2$, with $I = I_0$ when $r = 1$ metre. Thus $I = I_0/r^2$. Using a Cartesian coordinate system with origin at the centre of the lamp, we have $r = (x^2 + y^2 + z^2)^{1/2}$, so the scalar field function is

$$I(x, y, z) = \frac{I_0}{x^2 + y^2 + z^2} \quad \left((x^2 + y^2 + z^2)^{1/2} > a \right).$$

The domain of the function is the statement in brackets, expressing the fact that the function describes light intensity in the region outside the lamp. ∎

The intensity inside the lamp would be represented by a different function.

Exercise 2.1

A thin circular sheet of metal of radius R_1 (in metres) has a concentric hole of radius R_2 (in metres) cut out of it (see Figure 2.3). The outer perimeter is maintained at a constant temperature Θ_1 and the inner perimeter is maintained at a constant temperature Θ_2. At any point P on the sheet, specified by a position vector $\mathbf{r}$ measured from the centre, the temperature (in kelvins) is given by

$$\Theta = \Theta_1 + \frac{\Theta_2 - \Theta_1}{\ln(R_2/R_1)}\ln\left(\frac{|\mathbf{r}|}{R_1}\right).$$

(a) Choose a Cartesian coordinate system with origin at the centre of the circular metal sheet and hence specify a function of x and y that models the temperature. Describe the region of the plane over which the function is defined and state the domain.

(b) Express the function found in part (a) in plane polar coordinates $\langle r, \phi \rangle$.

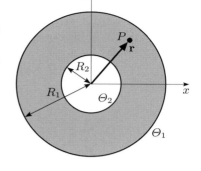

Figure 2.3

In this unit and in *Unit 24*, we use the notation $\langle r, \phi \rangle$ of *Unit 4* for plane polar coordinates.

2.2   Contour curves and contour surfaces

The scalar fields in the previous subsection were presented in three different ways. For the first scalar field, of temperature on a plate as given in Figure 2.1, we represented the field by showing the values of the temperature at a few points on the plate. For the second scalar field, the atmospheric pressure in the UK as shown in Figure 2.2, we represented the field by isobars (lines joining points at which the atmospheric pressure is the same) on a map of the UK. In both cases, the representation of the scalar field is not complete because, for instance, there is a temperature associated with *every* point of the flat plate, and not just the points shown in Figure 2.1. In the third mode, in Exercise 2.1 and Example 2.1, the scalar fields were represented by functions of two or three Cartesian variables.

Of these modes of representation, the isobar example gives a good way of visualizing the field pictorially. Figure 2.4 shows the temperature distribution (in degrees Celsius) over an unevenly heated flat plate similar to that shown in Figure 2.1. However, instead of giving the values of the temperature at different points as we did before, we have drawn curves through those points on the plate where the temperature is the same. Of course we cannot show all possible curves because that would require a curve through every point on the plate, so we choose certain values of the temperature. Then the curves give us a pictorial idea of the scalar field. So, for example, for each point on the curve AB the temperature is $300°C$. For a temperature field, the curves are called *isotherms* and, in this example, we have drawn the isotherms for multiples of $50°C$. In one part of the plate the isotherms are much closer together than those on the rest of the plate. The temperature is changing more rapidly in the region where the isotherms are close together.

We now extend this pictorial representation for pressure and temperature to more general two-dimensional scalar fields. Suppose that we have a two-dimensional scalar field $f(x, y)$, defined over a region R of the (x, y)-plane. We can represent this scalar field pictorially by drawing curves in the (x, y)-plane through those points that have equal values of f. Figure 2.5, for example, shows four such curves where C_1, C_2, C_3 and C_4 are constants. The curves that we have drawn are called *contour curves*. Each contour curve is labelled by a scalar value.

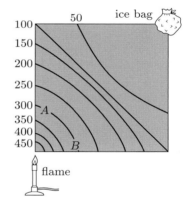

Figure 2.4

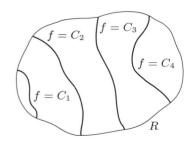

Figure 2.5

The isobars in a pressure field are contour curves of equal pressure, and isotherms in a temperature field are contour curves of equal temperature.

For example, consider the scalar field

$$f(x,y) = x^2 + y^2$$

defined over the rectangular domain $-1 \le x \le 1$, $-2 \le y \le 2$ (see Figure 2.6). The contour curves are defined by

$$f(x,y) = \text{constant},$$

or, in this case,

$$x^2 + y^2 = \text{constant}.$$

These curves are circles centred on the origin and are drawn as parts of circles within the rectangular region for which f is defined. Figure 2.6 shows the contour curves

$$f(x,y) = 1, \quad f(x,y) = 2, \quad f(x,y) = 3, \quad f(x,y) = 4.$$

Again we cannot draw *all* possible curves, only some of them.

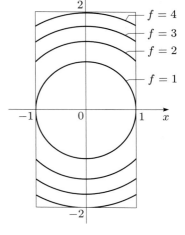

Figure 2.6

Definition

The family of curves given by $f(x,y) = C$, for different values of the constant C, are the **contour curves** of the two-dimensional scalar field f.

Exercise 2.2

Sketch the contour curves $f(x,y) = \frac{1}{2}$, $f(x,y) = -\frac{1}{4}$ and $f(x,y) = 1$ of the scalar field $f(x,y) = xy$, defined over the domain $x^2 + y^2 \le 4$.

For this exercise, you may wish to use the computer algebra package for the course.

You are probably familiar with the word 'contour' from Ordnance Survey or other topographical maps, where the contour curves join points that are at the same height above sea level. The contours can give us information about the shape of the land. Figure 2.7 provides an example, where the contour curves join points at the specified number of metres above sea level. See if you can answer Exercise 2.3 just from the contour curves in Figure 2.7.

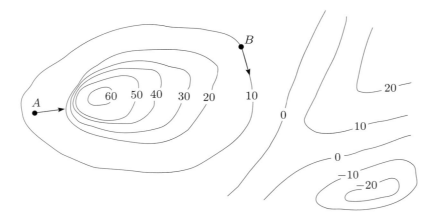

Figure 2.7

*Exercise 2.3
(a) Where would you expect to find (i) a hill and (ii) a lake?

(b) Where is the land fairly level?

(c) Imagine that you set off from A and walk in the direction of the arrow. Would you expect an easy walk or a hard climb?

Exercise 2.3 illustrates an important feature of a scalar field that can be deduced from its contour curves. For any scalar field, the change in value of the field depends on the direction in which you move. For example, if you set off from B in Figure 2.7 and walk in the direction of the arrow, then, initially, the field values will not change (you are contour walking). However, for movement as in Exercise 2.3(c), which is approximately perpendicular to the contours, the scalar field changes (increases or decreases) with changing position.

So far in this subsection we have considered two-dimensional fields. Now we turn our attention to three-dimensional scalar fields.

We can represent a three-dimensional scalar field $f(x, y, z)$ in an analogous way. If we join up points for which the three-dimensional scalar field $f(x, y, z)$ has the same constant value C, we obtain the *surface* with equation $f(x, y, z) = C$.

> **Definition**
>
> The family of surfaces given by $f(x, y, z) = C$, for different values of the constant C, are the **contour surfaces** of the scalar field f.

Contour surfaces give a pictorial representation of a three-dimensional scalar field. For example, those of the scalar field $I = I_0 / (x^2 + y^2 + z^2)$, given in Example 2.1, are concentric spheres with centres at the origin. Two of the contour surfaces, for $I = I_0/4$ and $I = I_0/9$, are shown in Figure 2.8.

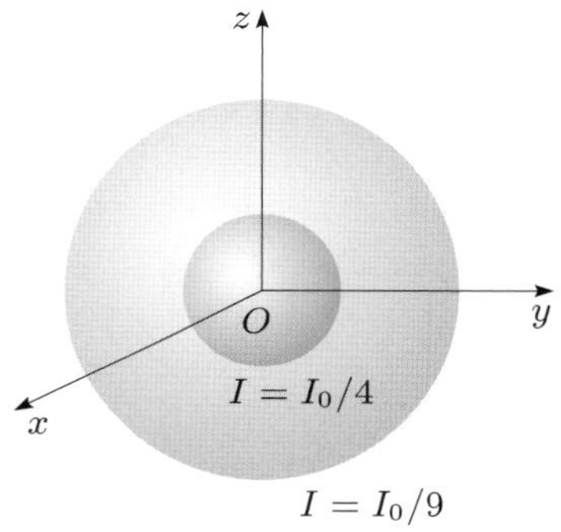

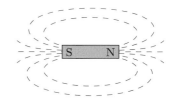

Figure 2.8

2.3 Vector fields

Figure 2.9 shows the pattern produced when iron filings are placed near a bar magnet. The iron filings align themselves in a symmetric pattern. The same pattern is revealed if we place small compasses at various points near the magnet. We find the arrow on each compass aligns itself in the same direction as the iron filings. The arrow shows the direction of the magnetic field at each point. The magnitude of the field can also be measured and is found to decrease as we move away from the magnet. The lengths and directions of the arrows in Figure 2.10 represent the magnitudes and directions of the magnetic field due to the bar magnet at various points on a plane through the magnet. There is a unique vector called the *magnetic field vector* at each point in the region of space around the magnet, and these vectors form a three-dimensional *vector field*.

Figure 2.9

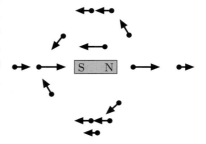

Figure 2.10

Here is an example of a two-dimensional vector field. The arrows in Figure 2.11 represent the surface velocity at various points on a river.

We assume the flow is steady. It is not changing with time.

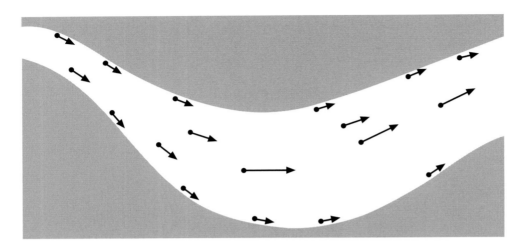

Figure 2.11

The surface velocity at a particular point is the velocity that a small floating object, such as a leaf, would have at that point. Near the river banks, the water is almost at rest, so the arrows are shorter in length (indicating a smaller speed near the edges of the river). At each point on the river surface there is a unique velocity, thus defining a two-dimensional vector field of velocity vectors on the surface. If we were interested in the velocity below the surface as well, we should need to consider the velocity vectors existing at points in the three-dimensional region forming the river itself and this would be a three-dimensional vector field.

In any vector field we have:

* some vector quantity (e.g. a surface velocity);
* a region of a plane or a region of space, i.e. a domain, over which the vector is defined (e.g. the surface of a river);
* the magnitudes and directions of the vectors at all points in the region.

We can model a two-dimensional vector field mathematically by introducing a vector function $\mathbf{F}$ such that a vector $\mathbf{F}(x, y)$ is defined at each point (x, y) of a two-dimensional domain. In three dimensions, $\mathbf{F}(x, y, z)$ is a vector at each point (x, y, z) in a three-dimensional domain.

Definition

A **vector field** is a distribution of vectors on a two- or three-dimensional region and is represented mathematically by a vector function of two or three spatial variables.

You met the idea of a vector field in *Unit 13*.

The domain of the vector function is the given region of a plane or of space in which the field exists. We shall use the terms *vector field* and *vector function* interchangeably, depending on whether we want to emphasize the physical or mathematical properties. Often we use the name of the physical quantity itself, such as *force field*, *velocity field* or *magnetic field*.

Example 2.2

The Earth's gravitational field is an example of a vector field in space. The gravitational force on a body (i.e. the weight of the body) on or above the Earth's surface and at a distance r from the centre of the Earth has magnitude inversely proportional to the square of the distance r and is directed towards the Earth's centre. Specify the vector field as a function of three Cartesian variables with the domain over which it is defined.

Solution

The vector quantity is the gravitational force $\mathbf{F}$ acting on the body due to the Earth's gravity. We introduce a Cartesian coordinate system with origin O at the centre of the Earth. The magnitude $F = |\mathbf{F}|$ is proportional to $1/r^2$, so

$$F(x, y, z) = \frac{C}{r^2} = \frac{C}{x^2 + y^2 + z^2},$$

for some constant C. The gravitational force on a body at P (see Figure 2.12) is $-F\widehat{\mathbf{r}}$, where $\widehat{\mathbf{r}}$ is a unit vector in the direction from O to P. Now $\widehat{\mathbf{r}} = \mathbf{r}/|\mathbf{r}|$, where $\mathbf{r} = x\mathbf{i} + y\mathbf{i} + z\mathbf{k}$ is the position vector of P, so

$$\widehat{\mathbf{r}}(x, y, z) = \frac{x\mathbf{i} + y\mathbf{j} + z\mathbf{k}}{\sqrt{x^2 + y^2 + z^2}}.$$

Thus the vector function we need is

$$\mathbf{F}(x, y, z) = -F(x, y, z)\,\widehat{\mathbf{r}}(x, y, z) = \frac{-C(x\mathbf{i} + y\mathbf{j} + z\mathbf{k})}{(x^2 + y^2 + z^2)^{3/2}}.$$

The domain is the region over which the vector field $\mathbf{F}$ is defined, i.e. the region of space on or outside the Earth's surface, specified by

$$(x^2 + y^2 + z^2)^{1/2} \geq R,$$

where R is the radius of the (spherical) Earth. ∎

The components of a vector field $\mathbf{F}$, relative to a given Cartesian coordinate system, are themselves *scalar* fields defined over the same region as $\mathbf{F}$. Thus, if $\mathbf{F}$ is a three-dimensional vector field defined on a domain D and

$$\mathbf{F}(x, y, z) = F_1(x, y, z)\mathbf{i} + F_2(x, y, z)\mathbf{j} + F_3(x, y, z)\mathbf{k},$$

then, separately, the three components $F_1(x, y, z) = \mathbf{F} \cdot \mathbf{i}$, $F_2(x, y, z) = \mathbf{F} \cdot \mathbf{j}$ and $F_3(x, y, z) = \mathbf{F} \cdot \mathbf{k}$ are scalar fields defined on D. For example, the x-component of the vector field $\mathbf{F}$ in Example 2.2 is the scalar field

$$F_1(x, y, z) = \mathbf{F} \cdot \mathbf{i} = \frac{-Cx}{(x^2 + y^2 + z^2)^{3/2}} \quad \left((x^2 + y^2 + z^2)^{1/2} \geq R\right).$$

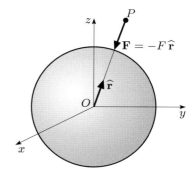

Figure 2.12

At the surface of the Earth, where the magnitude of the acceleration due to gravity is measured as g, this field can be approximated by the constant-magnitude vector field $\mathbf{F} = -mg\widehat{\mathbf{r}}$, where m is the mass of the body, so $C = mgR^2$.

Alternatively, we could use the column vector notation of *Unit 9* for vector fields and write a vector field in three dimensions as

$$\mathbf{F}(x, y, z) = \begin{bmatrix} F_1(x, y, z) \\ F_2(x, y, z) \\ F_3(x, y, z) \end{bmatrix}.$$

*Exercise 2.4

The weight $\mathbf{F}$ of a body of mass m inside the Earth (e.g. in a mine shaft) has a magnitude given by mgr/R, where r is the distance from the Earth's centre and R is the Earth's radius. The direction of $\mathbf{F}$ is towards the Earth's centre. Express $\mathbf{F}$ as a vector function $\mathbf{F}(x, y, z)$ using the same Cartesian coordinate system as in Example 2.2. What is the weight of the body at the Earth's centre?

You studied steady-state heat transfer by conduction in *Unit 15*. The pattern of heat flow in a conducting material is another example of a vector field. When the magnitude and direction of the heat flow vary from place to place in a conductor, the heat flow rate per unit area at a point P in the conductor is a vector $\mathbf{J}$ whose direction is the direction of the heat flow at P. The magnitude of $\mathbf{J}$ is the rate at which heat flows across a very small plane surface containing P and oriented at right angles to the direction of flow, divided by the area A of the surface (see Figure 2.13). So $|\mathbf{J}|$ is the heat flow rate per unit area at P and has units of joules per second per square metre (i.e. $\mathrm{J\,s^{-1}\,m^{-2}}$, or $\mathrm{W\,m^{-2}}$, since 1 watt (W) $= 1\,\mathrm{J\,s^{-1}}$). (The vector $\mathbf{J}$ is called the *heat flow vector* or the *heat conduction vector*.) To define $|\mathbf{J}|$ at P formally, we take the limit as the area A of the plane surface approaches zero, that is,

$$|\mathbf{J}| = \lim_{A \to 0} \frac{\text{heat flow rate across surface area } A}{A}.$$

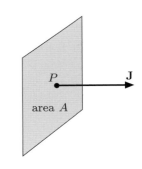

Figure 2.13

Figure 2.14 shows a selection of arrows representing a heat-flow vector field $\mathbf{J}$ in a cross-section of a wall of a heated house. Shown also are vertical lines representing the scalar temperature contours. These lines are the intersections of the temperature contour surfaces with the plane of the figure. The contours are labelled by the temperature, in degrees Celsius, for the case where the inside surface is 20°C and the outside surface is 6°C. Hence Figure 2.14 depicts two fields: a scalar (temperature) field and a vector (heat flow) field. As in *Unit 15*, it is assumed that the temperature has a different constant value on each face of the wall and that the wall is homogeneous. Then the vector $\mathbf{J}$ has the same magnitude and direction everywhere inside the wall. (In the notation of *Unit 15*, $|\mathbf{J}| = q/A$.)

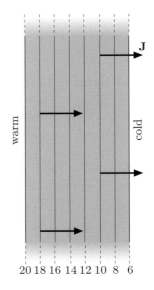

Figure 2.14

If we draw continuous curves in the domain such that, at any point, the tangent to the curve is parallel to the direction of the vector field at that point, then the curves are called the **vector field lines** of the vector field. For instance, the orientation of iron filings near a bar magnet suggests a family of continuous curves. Two such curves are shown in Figure 2.15. The arrow on a vector field line specifies the sense, i.e. the direction along the line, of the vector field. If we draw a curve showing the path of a leaf floating on the surface of a river, then, at each point on the path, the tangent to the path is parallel to the direction of the velocity vector of the leaf. This line is a vector field line for the velocity vector field. If we were to show the vector field lines of the heat flow vector $\mathbf{J}$ in Figure 2.14, they would be at right angles to the temperature contour surfaces shown as lines in that figure.

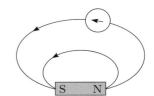

Figure 2.15

*Exercise 2.5 _____

Figure 2.16 shows the cross-section of a long cylindrical central heating pipe carrying hot water. The heat flow vector $\mathbf{J}$ in the metal of the pipe is given (in the steady state) by

$$\mathbf{J}(x, y, z) = \frac{C(x\mathbf{i} + y\mathbf{j})}{x^2 + y^2} \quad (a \le \sqrt{x^2 + y^2} \le b),$$

where a, b and C are positive constants, and the z-axis is the central axis of the pipe.

(a) Specify the x-component of $\mathbf{J}$.

(b) Describe the vector field lines of $\mathbf{J}$.

(c) How does the magnitude $|\mathbf{J}|$ vary with distance $\rho = \sqrt{x^2 + y^2}$ from the z-axis?

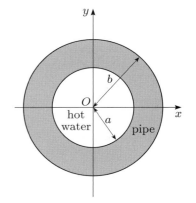

Figure 2.16

(d) Consider an imaginary cylindrical surface of length h with its axis on the z-axis and radius ρ such that $a \leq \rho \leq b$. By making use of your answers to parts (b) and (c), show that the rate at which heat flows outwards across the whole curved surface of this section of the cylinder is independent of the radius ρ. What does this result mean in terms of conservation of heat energy?

Note that although the vector field $\mathbf{J}$ of Exercise 2.5 exists in three dimensions, its z-component is zero and there are no variations in the z-direction. The field could therefore be represented by a two-dimensional vector function

$$\mathbf{J}(x, y) = \frac{C(x\mathbf{i} + y\mathbf{i})}{x^2 + y^2} \quad (a \leq \sqrt{x^2 + y^2} \leq b).$$

End-of-section Exercises

Exercise 2.6

The density σ of air is $1.205 \, \text{kg m}^{-3}$ at sea level. Assume that σ decreases exponentially with altitude and is reduced to $(1.205/e) \, \text{kg m}^{-3}$ at an altitude of 9.5×10^3 metres. Assuming the Earth's surface to be flat, choose a Cartesian coordinate system and hence express the density σ as a scalar field $\sigma(x, y, z)$. What shape are the contour surfaces?

Applied mathematicians and physicists often need to know how a quantity 'e-folds', that is, they need to know the distance (or time) in which the quantity reduces to $1/e$ of its original value.

**Exercise 2.7*

When a long thin straight wire carries a uniform surface distribution of static positive electric charge, the electric field vector $\mathbf{E}$ at any point outside the wire has magnitude $|\mathbf{E}|$ inversely proportional to the perpendicular distance from the centre of the wire and a direction pointing directly away from the wire. Introduce a Cartesian coordinate system and hence specify the vector field $\mathbf{E}(x, y, z)$. Take $|\mathbf{E}|$ to be the constant E_0 at unit distance from the wire. Describe the vector field lines.

Describing the wire as 'thin' implies that it has negligible radius. It is just a straight line.

3   *Gradient of a scalar field*

An important property of any field is the way in which the field value changes from one point to another. These spatial variations can be quite complicated even for a scalar field, since the change of field value in going from a point P to a nearby point Q may depend on the direction as well as the magnitude of the displacement $\overrightarrow{PQ}$. Consider Figure 3.1, which shows three contour curves of a scalar field f. The change in f is $7 - 6 = 1$ when the displacement $\overrightarrow{PQ}_1$ is made and about $5.5 - 6 = -0.5$ for a displacement $\overrightarrow{PQ}_2$ of the same magnitude as $\overrightarrow{PQ}_1$, but in a different direction. We shall show in this section that the way in which a scalar field varies in *any* direction can be found from the *gradient function*, which was introduced in *Unit 12*. There is a gradient function at each point in a scalar field and so the gradient function is a vector field.

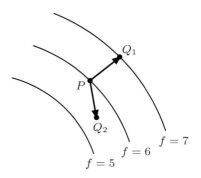

Figure 3.1

In *Unit 12* you saw how to use the gradient function to find the magnitude of the steepest upward slope at a point on a surface (and the direction in which that steepest slope occurs). The gradient function for a general two-dimensional scalar field $f(x, y)$ was expressed in terms of partial derivatives of f. You also saw in *Unit 12* how the gradient function can be used to calculate slopes in arbitrary directions. In Subsections 3.1 and 3.2 we review those ideas and later, in Subsection 3.3, we consider how the expression for the gradient function can be generalized to three dimensions.

Subsection 3.4 discusses the *vector differential operator* called 'del', which plays a unifying role in vector calculus. Finally, in Subsection 3.5, we see how to define the operator 'del' in plane polar coordinates.

You met 'del' in *Unit 12*, in conjunction with the gradient function.

3.1 Gradient function

A two-dimensional scalar field $f(x, y)$ is defined only in the (x, y)-plane. This leaves the z-axis of the coordinate system free for showing the scalar values f, i.e. we can put $z = f(x, y)$. Thus the set of points $(x, y, f(x, y))$ is a surface above (or below) the (x, y)-plane, giving a graphical picture of the scalar field. In general, the surface $(x, y, f(x, y))$ is a graphical representation of the scalar field f and shows how f varies with position in the (x, y)-plane.

You saw examples of such surfaces in *Unit 12*.

Consider a general two-dimensional scalar field f and a path in the (x, y)-plane parametrized by the arc length s, i.e. as s varies, the point $(x(s), y(s))$ moves along the path in the (x, y)-plane. The height z of the surface will also vary as s varies, i.e. $z = z(s)$. The rate of change of z with s at a point P in the (x, y)-plane is the slope or steepness of the surface for movement in the direction of the path, i.e. it is the vertical rise of z over a small horizontal change in arc length δs in the direction of the path at P and is given by the Chain Rule, which we can write as

$$\frac{dz}{ds} = \frac{\partial f}{\partial x}\frac{dx}{ds} + \frac{\partial f}{\partial y}\frac{dy}{ds}, \tag{3.1}$$

where all the derivatives and partial derivatives are to be evaluated at P.

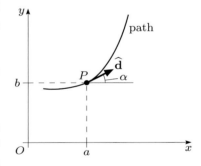

Figure 3.2

Let us first consider a small change in length along the path at P in the (x, y)-plane. Since it is small, we can take it to be in the direction of the tangent to the path at P, a direction given by a unit vector $\widehat{\mathbf{d}}$, say, as shown in Figure 3.2. If α is the angle at P between $\widehat{\mathbf{d}}$ and the positive direction of the x-axis, then $\cos \alpha = dx/ds$ and $\sin \alpha = dy/ds$, and Equation (3.1) may be rewritten as

$$\frac{dz}{ds} = \frac{\partial f}{\partial x}(a, b)\cos \alpha + \frac{\partial f}{\partial y}(a, b)\sin \alpha, \tag{3.2}$$

where we have shown explicitly that the partial derivatives are to be evaluated at the point P whose coordinates are (a, b). While the angle α depends on the direction of the path at P, the partial derivatives in Equation (3.2) are independent of any particular path through P, and depend only on the scalar field f and the coordinates (a, b) of P. We can take advantage of this by using the **gradient function**, in the (x, y)-plane at the point (a, b):

$$\mathbf{grad}\, f(a, b) = \frac{\partial f}{\partial x}(a, b)\mathbf{i} + \frac{\partial f}{\partial y}(a, b)\mathbf{j}.$$

The unit vector $\widehat{\mathbf{d}}$ may be written in terms of α as

$$\widehat{\mathbf{d}} = (\cos \alpha)\mathbf{i} + (\sin \alpha)\mathbf{j}.$$

In *Unit 12* you met the alternative notation $\boldsymbol{\nabla} f$ for $\mathbf{grad}\, f$, but we shall postpone using that notation for $\mathbf{grad}\, f$ until we have defined $\boldsymbol{\nabla}$ in Subsection 3.4.

So we can now write Equation (3.2) as a dot product of $\mathbf{grad}\, f(a,b)$ and $\widehat{\mathbf{d}}$,

$$\frac{dz}{ds} = \mathbf{grad}\, f(a,b) \cdot \widehat{\mathbf{d}} = |\mathbf{grad}\, f(a,b)| \cos\theta, \qquad (3.3)$$

where θ is the angle between $\mathbf{grad}\, f$ and $\widehat{\mathbf{d}}$, as shown in Figure 3.3.

You can see from Equation (3.3) that dz/ds, the slope or steepness of the surface (the graph of f), has its maximum value (when $\cos\theta = 1$) for movement parallel to the (x,y)-plane in a direction $\widehat{\mathbf{d}}$ that coincides with the direction of the gradient function. Then $\cos\theta = 1$ and we have

$$\left(\frac{dz}{ds}\right)_{\text{max}} = |\mathbf{grad}\, f(a,b)|.$$

Hence the direction of the gradient function at (a,b) shows the direction of maximum slope of the surface and the magnitude of the gradient function is equal to the magnitude of the maximum slope.

There is such a vector at each point in the (x,y)-plane and so $\mathbf{grad}\, f(x,y)$ is a vector field, often written simply as $\mathbf{grad}\, f$. In terms of the Cartesian unit vectors, we define it as follows.

> **Definition**
>
> The **gradient in Cartesian coordinates** (x,y) **of a two-dimensional scalar field** f is the vector field
>
> $$\mathbf{grad}\, f = \frac{\partial f}{\partial x}\mathbf{i} + \frac{\partial f}{\partial y}\mathbf{j}. \qquad (3.4)$$

Thus, to find the gradient function at a particular point, it is necessary to find the two partial derivatives at that point and substitute them into Equation (3.4).

The function f in the definition can represent any two-dimensional scalar field. For example, suppose $\Theta(x,y)$ is the temperature field of a flat plate in the (x,y)-plane. Then $\mathbf{grad}\, \Theta$ is a vector parallel to the plane of the plate pointing in the direction in which the temperature increases most rapidly with distance and $|\mathbf{grad}\, \Theta|$ is the value of the maximum rate of temperature change with distance.

The gradient function of a two-dimensional scalar field $f(x,y)$ is always parallel to the (x,y)-plane. It is a vector having only $\mathbf{i}$ and $\mathbf{j}$ components. You can think of it as lying in the (x,y)-plane, or you may prefer to imagine it positioned at the point $(x,y,f(x,y))$ and lying in a plane parallel to the (x,y)-plane. Equation (3.3) shows that we can use the gradient function to work out the slope, or steepness, dz/ds of a scalar field for movement in any direction parallel to the (x,y)-plane. This slope is the *derivative* of f in the *specified direction*.

> **Definition**
>
> The **derivative of a scalar field** f in a direction specified by a unit vector $\widehat{\mathbf{d}}$ is given by
>
> $$\mathbf{grad}\, f \cdot \widehat{\mathbf{d}}.$$

The dot product of two vectors $\mathbf{a}$ and $\mathbf{b}$ was defined in *Unit 4* as

$$\mathbf{a} \cdot \mathbf{b} = |\mathbf{a}|\,|\mathbf{b}| \cos\theta,$$

where θ is the angle between $\mathbf{a}$ and $\mathbf{b}$.

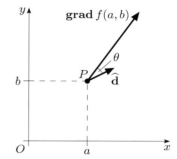

Figure 3.3

This definition is the same as that given in *Unit 12*, but expressed in terms of fields. As the gradient is a vector field, i.e. a vector function, it is sometimes referred to as the *gradient function*.

For a temperature field measured in degrees Celsius, the slope has units of degrees Celsius per metre, i.e. $^{\circ}\mathrm{C}\,\mathrm{m}^{-1}$.

This derivative is often referred to as a *directional derivative* or *slope*, the latter being particularly apt for a two-dimensional scalar field.

3.2 Calculating gradients

We can calculate gradient vectors of two-dimensional scalar fields $f(x, y)$, and derivatives in specified directions, by using the two definitions above.

Example 3.1

Evaluate **grad** f at the point $(0, 1)$ when $f(x, y) = \ln(x + 2y)$. Determine the magnitude of **grad** f and the unit vector in the direction of **grad** f at the point $(0, 1)$. What is the derivative of f in the direction of the unit vector $\widehat{\mathbf{d}} = (\mathbf{i} + \mathbf{j})/\sqrt{2}$ at $(0, 1)$?

Solution

The vector field **grad** f is found from the first partial derivatives of f,

$$\frac{\partial f}{\partial x} = \frac{1}{x + 2y}, \quad \frac{\partial f}{\partial y} = \frac{2}{x + 2y}.$$

So, from Equation (3.4),

$$\mathbf{grad}\, f = \left(\frac{1}{x + 2y}\right)\mathbf{i} + \left(\frac{2}{x + 2y}\right)\mathbf{j}.$$

This is the gradient vector field. Putting $x = 0$ and $y = 1$, we have, at the point $(0, 1)$, the gradient vector **grad** $f = \frac{1}{2}\mathbf{i} + \mathbf{j}$. The magnitude of **grad** f at $(0, 1)$ is $|\mathbf{grad}\, f| = (\frac{1}{4} + 1)^{1/2} = \sqrt{5}/2$. The unit vector in the direction of **grad** f at $(0, 1)$ is $\widehat{\mathbf{n}} = \mathbf{grad}\, f / |\mathbf{grad}\, f|$. Hence $\widehat{\mathbf{n}} = (\mathbf{i} + 2\mathbf{j})/\sqrt{5}$. The derivative of f in the direction of $\widehat{\mathbf{d}}$ is given at $(0, 1)$ by the dot product $\mathbf{grad}\, f \cdot \widehat{\mathbf{d}} = 3/(2\sqrt{2})$. ∎

*Exercise 3.1 ———————————————

Evaluate **grad** f at the point $(-1, 2)$ when $f(x, y) = x^2 y$. Find the derivative of f in the x-direction at $(-1, 2)$.

Example 3.2

Evaluate **grad** f at the point $(1, 2)$ when $f(x, y) = x^2 + y^2$. Show that the direction of **grad** f at $(1, 2)$ is normal to the tangent line to the contour curve of f at the point $(1, 2)$.

Solution

The first partial derivatives of f and their values at the point $(1, 2)$ are

$$\frac{\partial f}{\partial x} = 2x, \quad \frac{\partial f}{\partial x}(1, 2) = 2,$$

$$\frac{\partial f}{\partial y} = 2y, \quad \frac{\partial f}{\partial y}(1, 2) = 4.$$

Thus, from Equation (3.4),

$$\mathbf{grad}\, f(1, 2) = \frac{\partial f}{\partial x}(1, 2)\mathbf{i} + \frac{\partial f}{\partial y}(1, 2)\mathbf{j} = 2\mathbf{i} + 4\mathbf{j}.$$

The contour curves are obtained by setting f equal to a constant and are circles centred on the origin. The contour curve through the point $(1, 2)$ is shown in Figure 3.4, together with the tangent line and the normal to the tangent line through $(1, 2)$. The position vector of $(1, 2)$ is $\mathbf{i} + 2\mathbf{j}$ and this is normal to the tangent line. But **grad** $f(1, 2) = 2\mathbf{i} + 4\mathbf{j} = 2(\mathbf{i} + 2\mathbf{j})$. Hence **grad** $f(1, 2)$ is normal to the tangent to the contour curve at $(1, 2)$. ∎

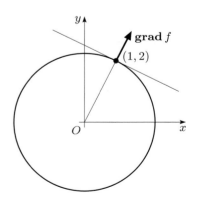

Figure 3.4

It is true generally that the gradient function at a point is normal to the tangent line to the contour curve at that point. This is clear from Figure 3.5, which shows a contour curve $f(x, y) = C$ passing through a point P, and a unit vector $\widehat{\mathbf{e}}$ on the tangent line at P. The scalar field f does not change along the contour curve, so the derivative of f in the direction tangential to the contour curve is zero and we must have $\mathbf{grad}\, f \cdot \widehat{\mathbf{e}} = 0$ at P. Hence $\mathbf{grad}\, f$ must be normal to $\widehat{\mathbf{e}}$.

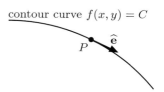

Figure 3.5

Exercise 3.2

Find a vector whose direction is normal to the curve $x^2 - 2xy + y^2 = 9$ at the point $(0, 3)$.

(*Hint*: The curve is a contour of the scalar field $f(x, y) = x^2 - 2xy + y^2$.)

3.3 Gradient function in three dimensions

You have seen that, for a two-dimensional scalar field $f(x, y)$, we can use the z-axis for showing the scalar values $z = f(x, y)$ and so construct the surface $(x, y, f(x, y))$. When we have a three-dimensional scalar field $f(x, y, z)$, such as the temperature distribution in a room, all three spatial coordinates (x, y, z) are needed to specify the domain of the function and there is no 'fourth spatial dimension' for showing the function values. However, we can still consider a parametrized path in space and use the Chain Rule in three dimensions to give the rate of change of f along the path. Proceeding as before, we find that the derivative of $f(x, y, z)$ in the direction of $\widehat{\mathbf{d}}$, a unit vector tangential to the path, parametrized by the arc length s at a point (a, b, c) is

$$\frac{df}{ds} = \mathbf{grad}\, f(a, b, c) \cdot \widehat{\mathbf{d}},$$

where the three-dimensional vector

$$\mathbf{grad}\, f(a, b, c) = \frac{\partial f}{\partial x}(a, b, c)\mathbf{i} + \frac{\partial f}{\partial y}(a, b, c)\mathbf{j} + \frac{\partial f}{\partial z}(a, b, c)\mathbf{k}$$

is the gradient vector of f at the point (a, b, c).

There is a gradient vector at each point in the domain of f, so $\mathbf{grad}\, f$ is a vector field in three dimensions.

Definitions

This **gradient in Cartesian coordinates** (x, y, z) **of a three-dimensional scalar field** f is the vector field

$$\mathbf{grad}\, f = \frac{\partial f}{\partial x}\mathbf{i} + \frac{\partial f}{\partial y}\mathbf{j} + \frac{\partial f}{\partial z}\mathbf{k}. \tag{3.5}$$

The **derivative** of f in a direction specified by a unit vector $\widehat{\mathbf{d}}$ is given by

$$\mathbf{grad}\, f \cdot \widehat{\mathbf{d}}.$$

This derivative may also be referred to as the *directional derivative*.

In three dimensions, the gradient vector at a point is always normal to the tangent plane to the contour surface passing through that point.

Example 3.3

Consider the scalar field $f(x, y, z) = -C/(x^2 + y^2 + z^2)^{1/2}$, where C is a positive constant. Show that the gravitational vector field $\mathbf{F} = -C\,\widehat{\mathbf{r}}/r^2$, where $\widehat{\mathbf{r}}$ is a unit vector in the direction of the position vector $\mathbf{r} = x\mathbf{i} + y\mathbf{j} + z\mathbf{k}$ and where $r = |\mathbf{r}| = \sqrt{x^2 + y^2 + z^2}$, can be expressed in terms of f by the relationship $\mathbf{F} = -\operatorname{\mathbf{grad}} f$.

The vector field $\mathbf{F}$ was considered in Example 2.2. The complete specification of the scalar field f would include a statement of the domain, $(x^2 + y^2 + z^2)^{1/2} \geq R$, where R is the radius of the Earth. We often omit the domain statement for convenience.

Solution

We have

$$f(x, y, z) = \frac{-C}{(x^2 + y^2 + z^2)^{1/2}},$$

so

$$\frac{\partial f}{\partial x} = \frac{Cx}{(x^2 + y^2 + z^2)^{3/2}}, \quad \frac{\partial f}{\partial y} = \frac{Cy}{(x^2 + y^2 + z^2)^{3/2}},$$

$$\frac{\partial f}{\partial z} = \frac{Cz}{(x^2 + y^2 + z^2)^{3/2}}.$$

Thus, from Equation (3.5),

$$\operatorname{\mathbf{grad}} f = \frac{C(x\mathbf{i} + y\mathbf{j} + z\mathbf{k})}{(x^2 + y^2 + z^2)^{3/2}} = \frac{C\,\widehat{\mathbf{r}}}{x^2 + y^2 + z^2},$$

where $\mathbf{r} = x\mathbf{i} + y\mathbf{j} + z\mathbf{k}$. Hence $-\operatorname{\mathbf{grad}} f$ is the vector function describing the gravitational vector field $\mathbf{F} = -C\,\widehat{\mathbf{r}}/r^2$. ∎

In Example 3.3, a vector field $\mathbf{F}$ is a scalar multiple of the gradient of a scalar field f. Scalar and vector fields that are used to model physical quantities in the real world are often related in this way. A similar relationship holds between the heat flow vector field $\mathbf{J}$ and the gradient function of a temperature field Θ in a heat-conducting material. This relationship is the vector form of Fourier's law, which you first met in *Unit 15*, and is given by

$$\mathbf{J} = -\kappa \operatorname{\mathbf{grad}} \Theta, \tag{3.6}$$

where κ is the thermal conductivity of the material.

To see the connection between this vector form of Fourier's law and the scalar form of the law that you saw in *Unit 15*, consider the case of steady-state conduction through a uniform slab of thickness b and cross-sectional area A. Figure 3.6 shows a cross-section of the slab with the vertical lines representing the contour surfaces of Θ (in °C) and the arrows representing the heat flow vector $\mathbf{J}$ at various points. The steady-state temperature in the slab falls linearly from the warmer surface in the plane $x = 0$, at a temperature Θ_1, to the cooler surface in the plane $x = b$, at a temperature Θ_2. (The case $\Theta_1 = 20°\mathrm{C}$ and $\Theta_2 = 0°\mathrm{C}$ is shown.) Thus, inside the slab, we have the temperature field

$$\Theta(x, y, z) = \Theta_1 - (\Theta_1 - \Theta_2)\frac{x}{b} \quad (0 \leq x \leq b),$$

so

$$\operatorname{\mathbf{grad}} \Theta = -\left(\frac{\Theta_1 - \Theta_2}{b}\right)\mathbf{i}.$$

If q is the total rate of heat flow through the slab, which is constant in the steady state, then $\mathbf{J} = (q/A)\mathbf{i}$. Substituting into Equation (3.6) gives

$$q = \frac{\kappa A (\Theta_1 - \Theta_2)}{b},$$

which is the equation for steady-state heat conduction obtained in *Unit 15*.

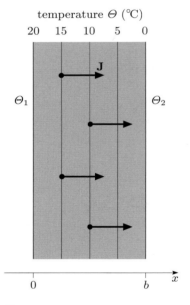

temperature Θ (°C)

| 20 | 15 | 10 | 5 | 0 |

Θ_1 **J** Θ_2

0 b x

Figure 3.6

$|\mathbf{J}|$ is the rate of heat flow across a unit area perpendicular to the direction of flow.

*Exercise 3.3

Evaluate **grad** Θ at the point $(-1, 1, 0)$ for the temperature field

$$\Theta(x, y, z) = A - B \ln\left(\frac{\sqrt{x^2 + y^2}}{a}\right),$$

where A, B and a are positive constants, and $\sqrt{x^2 + y^2} \geq a$.

A scalar field of this form can be used to model the temperature distribution in the wall of a conducting cylindrical pipe with its axis along the z-axis and inner radius a (as in Exercise 2.5). The pipe carries hot water at temperature A.

We shall return to this topic in *Unit 24*.

You have seen examples in which a vector field is equal to a constant multiple of the gradient of a scalar field. However, note that not all vector fields can be obtained as gradients of scalar fields.

3.4 Gradient as a vector operator

We can write the partial derivative $\partial f / \partial x$ of a scalar field f as $(\partial/\partial x)f$, where the symbol $\partial/\partial x$ is a **differential operator**. The operator acquires meaning only when given an **operand** on its right-hand side, i.e. a function f on which to operate. Thus the differential operator $\partial/\partial x$ acts on a scalar function f to give another scalar function $\partial f / \partial x$.

Consider the quantity $\mathbf{i}\,\partial/\partial x$. This, too, is a differential operator. It acts on a scalar function f to give the vector function $(\mathbf{i}\,\partial/\partial x)f = \mathbf{i}\,\partial f/\partial x$. For example, when $f(x, y, z) = x^3 - 2xy^2 + z$, we have the vector function

$$(\mathbf{i}\,\partial/\partial x)f = \mathbf{i}\,\partial f/\partial x = \mathbf{i}(3x^2 - 2y^2).$$

The operator $\mathbf{i}\,\partial/\partial x$ is an example of a **vector differential operator**.

Consider the expression for **grad** f in Equation (3.5). We can write it as

$$\mathbf{grad}\, f = \left(\mathbf{i}\frac{\partial}{\partial x} + \mathbf{j}\frac{\partial}{\partial y} + \mathbf{k}\frac{\partial}{\partial z}\right) f, \tag{3.7}$$

where the quantity in brackets is a vector differential operator commonly known as **del** (or **nabla** in some texts) and denoted by the bold symbol $\boldsymbol{\nabla}$.

The symbol $\boldsymbol{\nabla}$ was introduced in *Unit 12*.

Definition

The vector differential operator **del** is denoted by $\boldsymbol{\nabla}$ and in Cartesian coordinates is given by

$$\boldsymbol{\nabla} = \mathbf{i}\frac{\partial}{\partial x} + \mathbf{j}\frac{\partial}{\partial y} + \mathbf{k}\frac{\partial}{\partial z}. \tag{3.8}$$

We can now write the gradient function of f as **grad** f or as $\boldsymbol{\nabla} f$, i.e.

$$\mathbf{grad}\, f = \boldsymbol{\nabla} f.$$

This use of 'del' may appear to be nothing more than a notational device. However, as you will see later, this vector differential operator takes on the significance of a powerful unifying concept in vector calculus.

We used the alternative notation for the gradient function in two dimensions in *Unit 12*. In two dimensions the third component of $\boldsymbol{\nabla}$ is redundant, and we have

$$\boldsymbol{\nabla} = \mathbf{i}\frac{\partial}{\partial x} + \mathbf{j}\frac{\partial}{\partial y}.$$

Example 3.4

Find the vector field ∇f, where f is the scalar field

$$f(x, y, z) = x^2 - 2xz.$$

Solution

∇f is the same as **grad** f. Hence, using Equation (3.7),

$$\begin{aligned}
\nabla f &= \left(\mathbf{i}\frac{\partial}{\partial x} + \mathbf{j}\frac{\partial}{\partial y} + \mathbf{k}\frac{\partial}{\partial z} \right)(x^2 - 2xz) \\
&= \mathbf{i}(2x - 2z) + \mathbf{j}(0) + \mathbf{k}(-2x) \\
&= 2(x - z)\mathbf{i} - 2x\mathbf{k}. \quad \blacksquare
\end{aligned}$$

Finally, notice that we can use matrix notation to write the operator **del** as

$$\nabla = \mathbf{i}\frac{\partial}{\partial x} + \mathbf{j}\frac{\partial}{\partial y} + \mathbf{k}\frac{\partial}{\partial z} = \begin{bmatrix} \mathbf{i} & \mathbf{j} & \mathbf{k} \end{bmatrix} \begin{bmatrix} \frac{\partial}{\partial x} \\ \frac{\partial}{\partial y} \\ \frac{\partial}{\partial z} \end{bmatrix}. \tag{3.9}$$

This idea is useful when we need a formula for **del** in other coordinate systems, as you will see in the next subsection.

3.5 Gradient function in plane polar coordinates

It is sometimes more convenient to express a scalar field in terms of polar coordinates $\langle r, \theta \rangle$. (One example is when the field is symmetric under rotations about the origin, so it has the form $f(r)$.) In order to calculate the gradient of a field in these coordinates we need an expression for **grad** f in polar coordinates. The first step is to recall from Section 1 how the polar unit vectors $\mathbf{e}_r$ and $\mathbf{e}_\theta$ are related to the Cartesian unit vectors $\mathbf{i}$ and $\mathbf{j}$:

$$\begin{aligned}
\mathbf{e}_r &= \cos\theta\,\mathbf{i} + \sin\theta\,\mathbf{j}, \\
\mathbf{e}_\theta &= -\sin\theta\,\mathbf{i} + \cos\theta\,\mathbf{j},
\end{aligned}$$

or, in matrix form,

$$\begin{bmatrix} \mathbf{e}_r \\ \mathbf{e}_\theta \end{bmatrix} = \begin{bmatrix} \cos\theta & \sin\theta \\ -\sin\theta & \cos\theta \end{bmatrix} \begin{bmatrix} \mathbf{i} \\ \mathbf{j} \end{bmatrix}.$$

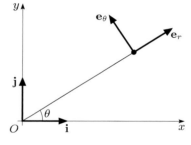

Figure 3.7

We can express $\mathbf{i}$ and $\mathbf{j}$ in terms of $\mathbf{e}_r$ and $\mathbf{e}_\theta$ by inverting this orthogonal matrix, obtaining

$$\begin{bmatrix} \mathbf{i} \\ \mathbf{j} \end{bmatrix} = \begin{bmatrix} \cos\theta & -\sin\theta \\ \sin\theta & \cos\theta \end{bmatrix} \begin{bmatrix} \mathbf{e}_r \\ \mathbf{e}_\theta \end{bmatrix}.$$

Now we use the Chain Rule from *Unit 12* to calculate $\dfrac{\partial f}{\partial r}$ in terms of $\dfrac{\partial f}{\partial x}$ and $\dfrac{\partial f}{\partial y}$. The form of the Chain Rule we need is

$$\frac{\partial f}{\partial r} = \frac{\partial f}{\partial x}\frac{\partial x}{\partial r} + \frac{\partial f}{\partial y}\frac{\partial y}{\partial r}.$$

But since $x = r\cos\theta$ and $y = r\sin\theta$, we have

$$\frac{\partial x}{\partial r} = \cos\theta \quad \text{and} \quad \frac{\partial y}{\partial r} = \sin\theta.$$

Hence

$$\frac{\partial f}{\partial r} = \cos\theta \, \frac{\partial f}{\partial x} + \sin\theta \, \frac{\partial f}{\partial y},$$

and since this is true for any function f, we have

$$\frac{\partial}{\partial r} = \cos\theta \, \frac{\partial}{\partial x} + \sin\theta \, \frac{\partial}{\partial y}.$$

Exercise 3.4

Derive a similar expression for $\dfrac{\partial}{\partial \theta}$ in terms of r, $\cos\theta$, $\sin\theta$, $\dfrac{\partial}{\partial x}$ and $\dfrac{\partial}{\partial y}$.

These two pieces of information may be summarized in matrix form as

$$\begin{bmatrix} \frac{\partial}{\partial r} \\ \frac{\partial}{\partial \theta} \end{bmatrix} = \begin{bmatrix} \cos\theta & \sin\theta \\ -r\sin\theta & r\cos\theta \end{bmatrix} \begin{bmatrix} \frac{\partial}{\partial x} \\ \frac{\partial}{\partial y} \end{bmatrix}.$$

Although the matrix is not orthogonal (because of the presence of r), it can be inverted to give

$$\begin{bmatrix} \frac{\partial}{\partial x} \\ \frac{\partial}{\partial y} \end{bmatrix} = \begin{bmatrix} \cos\theta & -\frac{1}{r}\sin\theta \\ \sin\theta & \frac{1}{r}\cos\theta \end{bmatrix} \begin{bmatrix} \frac{\partial}{\partial r} \\ \frac{\partial}{\partial \theta} \end{bmatrix}.$$

Now we can immediately write down the formula for **del** in plane polar coordinates, since

$$\begin{aligned}
\nabla &= \begin{bmatrix} \mathbf{i} & \mathbf{j} \end{bmatrix} \begin{bmatrix} \frac{\partial}{\partial x} \\ \frac{\partial}{\partial y} \end{bmatrix} \\
&= \left(\begin{bmatrix} \cos\theta & -\sin\theta \\ \sin\theta & \cos\theta \end{bmatrix} \begin{bmatrix} \mathbf{e}_r \\ \mathbf{e}_\theta \end{bmatrix} \right)^{T} \begin{bmatrix} \cos\theta & -\frac{1}{r}\sin\theta \\ \sin\theta & \frac{1}{r}\cos\theta \end{bmatrix} \begin{bmatrix} \frac{\partial}{\partial r} \\ \frac{\partial}{\partial \theta} \end{bmatrix} \\
&= \begin{bmatrix} \mathbf{e}_r \\ \mathbf{e}_\theta \end{bmatrix}^{T} \begin{bmatrix} \cos\theta & -\sin\theta \\ \sin\theta & \cos\theta \end{bmatrix}^{T} \begin{bmatrix} \cos\theta & -\frac{1}{r}\sin\theta \\ \sin\theta & \frac{1}{r}\cos\theta \end{bmatrix} \begin{bmatrix} \frac{\partial}{\partial r} \\ \frac{\partial}{\partial \theta} \end{bmatrix} \\
&= \begin{bmatrix} \mathbf{e}_r \\ \mathbf{e}_\theta \end{bmatrix}^{T} \begin{bmatrix} \cos\theta & \sin\theta \\ -\sin\theta & \cos\theta \end{bmatrix} \begin{bmatrix} \cos\theta & -\frac{1}{r}\sin\theta \\ \sin\theta & \frac{1}{r}\cos\theta \end{bmatrix} \begin{bmatrix} \frac{\partial}{\partial r} \\ \frac{\partial}{\partial \theta} \end{bmatrix} \\
&= \begin{bmatrix} \mathbf{e}_r \\ \mathbf{e}_\theta \end{bmatrix}^{T} \begin{bmatrix} 1 & 0 \\ 0 & \frac{1}{r} \end{bmatrix} \begin{bmatrix} \frac{\partial}{\partial r} \\ \frac{\partial}{\partial \theta} \end{bmatrix} \\
&= \mathbf{e}_r \frac{\partial}{\partial r} + \frac{1}{r}\mathbf{e}_\theta \frac{\partial}{\partial \theta}. \qquad\qquad (3.10)
\end{aligned}$$

Exercise 3.5

Find the gradient vector at a point $\langle r, \theta \rangle$ of the scalar function given by

$$f(r, \theta) = r^2 - 2r\cos\theta.$$

End-of-section Exercises

Exercise 3.6 ————————————————————————

For $f(x, y, z) = x^2 y^2 z^2$ find:

(a) the maximum value of the derivative of f at the point $(-1, 1, 1)$ and the unit vector that specifies the direction in which this maximum occurs;

(b) the derivative of f at the point $(2, 1, -1)$ in the direction of the unit vector $\widehat{\mathbf{d}} = \frac{3}{5}\mathbf{i} + \frac{4}{5}\mathbf{k}$.

Exercise 3.7 ————————————————————————

Consider the scalar field $f(x, y, z) = e^{-a(x^2+y^2)-bz}$, where a and b are positive constants. Show that

$$\nabla f = -(2a(x\mathbf{i} + y\mathbf{j}) + b\mathbf{k})f,$$

and evaluate ∇f at the origin. Find the x-component of $\nabla f(1, 2, 3)$.

Exercise 3.8 ————————————————————————

A two-dimensional scalar field has the form $f(x, y) = (x^2 + y^2)^{1/2}$.

(a) Find the vector field **grad** f and evaluate **grad** f at the point $(1, 1)$.

(b) Specify the unit vector $\widehat{\mathbf{d}}$ at $\frac{\pi}{6}$ to the positive x-direction and at $\frac{\pi}{3}$ to the positive y-direction. What is the derivative of f in the direction of $\widehat{\mathbf{d}}$ at $(1, 1)$?

Exercise 3.9 ————————————————————————

Determine the vector field **grad** g, where $g(x, y) = x^2 y - y^2 x$. Find the magnitude and direction of the steepest slope on the surface $z = g(x, y)$ at the point $(1, 1)$.

4 *Three-dimensional polar coordinate systems*

Often the first step in solving a problem is to choose an appropriate coordinate system, one that will express the problem in the simplest possible form. This may involve choosing the origin and the orientation of a Cartesian coordinate system. On the other hand, there are many problems for which other types of coordinate system are more appropriate. For example, in *Unit 20* you saw how useful a plane polar coordinate system can be for problems involving circular motion.

This section introduces two non-Cartesian coordinate systems, which are especially useful for representing three-dimensional fields that have cylindrical or spherical symmetry. Such symmetries are usually easy to recognize. A three-dimensional scalar field has **cylindrical symmetry** when the field values depend only on the distance from a fixed straight line. If we call this line the z-axis, then the field depends only on the single variable $\rho = \sqrt{x^2 + y^2}$. The scalar field of Exercise 3.3 is an example of a cylindrically symmetric field. A three-dimensional scalar field has **spherical symmetry** when the field values depend only on the distance from a fixed point, which may be taken as the origin. The light intensity field I of Example 2.1, which varies only with $r = \sqrt{x^2 + y^2 + z^2}$, is an example of a spherically symmetric field.

4.1 Cylindrical polar coordinates

A cylindrical polar coordinate system extends the familiar plane polar coordinates $\langle r, \theta \rangle$ to three dimensions. The coordinate r is now labelled ρ, since it represents the distance from the z-axis (rather than from the origin). The z-coordinate of the Cartesian coordinate system provides the third variable, to give the following system.

Some texts continue to use r in place of ρ.

Cylindrical polar coordinates

Any point P can be represented by the triple $\langle \rho, \theta, z \rangle$, where z is the distance of P from the (x, y)-plane and $\langle \rho, \theta \rangle$ are the plane polar coordinates of the projection N of P onto the (x, y)-plane (see Figure 4.1). Cylindrical polar coordinates are related to the Cartesian coordinates (x, y, z) by

$$x = \rho \cos \theta, \quad y = \rho \sin \theta, \quad z = z, \tag{4.1}$$

$$\rho = (x^2 + y^2)^{1/2}, \quad \sin \theta = y/\rho, \quad \cos \theta = x/\rho. \tag{4.2}$$

We require that

$$\rho \geq 0, \quad -\pi < \theta \leq \pi, \quad z \in \mathbb{R}.$$

The value of θ for points on the z-axis ($\rho = 0$) is undefined. By convention, we put $\theta = 0$ for such points.

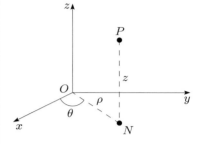

Figure 4.1

The convention in this course is that the angle θ is measured anticlockwise from the x-axis and is in the range $-\pi < \theta \leq \pi$. In some texts the range of θ is taken as $0 \leq \theta < 2\pi$.

In three dimensions we use the symbol ρ for the distance $\sqrt{x^2 + y^2}$ from the z-axis. The symbol r is reserved for the distance $\sqrt{x^2 + y^2 + z^2}$ from the origin.

In Cartesian coordinates, the surfaces $x = $ constant, $y = $ constant and $z = $ constant are planes. In cylindrical polar coordinates, the surfaces $\rho = $ constant (> 0) are circular cylinders with axis the z-axis and radius ρ (see Figure 4.2). The surfaces $\theta = $ constant $(\neq 0)$ are half-planes that do not contain the z-axis (see Figure 4.3). The surfaces $z = $ constant are planes perpendicular to the z-axis (see Figure 4.4).

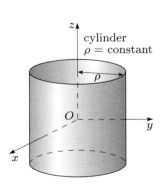

Figure 4.2

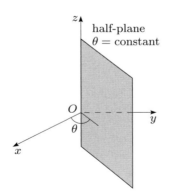

Figure 4.3

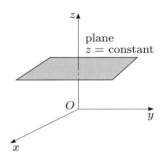

Figure 4.4

Example 4.1

(a) All the z-values remain unchanged. The first column of Table 4.1 gives the Cartesian coordinates of four points. Determine the cylindrical polar coordinates of these points and hence complete the table.

Table 4.1

Cartesian coordinates (x, y, z)	Cylindrical polar coordinates $\langle \rho, \theta, z \rangle$
$(5, 0, 0)$	
$(0, 5, 0)$	
$(-3, 3, 2)$	
$(1, \sqrt{3}, 3)$	

(b) Express the scalar field

$$f(x, y, z) = \frac{x\left(x^2 + y^2 + 3\right)}{x^2 + y^2} \quad \left(x^2 + y^2 > 0, \ z > 1\right)$$

in cylindrical polar form and determine, if possible, the field value at the point where $\rho = 4$, $\theta = \frac{\pi}{3}$ and $z = 2$.

Solution

(a) All the z-values remain unchanged. The first two points are both at a distance 5 from the z-axis and lie in the (x, y)-plane, so $\rho = 5$ and $z = 0$ for both of them. The angle θ is measured in the (x, y)-plane anticlockwise from the x-axis (see Figure 4.1), so $\theta = 0$ for the first point and $\theta = \frac{\pi}{2}$ for the second point.

The third point is at a distance $((-3)^2 + 3^2)^{1/2} = 3\sqrt{2}$ from the z-axis, so $\rho = 3\sqrt{2}$. The angle θ is in the second quadrant of the (x, y)-plane and has the value $\frac{3\pi}{4}$. More formally, we could use Equations (4.2) to obtain $\rho = ((-3)^2 + 3^2)^{1/2} = 3\sqrt{2}$, $\cos\theta = -\frac{3}{3\sqrt{2}}$ and $\sin\theta = \frac{3}{3\sqrt{2}}$, from which $\theta = \frac{3\pi}{4}$.

Using Equations (4.2) for the fourth point, $\rho = (1^2 + (\sqrt{3})^2)^{1/2} = 2$, $\cos\theta = \frac{1}{2}$ and $\sin\theta = \frac{\sqrt{3}}{2}$, from which $\theta = \frac{\pi}{3}$.

So the entries for the second column of the table are

$$\langle 5, 0, 0 \rangle, \quad \langle 5, \tfrac{\pi}{2}, 0 \rangle, \quad \langle 3\sqrt{2}, \tfrac{3\pi}{4}, 2 \rangle, \quad \langle 2, \tfrac{\pi}{3}, 3 \rangle.$$

(b) Using Equations (4.1), we see that $x^2 + y^2 + 3 = \rho^2\left(\cos^2\theta + \sin^2\theta\right) + 3 = \rho^2 + 3$ and $x/\left(x^2 + y^2\right) = (\rho\cos\theta)/\rho^2 = (\cos\theta)/\rho$. Hence

$$f(\rho, \theta, z) = \frac{\left(\rho^2 + 3\right)\cos\theta}{\rho} \quad (\rho > 0, \ z > 1).$$

First we confirm that the point with cylindrical polar coordinates $\langle 4, \frac{\pi}{3}, 2 \rangle$ is within the domain of the function. It clearly satisfies $\rho > 0$ and $z > 1$. No condition is explicitly placed on θ, so we assume that θ can have any value within its range. Thus the point is within the domain of f and

$$f(4, \tfrac{\pi}{3}, 2) = \frac{\left(4^2 + 3\right)\cos\frac{\pi}{3}}{4} = \frac{19}{8}. \quad \blacksquare$$

Exercise 4.1

Consider the scalar field

$$\lambda(\rho, \theta, z) = \left(\cos(\tfrac{\pi}{2} z)\right)/\rho \quad (\rho > 0, -1 \leq z \leq 1).$$

(a) Describe, in geometric terms, the domain of the function.

(b) Determine, where possible, the values of λ at points P, Q and R on the positive x-, y- and z-axes, respectively, each at unit distance from the origin.

(c) Determine the value of λ at all points on a circle of radius 2, with its centre on the z-axis, in the plane $z = \tfrac{1}{4}$.

The cylindrical polar coordinate system can also be used to represent vector fields. However, before we can do this, we need to specify a set of three unit vectors in cylindrical polar coordinates that play the same role as $\mathbf{i}$, $\mathbf{j}$ and $\mathbf{k}$ in Cartesian systems. Figure 4.5(a) shows three mutually perpendicular unit vectors at a point P with cylindrical polar coordinates $\langle \rho, \theta, z \rangle$, as follows.

- The unit vector $\mathbf{e}_\rho$ at P points in the direction of increasing ρ, i.e. perpendicularly away from the z-axis at P.

- The unit vector $\mathbf{e}_\theta$ at P points in the direction of increasing θ, i.e. tangential to the circle through P and centred at $\langle 0, 0, z \rangle$.

- The unit vector $\mathbf{e}_z$ is the same as the Cartesian unit vector $\mathbf{k}$, i.e. it is in the positive z-direction.

In the plane polar coordinate notation $\langle r, \theta \rangle$ of Section 1 and Subsection 3.5, the unit vectors $\mathbf{e}_\rho$ and $\mathbf{e}_\theta$ are $\mathbf{e}_r$ and $\mathbf{e}_\theta$, respectively.

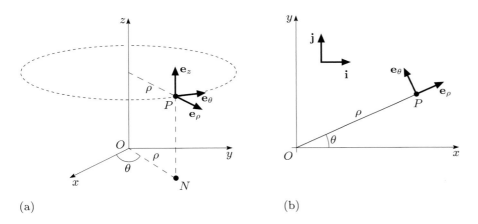

(a)   (b)

Figure 4.5   Unit vectors $\mathbf{e}_\rho$ and $\mathbf{e}_\theta$ lie in a plane parallel to the (x, y)-plane, with $\mathbf{e}_\rho$ pointing away from the z-axis and $\mathbf{e}_\theta$ perpendicular to $\mathbf{e}_\rho$ in the direction of increasing θ.

You can see from Figure 4.5(b) that these unit vectors are related to the Cartesian unit vectors in the following way.

Cylindrical polar unit vectors and Cartesian unit vectors

The cylindrical polar unit vectors $\mathbf{e}_\rho$, $\mathbf{e}_\theta$ and $\mathbf{e}_z$ can be expressed in terms of the Cartesian unit vectors $\mathbf{i}$, $\mathbf{j}$ and $\mathbf{k}$ as

$$\mathbf{e}_\rho = \mathbf{i}\cos\theta + \mathbf{j}\sin\theta = \frac{x\mathbf{i} + y\mathbf{j}}{\sqrt{x^2 + y^2}},$$

$$\mathbf{e}_\theta = -\mathbf{i}\sin\theta + \mathbf{j}\cos\theta = \frac{-y\mathbf{i} + x\mathbf{j}}{\sqrt{x^2 + y^2}}, \qquad (4.3)$$

$$\mathbf{e}_z = \mathbf{k}.$$

We can write this information more economically in matrix form as

$$\begin{bmatrix} \mathbf{e}_\rho \\ \mathbf{e}_\theta \\ \mathbf{e}_z \end{bmatrix} = \begin{bmatrix} \cos\theta & \sin\theta & 0 \\ -\sin\theta & \cos\theta & 0 \\ 0 & 0 & 1 \end{bmatrix} \begin{bmatrix} \mathbf{i} \\ \mathbf{j} \\ \mathbf{k} \end{bmatrix}.$$

The matrix is orthogonal, so its inverse is its transpose

$$\begin{bmatrix} \mathbf{i} \\ \mathbf{j} \\ \mathbf{k} \end{bmatrix} = \begin{bmatrix} \cos\theta & -\sin\theta & 0 \\ \sin\theta & \cos\theta & 0 \\ 0 & 0 & 1 \end{bmatrix} \begin{bmatrix} \mathbf{e}_\rho \\ \mathbf{e}_\theta \\ \mathbf{e}_z \end{bmatrix}. \tag{4.4}$$

Unlike the Cartesian unit vectors, the cylindrical polar unit vectors $\mathbf{e}_\rho$, $\mathbf{e}_\theta$ and $\mathbf{e}_z$ are not all constant vectors, since the directions of $\mathbf{e}_\rho$ and $\mathbf{e}_\theta$ depend on the position of P. In other words, $\mathbf{e}_\rho$ and $\mathbf{e}_\theta$ are non-constant vector fields.

Since the cylindrical polar unit vectors are mutually perpendicular at each point, we have the following definition.

Cylindrical polar components

A vector $\mathbf{F}$ can be expressed in terms of the cylindrical polar unit vectors $\mathbf{e}_\rho$, $\mathbf{e}_\theta$ and $\mathbf{e}_z$ as

$$\mathbf{F} = F_\rho \mathbf{e}_\rho + F_\theta \mathbf{e}_\theta + F_z \mathbf{e}_z,$$

where $F_\rho = \mathbf{F} \cdot \mathbf{e}_\rho$, $F_\theta = \mathbf{F} \cdot \mathbf{e}_\theta$ and $F_z = \mathbf{F} \cdot \mathbf{e}_z$. The scalar quantities F_ρ, F_θ and F_z are the **cylindrical polar components** of $\mathbf{F}$.

Example 4.2

Consider the vector field

$$\mathbf{F}(x, y, z) = \frac{C(x\mathbf{i} + y\mathbf{j})}{x^2 + y^2} \quad \left(a \le \sqrt{x^2 + y^2} \le b \right),$$

where a, b and C are positive constants.

(a) Express this vector field in cylindrical polar coordinates.

(b) Assuming that $C = 1$, $a = 2$ and $b = 4$, determine the magnitude and direction of the vector field at the point $\langle 3, \pi, 7 \rangle$. What are the cylindrical polar components of $\mathbf{F}$ at this point?

Solution

(a) We can write

$$\mathbf{F}(x, y, z) = \frac{C}{\sqrt{x^2 + y^2}} \frac{x\mathbf{i} + y\mathbf{j}}{\sqrt{x^2 + y^2}} \quad \left(a \le \sqrt{x^2 + y^2} \le b \right).$$

Thus, using Equations (4.2) and (4.3),

$$\mathbf{F}(\rho, \theta, z) = \frac{C}{\rho} \mathbf{e}_\rho \quad (a \le \rho \le b). \tag{4.5}$$

(b) From Equation (4.5), the magnitude of the vector field at $\langle 3, \pi, 7 \rangle$ is $|\mathbf{F}(3, \pi, 7)| = |C/\rho| = \frac{1}{3}$, and the direction of the vector field is given by $\mathbf{e}_\rho$, i.e. in the direction perpendicularly away from the z-axis through the point. Again from Equation (4.5), the cylindrical polar components of $\mathbf{F}$ at $\langle 3, \pi, 7 \rangle$ are $F_\rho = \frac{1}{3}$ and $F_\theta = F_z = 0$. ∎

4.2 Grad in cylindrical polar coordinates

If we are given a scalar field f in cylindrical polar coordinates, we can work out the vector field **grad** f without first having to convert the cylindrical polar coordinates into Cartesian coordinates. In order to do this, we need an expression for **grad** f in terms of partial derivatives with respect to the cylindrical polar variables. We start by finding relationships between $\partial/\partial\rho$, $\partial/\partial\theta$, $\partial/\partial z$ and $\partial/\partial x$, $\partial/\partial y$, $\partial/\partial z$. This is done easily using the Chain Rule.

First we recall the relationship between Cartesian coordinates and cylindrical polar coordinates from Equations (4.1):

$$x = \rho\cos\theta, \quad y = \rho\sin\theta, \quad z = z.$$

Now applying the Chain Rule gives, for any function f,

$$\frac{\partial f}{\partial \rho} = \frac{\partial x}{\partial \rho}\frac{\partial f}{\partial x} + \frac{\partial y}{\partial \rho}\frac{\partial f}{\partial y} + \frac{\partial z}{\partial \rho}\frac{\partial f}{\partial z}$$

$$= \cos\theta\,\frac{\partial f}{\partial x} + \sin\theta\,\frac{\partial f}{\partial y},$$

since $\dfrac{\partial z}{\partial \rho} = 0$.

We deduce that

$$\frac{\partial}{\partial \rho} = \cos\theta\,\frac{\partial}{\partial x} + \sin\theta\,\frac{\partial}{\partial y}.$$

Similarly, we can find an expression for $\partial/\partial\theta$:

$$\frac{\partial}{\partial \theta} = \frac{\partial x}{\partial \theta}\frac{\partial}{\partial x} + \frac{\partial y}{\partial \theta}\frac{\partial}{\partial y} + \frac{\partial z}{\partial \theta}\frac{\partial}{\partial z}$$

$$= -\rho\sin\theta\,\frac{\partial}{\partial x} + \rho\cos\theta\,\frac{\partial}{\partial y}.$$

Fortunately, there is no additional work for $\partial/\partial z$ because

$$\frac{\partial}{\partial z} = \frac{\partial}{\partial z}.$$

We can write these three operator equations in matrix form as

$$\begin{bmatrix} \frac{\partial}{\partial \rho} \\ \frac{\partial}{\partial \theta} \\ \frac{\partial}{\partial z} \end{bmatrix} = \begin{bmatrix} \cos\theta & \sin\theta & 0 \\ -\rho\sin\theta & \rho\cos\theta & 0 \\ 0 & 0 & 1 \end{bmatrix} \begin{bmatrix} \frac{\partial}{\partial x} \\ \frac{\partial}{\partial y} \\ \frac{\partial}{\partial z} \end{bmatrix}.$$

This is very similar to the operator equations derived for plane polar coordinates in Subsection 3.5.

This matrix is not orthogonal for $\rho \neq 1$, but we can deduce that its inverse is

$$\begin{bmatrix} \cos\theta & \sin\theta & 0 \\ -\rho\sin\theta & \rho\cos\theta & 0 \\ 0 & 0 & 1 \end{bmatrix}^{-1} = \begin{bmatrix} \cos\theta & -\frac{1}{\rho}\sin\theta & 0 \\ \sin\theta & \frac{1}{\rho}\cos\theta & 0 \\ 0 & 0 & 1 \end{bmatrix}.$$

This allows us to express $\partial/\partial x$, $\partial/\partial y$ and $\partial/\partial z$ in terms of $\partial/\partial\rho$, $\partial/\partial\theta$ and $\partial/\partial z$:

$$\begin{bmatrix} \frac{\partial}{\partial x} \\ \frac{\partial}{\partial y} \\ \frac{\partial}{\partial z} \end{bmatrix} = \begin{bmatrix} \cos\theta & -\frac{1}{\rho}\sin\theta & 0 \\ \sin\theta & \frac{1}{\rho}\cos\theta & 0 \\ 0 & 0 & 1 \end{bmatrix} \begin{bmatrix} \frac{\partial}{\partial \rho} \\ \frac{\partial}{\partial \theta} \\ \frac{\partial}{\partial z} \end{bmatrix}. \tag{4.6}$$

Recall from Equation (3.9) that

$$\nabla = \mathbf{i}\,\frac{\partial}{\partial x} + \mathbf{j}\,\frac{\partial}{\partial y} + \mathbf{k}\,\frac{\partial}{\partial z} = \begin{bmatrix} \mathbf{i} & \mathbf{j} & \mathbf{k} \end{bmatrix} \begin{bmatrix} \frac{\partial}{\partial x} \\ \frac{\partial}{\partial y} \\ \frac{\partial}{\partial z} \end{bmatrix}.$$

Now from Equation (4.4) we have

$$\begin{bmatrix} \mathbf{i} & \mathbf{j} & \mathbf{k} \end{bmatrix} = \begin{bmatrix} \mathbf{i} \\ \mathbf{j} \\ \mathbf{k} \end{bmatrix}^T = \left(\begin{bmatrix} \cos\theta & -\sin\theta & 0 \\ \sin\theta & \cos\theta & 0 \\ 0 & 0 & 1 \end{bmatrix} \begin{bmatrix} \mathbf{e}_\rho \\ \mathbf{e}_\theta \\ \mathbf{e}_z \end{bmatrix} \right)^T$$

$$= \begin{bmatrix} \mathbf{e}_\rho & \mathbf{e}_\theta & \mathbf{e}_z \end{bmatrix} \begin{bmatrix} \cos\theta & -\sin\theta & 0 \\ \sin\theta & \cos\theta & 0 \\ 0 & 0 & 1 \end{bmatrix}^T.$$

Substituting for $[\partial/\partial x \quad \partial/\partial y \quad \partial/\partial z]^T$ from Equation (4.6), we see that

$$\nabla = \begin{bmatrix} \mathbf{e}_\rho & \mathbf{e}_\theta & \mathbf{e}_z \end{bmatrix} \begin{bmatrix} \cos\theta & -\sin\theta & 0 \\ \sin\theta & \cos\theta & 0 \\ 0 & 0 & 1 \end{bmatrix}^T \begin{bmatrix} \cos\theta & -\frac{1}{\rho}\sin\theta & 0 \\ \sin\theta & \frac{1}{\rho}\cos\theta & 0 \\ 0 & 0 & 1 \end{bmatrix} \begin{bmatrix} \frac{\partial}{\partial\rho} \\ \frac{\partial}{\partial\theta} \\ \frac{\partial}{\partial z} \end{bmatrix}$$

$$= \begin{bmatrix} \mathbf{e}_\rho & \mathbf{e}_\theta & \mathbf{e}_z \end{bmatrix} \begin{bmatrix} \cos\theta & \sin\theta & 0 \\ -\sin\theta & \cos\theta & 0 \\ 0 & 0 & 1 \end{bmatrix} \begin{bmatrix} \cos\theta & -\frac{1}{\rho}\sin\theta & 0 \\ \sin\theta & \frac{1}{\rho}\cos\theta & 0 \\ 0 & 0 & 1 \end{bmatrix} \begin{bmatrix} \frac{\partial}{\partial\rho} \\ \frac{\partial}{\partial\theta} \\ \frac{\partial}{\partial z} \end{bmatrix}$$

$$= \begin{bmatrix} \mathbf{e}_\rho & \mathbf{e}_\theta & \mathbf{e}_z \end{bmatrix} \begin{bmatrix} 1 & 0 & 0 \\ 0 & \frac{1}{\rho} & 0 \\ 0 & 0 & 1 \end{bmatrix} \begin{bmatrix} \frac{\partial}{\partial\rho} \\ \frac{\partial}{\partial\theta} \\ \frac{\partial}{\partial z} \end{bmatrix}.$$

Performing the multiplication gives the required formula.

Gradient function in cylindrical polar coordinates

The **gradient function in cylindrical polar coordinates** of a scalar field f is

$$\operatorname{grad} f = \mathbf{e}_\rho \frac{\partial f}{\partial \rho} + \mathbf{e}_\theta \frac{1}{\rho}\frac{\partial f}{\partial \theta} + \mathbf{e}_z \frac{\partial f}{\partial z}, \tag{4.7}$$

where $\mathbf{e}_\rho$, $\mathbf{e}_\theta$ and $\mathbf{e}_z$ are unit vectors in the ρ-direction, θ-direction and z-direction.

When the scalar field has cylindrical symmetry, the scalar field does not vary with θ or z, so the equation simplifies to

$$\operatorname{grad} f = \mathbf{e}_\rho \frac{\partial f}{\partial \rho}. \tag{4.8}$$

Example 4.3

Consider the scalar field $f(\rho, \theta, z) = \ln\rho$ $(\rho > 0)$. Determine the vector field **grad** f. Specify the magnitude and direction of the gradient vector at a point 5 units perpendicularly away from the z-axis. Check your answer for **grad** f by expressing the scalar function f in Cartesian coordinates and using the Cartesian expression for the gradient function.

Solution

We can use the form for **grad** f in Equation (4.8), since the function varies with ρ only. Hence the vector field is

$$\mathbf{grad}\, f = \mathbf{e}_\rho \frac{\partial}{\partial \rho}(\ln \rho) = \mathbf{e}_\rho \left(\frac{1}{\rho}\right) = \frac{1}{\rho}\mathbf{e}_\rho \quad (\rho > 0).$$

At a perpendicular distance of 5 units from the z-axis, we have $\rho = 5$, so $|\mathbf{grad}\, f| = \frac{1}{5}$. The direction of **grad** f is along the line perpendicularly out from the z-axis, passing through the point.

Since $\rho = (x^2 + y^2)^{1/2}$, in Cartesian coordinates the scalar field is

$$f(x, y, z) = \ln((x^2 + y^2)^{1/2}) = \tfrac{1}{2}\ln\left(x^2 + y^2\right).$$

Hence, from Equation (3.5), as before,

$$\mathbf{grad}\, f = \tfrac{1}{2}\left(\frac{2x}{x^2 + y^2}\mathbf{i} + \frac{2y}{x^2 + y^2}\mathbf{j}\right) = \frac{x\mathbf{i} + y\mathbf{j}}{x^2 + y^2} = \frac{1}{\rho}\mathbf{e}_\rho. \quad \blacksquare$$

*Exercise 4.2 ⎯⎯⎯⎯⎯⎯⎯⎯⎯⎯⎯⎯⎯⎯⎯⎯⎯⎯⎯⎯⎯⎯

Consider the scalar field $U(x, y, z) = 1/(x^2 + y^2)$, where $x^2 + y^2 > 0$. Find ∇U using the Cartesian form of the gradient function. Express U in cylindrical polar coordinates and hence confirm your answer for the gradient function. Sketch some contour surfaces of U and vector field lines for ∇U.

Exercise 4.3 ⎯⎯⎯⎯⎯⎯⎯⎯⎯⎯⎯⎯⎯⎯⎯⎯⎯⎯⎯⎯⎯⎯⎯⎯

Determine the cylindrical polar components of the vector field **grad** f for the scalar field $f(\rho, \theta, z) = (\cos z)/\rho$, where $\rho > 0$.

4.3 Spherical polar coordinates

In the spherical polar coordinate system, one of the three coordinates of any point is specified as the magnitude r of the position vector $\mathbf{r}$ of the point. Hence, for fixed r, all points with coordinate r lie on the surface of a sphere of radius r centred on the origin. To specify position on the sphere, two angle coordinates θ and ϕ are used, based on the idea of locating a point on the Earth's surface by giving the latitude and the longitude (see Figure 4.6(a)).

The role of θ here is different from that in cylindrical polar coordinates. Here ϕ denotes the angle θ used in cylindrical polar coordinates. In some texts the roles of θ and ϕ may be reversed. The notation here matches that used in other Open University courses.

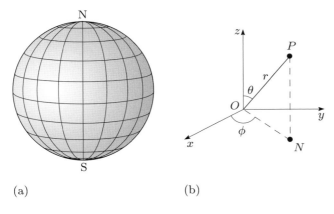

(a)   (b)

Figure 4.6

The **polar angle** θ is a measure of latitude on the sphere, with θ increasing from 'north pole' to 'south pole', so $\theta = 0$ for points on the positive z-axis, $\theta = \frac{\pi}{2}$ for points in the (x, y)-plane and $\theta = \pi$ for points on the negative z-axis. The **azimuthal angle** ϕ is a measure of longitude on the sphere and is the same as the coordinate θ in the cylindrical polar coordinate system.

It may help to think of ϕ as increasing 'west to east'; compare Figures 4.5(a) and 4.6(b).

Spherical polar coordinates

Any point P (see Figure 4.6(b)) can be represented by the triple $\langle r, \theta, \phi \rangle$, where r is the distance of P from the origin, and θ and ϕ are the polar and azimuthal angles, respectively. In Figure 4.6(b), N is the projection of P onto the (x, y)-plane. The spherical polar coordinates of P are related to the Cartesian coordinates (x, y, z) by

$$x = ON \cos \phi = r \sin \theta \cos \phi,$$
$$y = ON \sin \phi = r \sin \theta \sin \phi,$$
$$z = r \cos \theta,$$
$$r = \sqrt{x^2 + y^2 + z^2}.$$

We require that

$$r \geq 0, \quad -\pi < \phi \leq \pi, \quad 0 \leq \theta \leq \pi.$$

There are explicit expressions for θ and ϕ in terms of the other variables, but we do not need them in this course.

The surface $r = $ constant is a sphere (see Figure 4.7). The surface $\theta = $ constant is a cone (see Figure 4.8), or a plane if $\theta = \frac{\pi}{2}$, or a half-line if $\theta = 0$ or $\theta = \pi$. The surface $\phi = $ constant $(\neq 0)$ is a half-plane that does not contain the z-axis (see Figure 4.9). By convention, only the half-plane $\phi = 0$ contains the z-axis on its boundary.

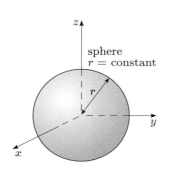

Figure 4.7

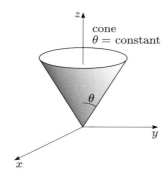

Figure 4.8

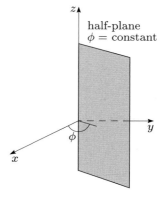

Figure 4.9

*Exercise 4.4

Give the spherical polar coordinates of points with Cartesian coordinates:
(a) $(5, 0, 0)$;   (b) $(0, 5, 0)$.

The mutually perpendicular unit vectors for the spherical polar coordinate system are shown in Figure 4.10. They are related to the Cartesian unit vectors in the following way.

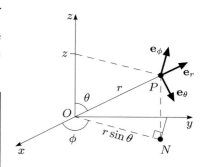

Figure 4.10

Spherical polar unit vectors and Cartesian unit vectors

The unit vectors $\mathbf{e}_r$, $\mathbf{e}_\theta$ and $\mathbf{e}_\phi$ can be expressed in terms of the Cartesian unit vectors $\mathbf{i}$, $\mathbf{j}$ and $\mathbf{k}$ as

$$\mathbf{e}_r = \mathbf{i} \sin \theta \cos \phi + \mathbf{j} \sin \theta \sin \phi + \mathbf{k} \cos \theta,$$
$$\mathbf{e}_\theta = \mathbf{i} \cos \theta \cos \phi + \mathbf{j} \cos \theta \sin \phi - \mathbf{k} \sin \theta, \quad (4.9)$$
$$\mathbf{e}_\phi = -\mathbf{i} \sin \phi + \mathbf{j} \cos \phi.$$

The directions of the unit vectors for the spherical polar coordinate system at a point P depend on the θ- and ϕ-coordinates of P (but not on r).

Once again, this information is more compactly expressed as a matrix equation

$$\begin{bmatrix} \mathbf{e}_r \\ \mathbf{e}_\theta \\ \mathbf{e}_\phi \end{bmatrix} = \begin{bmatrix} \sin\theta\cos\phi & \sin\theta\sin\phi & \cos\theta \\ \cos\theta\cos\phi & \cos\theta\sin\phi & -\sin\theta \\ -\sin\phi & \cos\phi & 0 \end{bmatrix} \begin{bmatrix} \mathbf{i} \\ \mathbf{j} \\ \mathbf{k} \end{bmatrix}$$

and, since the matrix is orthogonal, we have

$$\begin{bmatrix} \mathbf{i} \\ \mathbf{j} \\ \mathbf{k} \end{bmatrix} = \begin{bmatrix} \sin\theta\cos\phi & \sin\theta\sin\phi & \cos\theta \\ \cos\theta\cos\phi & \cos\theta\sin\phi & -\sin\theta \\ -\sin\phi & \cos\phi & 0 \end{bmatrix}^{-1} \begin{bmatrix} \mathbf{e}_r \\ \mathbf{e}_\theta \\ \mathbf{e}_\phi \end{bmatrix}$$

$$= \begin{bmatrix} \sin\theta\cos\phi & \cos\theta\cos\phi & -\sin\phi \\ \sin\theta\sin\phi & \cos\theta\sin\phi & \cos\phi \\ \cos\theta & -\sin\theta & 0 \end{bmatrix} \begin{bmatrix} \mathbf{e}_r \\ \mathbf{e}_\theta \\ \mathbf{e}_\phi \end{bmatrix}. \qquad (4.10)$$

Since the unit vectors $\mathbf{e}_r$, $\mathbf{e}_\theta$ and $\mathbf{e}_\phi$ are mutually perpendicular, we have the following definition.

Spherical polar components

A vector $\mathbf{F}$ can be expressed in terms of the spherical polar unit vectors $\mathbf{e}_r$, $\mathbf{e}_\theta$ and $\mathbf{e}_\phi$ as

$$\mathbf{F} = F_r\mathbf{e}_r + F_\theta\mathbf{e}_\theta + F_\phi\mathbf{e}_\phi, \qquad (4.11)$$

where $F_r = \mathbf{F}\cdot\mathbf{e}_r$, $F_\theta = \mathbf{F}\cdot\mathbf{e}_\theta$ and $F_\phi = \mathbf{F}\cdot\mathbf{e}_\phi$. The scalars F_r, F_θ and F_ϕ are the **spherical polar components** of $\mathbf{F}$.

Exercise 4.5 _____

Specify the spherical polar components of the vector field

$$\mathbf{F}(r,\theta,\phi) = \frac{1}{r}\,\mathbf{e}_\phi \quad (r > 0).$$

Grad in spherical polar coordinates

The gradient function can be expressed in spherical polar coordinates as follows.

The derivation is similar to (but more complicated than) that for cylindrical polar coordinates.

Gradient function in spherical polar coordinates

The **gradient function in spherical polar coordinates** of a scalar field f is

$$\mathbf{grad}\,f = \mathbf{e}_r\frac{\partial f}{\partial r} + \mathbf{e}_\theta\frac{1}{r}\frac{\partial f}{\partial \theta} + \mathbf{e}_\phi\frac{1}{r\sin\theta}\frac{\partial f}{\partial \phi}, \qquad (4.12)$$

where $\mathbf{e}_r$, $\mathbf{e}_\theta$ and $\mathbf{e}_\phi$ are unit vectors in the r-, θ- and ϕ-directions.

For spherically symmetric fields, in which the field values do not vary with θ or ϕ, the gradient simplifies to

$$\mathbf{grad}\,f = \mathbf{e}_r\frac{\partial f}{\partial r}. \qquad (4.13)$$

Example 4.4

Consider the scalar field expressed in Cartesian coordinates as

$$V(x, y, z) = \frac{-I_0}{(x^2 + y^2 + z^2)^{1/2}} \quad \left((x^2 + y^2 + z^2)^{1/2} > a > 0\right),$$

where I_0 is a positive constant. Express this field in spherical polar coordinates and hence show that $|\mathbf{grad}\, V| = I$, where I is the light intensity field specified in Example 2.1 as $I = I_0/(x^2 + y^2 + z^2)$.

Solution

We know that $x^2 + y^2 + z^2 = r^2$, so

$$V(r, \theta, \phi) = -I_0/r \quad (r > a).$$

By definition, $r \geq 0$.

The field is spherically symmetric, so we can use Equation (4.13) to obtain

$$\mathbf{grad}\, V = \mathbf{e}_r \frac{\partial}{\partial r}\left(\frac{-I_0}{r}\right) = \frac{I_0}{r^2}\mathbf{e}_r.$$

Hence $|\mathbf{grad}\, V| = I_0/r^2 = I_0/(x^2 + y^2 + z^2)$, which is the light intensity field I of Example 2.1. ∎

*Exercise 4.6

Specify the spherical polar components of the vector field $\mathbf{grad}\, V$ in Example 4.4.

End-of-section Exercises

Exercise 4.7

(a) Describe the geometric shapes of the surfaces defined in a cylindrical polar system by the following.

   (i) $\rho = 2$ (ii) $\theta = \frac{\pi}{2}$

(b) Show that the cylindrical polar unit vectors $\mathbf{e}_\rho$ and $\mathbf{e}_\theta$ are mutually perpendicular.

   (*Hint*: Use the fact that the Cartesian unit vectors are mutually perpendicular.)

(c) Find the gradient of the scalar field $F(\rho, \theta, z) = \rho e^{-z}$ at a point on the positive x-axis 5 units from the origin.

Exercise 4.8

(a) Describe the geometric shape of the surface defined in a spherical polar coordinate system by $\theta = \frac{\pi}{6}$.

(b) Use Equation (4.9) to confirm that the spherical polar unit vector $\mathbf{e}_r$ is of unit magnitude.

(c) Find the gradient in spherical polar coordinates of the scalar field $U(x, y, z) = \sqrt{x^2 + y^2 + z^2}$ at the point $\langle 5, \frac{\pi}{2}, \pi \rangle$. Give your answer in terms of the Cartesian unit vectors.

Exercise 4.9

Specify the cylindrical polar components of the vector field

$$u(\rho, \theta, z) = e^{-z^2} \mathbf{e}_\rho + \frac{1}{\rho}\, \mathbf{e}_\theta.$$

Exercise 4.10

Consider the scalar field

$$V(r, \theta, \phi) = \frac{M(3\cos^2\theta - 1)}{r^3} \quad (r > 0),$$

where M is a positive constant. Three points A, B and C have the following positions: A is on the positive y-axis 3 units from the origin, B has Cartesian coordinates $(0, 0, 1)$ and C has spherical polar coordinates $\langle 1, \pi, 0 \rangle$.

On the z-axis, where ϕ is not defined, by convention we have $\phi = 0$.

(a) Determine, where possible, the value of the scalar field V at the three points A, B and C.

(b) If $V(r, \theta, \phi)$ represents the potential energy of a particle at a point, then the force acting on the particle at that point is given by

This result, relating force and potential energy, is obtained in *Unit 24*.

$$\mathbf{F} = -\operatorname{\mathbf{grad}} V.$$

Determine the magnitude and direction of the force on the particle when the particle is at A.

Outcomes

After studying this unit you should be able to:

- interpret and sketch contour curves for a given scalar field;
- determine scalar field values at specified points for a given scalar field;
- interpret and sketch vector field lines for a given vector field;
- determine vector field values at specified points for a given vector field;
- determine the gradient function of a scalar field and calculate the derivative of a scalar field in a specified direction;
- convert between the Cartesian coordinates of a point and the cylindrical and spherical polar coordinates of the point;
- express a scalar or vector field in cylindrical or spherical polar coordinates, given the field in Cartesian coordinates.

Solutions to the exercises

Section 1

1.1 Since $\mathbf{A}^T\mathbf{A} = \mathbf{I}$, we have

$$\det(\mathbf{A}^T\mathbf{A}) = \det(\mathbf{A}^T)\det(\mathbf{A}) = 1.$$

However, $\det(\mathbf{A}^T) = \det(\mathbf{A})$, so the above becomes

$$(\det(\mathbf{A}))^2 = 1.$$

We can therefore deduce that $\det(\mathbf{A}) = \pm 1$. (For rotations $\det(\mathbf{A}) = 1$, and the minus sign arises only for a reflection. We do not investigate reflections since we are concentrating on right-handed systems.)

1.2 In each case we compute $\mathbf{A}^T\mathbf{A}$ and compare it with the identity matrix $\mathbf{I}$.

(a) $\begin{bmatrix} 1 & 0 \\ 1 & 1 \end{bmatrix}\begin{bmatrix} 1 & 1 \\ 0 & 1 \end{bmatrix} = \begin{bmatrix} 1 & 1 \\ 1 & 2 \end{bmatrix} \neq \mathbf{I}$

(b) $\begin{bmatrix} \frac{1}{\sqrt{2}} & \frac{1}{\sqrt{2}} \\ -\frac{1}{\sqrt{2}} & \frac{1}{\sqrt{2}} \end{bmatrix}\begin{bmatrix} \frac{1}{\sqrt{2}} & -\frac{1}{\sqrt{2}} \\ \frac{1}{\sqrt{2}} & \frac{1}{\sqrt{2}} \end{bmatrix} = \mathbf{I}$

(c) $\begin{bmatrix} 2 & 0 \\ 0 & 1 \end{bmatrix}\begin{bmatrix} 2 & 0 \\ 0 & 1 \end{bmatrix} = \begin{bmatrix} 4 & 0 \\ 0 & 1 \end{bmatrix} \neq \mathbf{I}$

(d) $\begin{bmatrix} \frac{1}{2} & \frac{\sqrt{3}}{2} \\ -\frac{\sqrt{3}}{2} & \frac{1}{2} \end{bmatrix}\begin{bmatrix} \frac{1}{2} & -\frac{\sqrt{3}}{2} \\ \frac{\sqrt{3}}{2} & \frac{1}{2} \end{bmatrix} = \mathbf{I}$

(e) $\begin{bmatrix} \frac{1}{2} & 0 & \frac{\sqrt{3}}{2} \\ 0 & 1 & 0 \\ -\frac{\sqrt{3}}{2} & 0 & \frac{1}{2} \end{bmatrix}\begin{bmatrix} \frac{1}{2} & 0 & -\frac{\sqrt{3}}{2} \\ 0 & 1 & 0 \\ \frac{\sqrt{3}}{2} & 0 & \frac{1}{2} \end{bmatrix} = \mathbf{I}$

Hence the matrices in (b), (d) and (e) are orthogonal and the others are not.

1.3 There are many possible choices — in fact, infinitely many ways. One example is $\begin{bmatrix} 2 & 1 & 0 \\ 1 & 1 & 0 \\ 0 & 0 & 1 \end{bmatrix}$, which certainly has determinant 1. However this matrix cannot be orthogonal because, when it is multiplied by the vector $[1 \quad 0 \quad 0]^T$, the result is $[2 \quad 1 \quad 0]^T$, a vector of different length.

Section 2

2.1 (a) Let the Cartesian coordinate system be in the plane of the sheet with $|\mathbf{r}| = \sqrt{x^2 + y^2}$. Then the scalar field function is

$$\Theta(x, y) = \Theta_1 + \frac{(\Theta_2 - \Theta_1)\ln\left(\sqrt{x^2 + y^2}/R_1\right)}{\ln(R_2/R_1)}.$$

The scalar field is defined over the region of the sheet. So the domain of the function is $R_2 \leq \sqrt{x^2 + y^2} \leq R_1$.

(b) In plane polar coordinates, $|\mathbf{r}| = r$, so the scalar field function is

$$\Theta(r, \theta) = \Theta_1 + \frac{(\Theta_2 - \Theta_1)\ln(r/R_1)}{\ln(R_2/R_1)},$$

with domain $R_2 \leq r \leq R_1$.

2.2 The domain of f is the area of the plane inside and on the circle $x^2 + y^2 = 4$ with radius 2. The contour curves are hyperbolae given by $xy = C$, where C is a constant, or, equivalently, by $y = C/x$. The figure shows the contour curves for $C = \frac{1}{2}$, $C = -\frac{1}{4}$ and $C = 1$.

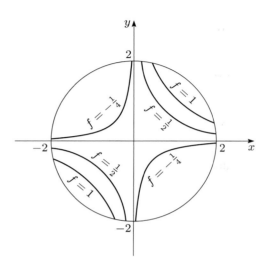

2.3 (a) (i) There is a hill summit inside the 60 m contour. (ii) There might be a lake in the depression in the region of the -10 m and -20 m contours.

(b) The land is fairly level in the vicinity of the 0 m and 10 m contours, since the contour curves are widely spaced in this region.

(c) Starting at A and walking in the direction of the arrow, you would soon experience a hard climb as you ascend the closely spaced contours leading to the top of the hill. Then there is a fairly gentle descent to the relatively level area, with a low point near the 0 m contour, and finally a gentle climb.

2.4 We have

$$\mathbf{F} = \frac{mgr}{R}(-\hat{\mathbf{r}}) = -\frac{mg}{R}\mathbf{r},$$

since $r\hat{\mathbf{r}} = \mathbf{r}$, so

$$\mathbf{F}(x, y, z) = \frac{-mg}{R}(x\mathbf{i} + y\mathbf{j} + z\mathbf{k}).$$

At the Earth's centre, we have $\mathbf{F}(0, 0, 0) = \mathbf{0}$.

2.5 (a) The x-component of the vector field $\mathbf{J}$ is

$$J_1(x, y, z) = \mathbf{J} \cdot \mathbf{i} = Cx/(x^2 + y^2).$$

(b) The vector $x\mathbf{i} + y\mathbf{j}$ points perpendicularly away from the z-axis. Hence the vector field lines of $\mathbf{J}$ are directed radially out from the axis of the pipe.

(c) The magnitude of $\mathbf{J}$ is given by

$$|\mathbf{J}| = \left|C(x\mathbf{i} + y\mathbf{j})/(x^2 + y^2)\right|$$
$$= C(x^2 + y^2)^{-1/2} = C/\rho.$$

Hence $|\mathbf{J}|$ is inversely proportional to ρ.

(d) The rate of flow outwards is the outward flow rate per unit area times the area of the surface, i.e.

$$|\mathbf{J}|(2\pi\rho h) = (C/\rho)(2\pi\rho h) = 2\pi Ch,$$

which is independent of ρ. This means that heat energy is being conducted through the material of the pipe, from the water surface to the outside surface of the pipe, without any loss or gain of heat in the material of the pipe.

2.6 Choose a coordinate system with the Earth's surface in the (x, y)-plane and the z-axis pointing vertically upwards. Then $\sigma(x, y, z) = Ae^{-\alpha z}$, for constants $A > 0$ and $\alpha > 0$. Knowing that $\sigma = 1.205$ at $z = 0$ tells us that $A = 1.205$. We are also told that $\sigma = 1.205/e$ when $z = 9.5 \times 10^3$. This gives $1.205/e = 1.205 e^{-\alpha \times 9.5 \times 10^3}$, from which $\alpha = 1/(9.5 \times 10^3)$. Hence the scalar field is

$$\sigma(x, y, z) = 1.205 e^{-z/(9.5 \times 10^3)}.$$

The domain is $z \geq 0$.

Since the field depends only on z, the contour surfaces are horizontal planes, i.e. $z = $ constant.

2.7 Introduce a Cartesian coordinate system with the z-axis along the axis of the wire. Then the magnitude $|\mathbf{E}|$ is inversely proportional to the distance $\rho = (x^2 + y^2)^{1/2}$ from the z-axis. The direction of $\mathbf{E}$ is directly away from the wire, in the direction of the vector $x\mathbf{i} + y\mathbf{j}$. The unit vector in this direction is $\mathbf{e}_\rho = (x\mathbf{i} + y\mathbf{j})/(x^2 + y^2)^{1/2}$. Hence the electric field vector at distance ρ is $\mathbf{E} = E_0 \mathbf{e}_\rho/\rho$, which has magnitude E_0 when $\rho = 1$, as required. Thus, in Cartesian coordinates, we have the vector field

$$\mathbf{E}(x, y, z) = E_0(x\mathbf{i} + y\mathbf{j})/(x^2 + y^2) \quad (x^2 + y^2 > 0).$$

The domain statement excludes the z-axis, where the function is not defined. The vector field lines are straight lines perpendicular to the z-axis and directed away from the z-axis.

Section 3

3.1 The scalar field is $f(x, y) = x^2 y$, so we have

$$\frac{\partial f}{\partial x} = 2xy, \quad \frac{\partial f}{\partial x}(-1, 2) = -4,$$

$$\frac{\partial f}{\partial y} = x^2, \quad \frac{\partial f}{\partial y}(-1, 2) = 1.$$

Thus, from Equation (3.4),

$$\mathbf{grad}\, f(-1, 2) = \frac{\partial f}{\partial x}\mathbf{i} + \frac{\partial f}{\partial y}\mathbf{j} = -4\mathbf{i} + \mathbf{j}.$$

The derivative in the x-direction is $\mathbf{grad}\, f \cdot \mathbf{i} = \partial f/\partial x$, which has the value -4 at $(-1, 2)$.

3.2 The curve $x^2 - 2xy + y^2 = 9$ is a contour of $f(x, y) = x^2 - 2xy + y^2$ passing through $(0, 3)$, and $\mathbf{grad}\, f$ evaluated at $(0, 3)$ is normal to this contour. We have

$$\mathbf{grad}\, f = (2x - 2y)\mathbf{i} + (-2x + 2y)\mathbf{j},$$

$$\mathbf{grad}\, f(0, 3) = -6\mathbf{i} + 6\mathbf{j}.$$

This, or any non-zero scalar multiple of it, is the required vector.

3.3 The partial derivatives are

$$\frac{\partial \Theta}{\partial x} = \frac{-Ba}{\sqrt{x^2 + y^2}} \times \frac{\frac{1}{2}(x^2 + y^2)^{-1/2}}{a} \times 2x$$

$$= -\frac{Bx}{x^2 + y^2},$$

$$\frac{\partial \Theta}{\partial y} = -\frac{By}{x^2 + y^2}, \quad \frac{\partial \Theta}{\partial z} = 0.$$

Thus, using Equation (3.5),

$$\mathbf{grad}\, \Theta = \left(-\frac{Bx}{x^2 + y^2}\right)\mathbf{i} + \left(-\frac{By}{x^2 + y^2}\right)\mathbf{j},$$

$$\mathbf{grad}\, \Theta(-1, 1, 0) = \tfrac{1}{2}B\mathbf{i} - \tfrac{1}{2}B\mathbf{j} = \tfrac{1}{2}B(\mathbf{i} - \mathbf{j}).$$

3.4 We have

$$\frac{\partial f}{\partial \theta} = \frac{\partial f}{\partial x}\frac{\partial x}{\partial \theta} + \frac{\partial f}{\partial y}\frac{\partial y}{\partial \theta}$$

$$= -r\sin\theta \frac{\partial f}{\partial x} + r\cos\theta \frac{\partial f}{\partial y}.$$

Hence

$$\frac{\partial}{\partial \theta} = -r\sin\theta \frac{\partial}{\partial x} + r\cos\theta \frac{\partial}{\partial y}.$$

3.5 We have $f(r, \theta) = r^2 - 2r\cos\theta$. Thus

$$\mathbf{grad}\, f = \left(\mathbf{e}_r \frac{\partial}{\partial r} + \frac{1}{r}\mathbf{e}_\theta \frac{\partial}{\partial \theta}\right) f$$

$$= \frac{\partial f}{\partial r}\mathbf{e}_r + \frac{1}{r}\frac{\partial f}{\partial \theta}\mathbf{e}_\theta$$

$$= (2r - 2\cos\theta)\mathbf{e}_r + 2\sin\theta\,\mathbf{e}_\theta.$$

3.6 (a) We need the magnitude and direction of $\mathbf{grad}\, f$ at $(-1, 1, 1)$. From Equation (3.5),

$$\mathbf{grad}\, f = 2xy^2 z^2\mathbf{i} + 2x^2 yz^2\mathbf{j} + 2x^2 y^2 z\mathbf{k}.$$

The maximum value of the derivative is $|\mathbf{grad}\, f|$ and it occurs in the direction of the unit vector $\mathbf{grad}\, f/|\mathbf{grad}\, f|$. At the point $(-1, 1, 1)$, we have

$$|\mathbf{grad}\, f| = |-2\mathbf{i} + 2\mathbf{j} + 2\mathbf{k}| = 2\sqrt{3},$$

$$\frac{\mathbf{grad}\, f}{|\mathbf{grad}\, f|} = -\frac{1}{\sqrt{3}}\mathbf{i} + \frac{1}{\sqrt{3}}\mathbf{j} + \frac{1}{\sqrt{3}}\mathbf{k}.$$

(b) The derivative of f in the direction of $\widehat{\mathbf{d}} = \tfrac{3}{5}\mathbf{i} + \tfrac{4}{5}\mathbf{k}$ is

$$\mathbf{grad}\, f \cdot \widehat{\mathbf{d}} = \tfrac{6}{5}xy^2 z^2 + \tfrac{8}{5}x^2 y^2 z.$$

At the point $(2, 1, -1)$, this gives

$$\mathbf{grad}\, f \cdot \widehat{\mathbf{d}} = -4.$$

3.7 We have

$$\frac{\partial f}{\partial x} = e^{-a(x^2 + y^2) - bz} \times (-2ax) = (-2ax)f(x, y, z),$$

$$\frac{\partial f}{\partial y} = e^{-a(x^2 + y^2) - bz} \times (-2ay) = (-2ay)f(x, y, z),$$

$$\frac{\partial f}{\partial z} = e^{-a(x^2 + y^2) - bz} \times (-b) = (-b)f(x, y, z).$$

Thus, from Equation (3.5),

$$\nabla f = (-2ax)f(x,y,z)\mathbf{i}$$
$$+ (-2ay)f(x,y,z)\mathbf{j}$$
$$+ (-b)f(x,y,z)\mathbf{k}$$
$$= -(2a(x\mathbf{i}+y\mathbf{j})+b\mathbf{k})f(x,y,z),$$

as required. At the origin,

$$\nabla f(0,0,0) = -be^0\mathbf{k} = -b\mathbf{k}.$$

The x-component of $\nabla f(1,2,3)$ is

$$\nabla f(1,2,3)\cdot\mathbf{i} = (-2a)f(1,2,3)$$
$$= -2ae^{-a(1^2+2^2)-3b}$$
$$= -2ae^{-5a-3b}.$$

3.8 (a) We have

$$\frac{\partial f}{\partial x} = \tfrac{1}{2}(x^2+y^2)^{-1/2}(2x) = \frac{x}{\sqrt{x^2+y^2}},$$

$$\frac{\partial f}{\partial y} = \frac{y}{\sqrt{x^2+y^2}}.$$

Thus, from Equation (3.4),

$$\mathbf{grad}\, f = \frac{1}{\sqrt{x^2+y^2}}(x\mathbf{i}+y\mathbf{j}),$$

$$\mathbf{grad}\, f(1,1) = \frac{1}{\sqrt{2}}(\mathbf{i}+\mathbf{j}).$$

(b) The unit vector $\widehat{\mathbf{d}}$ is shown in the figure.

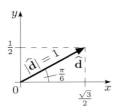

We have

$$\widehat{\mathbf{d}} = (\cos\tfrac{\pi}{6})\mathbf{i} + (\cos\tfrac{\pi}{3})\mathbf{j} = \tfrac{\sqrt{3}}{2}\mathbf{i} + \tfrac{1}{2}\mathbf{j}.$$

The required derivative is

$$\mathbf{grad}\, f(1,1)\cdot\widehat{\mathbf{d}} = \left(\tfrac{1}{\sqrt{2}}(\mathbf{i}+\mathbf{j})\right)\cdot\left(\tfrac{\sqrt{3}}{2}\mathbf{i}+\tfrac{1}{2}\mathbf{j}\right)$$
$$= \tfrac{\sqrt{3}}{2\sqrt{2}} + \tfrac{1}{2\sqrt{2}}$$
$$= \tfrac{1+\sqrt{3}}{2\sqrt{2}} \simeq 0.9659.$$

3.9 We have

$$\frac{\partial g}{\partial x} = 2xy - y^2, \quad \frac{\partial g}{\partial y} = x^2 - 2xy.$$

Thus, from Equation (3.4),

$$\mathbf{grad}\, g = (2xy-y^2)\mathbf{i} + (x^2-2xy)\mathbf{j},$$

$$\mathbf{grad}\, g(1,1) = \mathbf{i} - \mathbf{j}.$$

This gradient vector specifies the magnitude and direction of the steepest slope of the surface $z = g(x,y)$ at the point $(1,1)$. Hence the required steepest slope is $|\mathbf{grad}\, g(1,1)| = |\mathbf{i}-\mathbf{j}| = \sqrt{2}$. The direction of steepest slope is specified by the vector $\mathbf{i}-\mathbf{j}$.

Section 4

4.1 (a) The domain is the slab of space between (and including) the planes $z = 1$ and $z = -1$, but excluding the z-axis.

(b) At P we have $\lambda(1,0,0) = (\cos 0)/1 = 1$.
At Q we have $\lambda(1,\tfrac{\pi}{2},0) = (\cos 0)/1 = 1$.
At R we have $\rho = 0$, so R is not in the domain of λ.

(c) The points on the circle all have $\rho = 2$, so the required field value is $\lambda(2,\theta,\tfrac{1}{4}) = (\cos\tfrac{\pi}{8})/2 \simeq 0.4619$.

4.2 The partial derivatives of U are

$$\frac{\partial U}{\partial x} = -\frac{2x}{(x^2+y^2)^2}, \quad \frac{\partial U}{\partial y} = -\frac{2y}{(x^2+y^2)^2},$$

$$\frac{\partial U}{\partial z} = 0.$$

Hence, since $\nabla U = \mathbf{grad}\, U$, from Equation (3.5),

$$\nabla U = -\frac{2}{(x^2+y^2)^2}(x\mathbf{i}+y\mathbf{j}).$$

Converting to cylindrical polar coordinates using Equation (4.2), $U(\rho,\theta,z) = 1/\rho^2$. This is a cylindrically symmetric scalar field, since it depends only on ρ. So we can use Equation (4.8) to obtain

$$\nabla U = \mathbf{e}_\rho\frac{\partial U}{\partial\rho} = \mathbf{e}_\rho(-2)\frac{1}{\rho^3} = -\frac{2}{\rho^3}\,\mathbf{e}_\rho.$$

But, from Equation (4.3), $\mathbf{e}_\rho = (x\mathbf{i}+y\mathbf{j})/\sqrt{x^2+y^2}$ and, from Equation (4.2), $1/\rho^3 = (x^2+y^2)^{-3/2}$, hence the two expressions for ∇U are identical.

The contour surfaces of U are found by putting $U = 1/\rho^2$ equal to a constant. Hence the contours are the surfaces where ρ is constant. Each such surface is cylindrical with its axis along the z-axis. We can sketch the intersections (circles) of the contours with a plane $z = $ constant. The vector field lines of ∇U are directed perpendicularly inwards towards the z-axis. (The vector field lines are not continuous through the z-axis, which is not in the domain of U.)

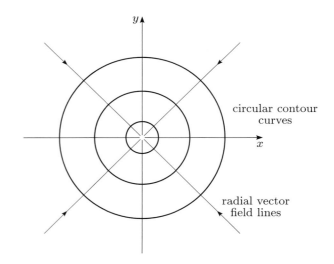

circular contour curves

radial vector field lines

4.3 The partial derivatives are
$$\frac{\partial f}{\partial \rho} = -\frac{\cos z}{\rho^2}, \quad \frac{\partial f}{\partial \theta} = 0, \quad \frac{\partial f}{\partial z} = -\frac{\sin z}{\rho}.$$
Hence, using Equation (4.7),
$$\mathbf{grad}\, f = \mathbf{e}_\rho \left(-\frac{\cos z}{\rho^2}\right) + \mathbf{e}_z \left(-\frac{\sin z}{\rho}\right).$$
So the components $(\mathbf{grad}\, f)_\rho$, $(\mathbf{grad}\, f)_\theta$ and $(\mathbf{grad}\, f)_z$ are $(-\cos z)/\rho^2$, 0 and $(-\sin z)/\rho$, respectively.

4.4 (a) Here $r = \sqrt{5^2 + 0^2 + 0^2} = 5$. The point is in the (x, y)-plane, so $\theta = \frac{\pi}{2}$. The point is on the x-axis, so $\phi = 0$. Hence the spherical polar coordinates are $\langle 5, \frac{\pi}{2}, 0 \rangle$.

(b) The point is on the positive y-axis 5 units from the origin, so the spherical polar coordinates are $\langle 5, \frac{\pi}{2}, \frac{\pi}{2} \rangle$.

4.5 Using Equation (4.11), the spherical polar components of $\mathbf{F}$ are
$$F_r = F_\theta = 0, \quad F_\phi = \frac{1}{r}.$$

4.6 Using Equation (4.12), the spherical polar components are
$$(\mathbf{grad}\, V)_r = I_0/r^2, \quad (\mathbf{grad}\, V)_\theta = (\mathbf{grad}\, V)_\phi = 0.$$

4.7 (a) (i) $\rho = 2$ defines a cylindrical surface of radius 2 with its axis along the z-axis.

(ii) $\theta = \frac{\pi}{2}$ defines a half-plane containing the positive y-axis but not the z-axis.

(b) We have
$$\mathbf{e}_\rho \cdot \mathbf{e}_\theta = \left(\frac{x\mathbf{i} + y\mathbf{j}}{\sqrt{x^2 + y^2}}\right) \cdot \left(\frac{-y\mathbf{i} + x\mathbf{j}}{\sqrt{x^2 + y^2}}\right)$$
$$= \frac{-xy + xy}{x^2 + y^2} = 0,$$
so $\mathbf{e}_\rho$ and $\mathbf{e}_\theta$ are mutually perpendicular.

(c) The partial derivatives of F are
$$\frac{\partial F}{\partial \rho} = e^{-z}, \quad \frac{\partial F}{\partial \theta} = 0, \quad \frac{\partial F}{\partial z} = -\rho e^{-z}.$$
Hence, from Equation (4.7), the gradient of F is
$$\boldsymbol{\nabla} F = \mathbf{grad}\, F = e^{-z} \mathbf{e}_\rho + -\rho e^{-z} \mathbf{e}_z.$$
At the point $\rho = 5$, $\theta = 0$, $z = 0$,
$$\boldsymbol{\nabla} F(5, 0, 0) = \mathbf{e}_\rho - 5\mathbf{e}_z.$$

4.8 (a) $\theta = \frac{\pi}{6}$ defines a cone with its axis along the positive z-axis, its apex at the origin and half-angle $\frac{\pi}{6}$.

(b) We have
$$|\mathbf{e}_r|^2 = \mathbf{e}_r \cdot \mathbf{e}_r$$
$$= (\mathbf{i} \sin \theta \cos \phi + \mathbf{j} \sin \theta \sin \phi + \mathbf{k} \cos \theta)$$
$$\quad \cdot (\mathbf{i} \sin \theta \cos \phi + \mathbf{j} \sin \theta \sin \phi + \mathbf{k} \cos \theta)$$
$$= (\sin \theta \cos \phi)^2 + (\sin \theta \sin \phi)^2 + \cos^2 \theta$$
$$= \sin^2 \theta (\cos^2 \phi + \sin^2 \phi) + \cos^2 \theta$$
$$= \sin^2 \theta + \cos^2 \theta = 1.$$

(c) We use spherical polar coordinates. Then $U = r$ and the only non-zero partial derivative is $\partial U / \partial r = 1$. Hence $\mathbf{grad}\, U = (1)\mathbf{e}_r = \mathbf{e}_r$. The point $\langle 5, \frac{\pi}{2}, \pi \rangle$ is on the negative x-axis, so $\mathbf{e}_r = -\mathbf{i}$ at this point.

(Alternatively, using Equation (4.9),
$$\mathbf{e}_r = \mathbf{i} \sin \theta \cos \phi + \mathbf{j} \sin \theta \sin \phi + \mathbf{k} \cos \theta$$
$$= \mathbf{i}(-1) + \mathbf{0} + \mathbf{0} = -\mathbf{i}.)$$

4.9 The cylindrical polar components are
$$u_\rho = e^{-z^2}, \quad u_\theta = \frac{1}{\rho}, \quad u_z = 0.$$

4.10 (a) At A, $r = 3$, $\theta = \frac{\pi}{2}$, $\phi = \frac{\pi}{2}$ and $V(3, \frac{\pi}{2}, \frac{\pi}{2}) = -M/3^3 = -M/27$.
At B, $r = 1$, $\theta = 0$, $\phi = 0$ and $V(1, 0, 0) = 2M$. (B is on the z-axis where $\phi = 0$, by convention.)
At C, $r = 1$, $\theta = \pi$, $\phi = 0$ and $V(1, \pi, 0) = 2M$.

(b) To find $\mathbf{grad}\, V$, we first determine the partial derivatives
$$\frac{\partial V}{\partial r} = -\frac{3M(3\cos^2 \theta - 1)}{r^4},$$
$$\frac{\partial V}{\partial \theta} = \frac{M(6\cos\theta(-\sin\theta))}{r^3},$$
$$\frac{\partial V}{\partial \phi} = 0.$$
Evaluating these at A yields
$$\frac{\partial V}{\partial r}(3, \tfrac{\pi}{2}, \tfrac{\pi}{2}) = \frac{M}{27}, \quad \frac{\partial V}{\partial \theta}(3, \tfrac{\pi}{2}, \tfrac{\pi}{2}) = 0.$$
Hence, at A, $\mathbf{grad}\, V = \frac{M}{27} \mathbf{e}_r$. The magnitude of the force $\mathbf{F}$ is $|-\mathbf{grad}\, V| = \frac{M}{27}$, and the direction is given by the direction of $-\mathbf{e}_r$ at A, i.e. the negative y-direction.

UNIT 24   Vector calculus

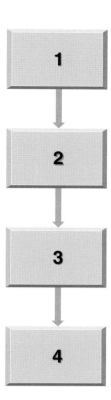

Study guide for Unit 24

Although this unit is quite short, it contains many important concepts and a great many exercises. The material relies rather heavily on *Units 4* and *12* and especially on *Unit 23*.

The sections are best studied in order.

Introduction

In *Unit 23* you saw that the spatial variations of a scalar field can be described by the gradient vector field, which can be expressed in terms of the three partial derivatives of the scalar field. Vector fields are more complicated than scalar fields. For a given Cartesian coordinate system there are nine partial derivatives associated with a vector field $\mathbf{F} = F_1\mathbf{i} + F_2\mathbf{j} + F_3\mathbf{k}$ at each field point. In the first two sections we shall introduce two new fields that are combinations of these partial derivatives and that represent important physical properties of the vector field $\mathbf{F}$. One of these fields, a scalar field called the *divergence* of $\mathbf{F}$, is the subject of Section 1. The other, a vector field called the *curl* of $\mathbf{F}$, is the subject of Section 2. In Section 3 we measure the work done by a force in moving a particle from one point to another in a vector field, by introducing the scalar line integral. Finally, Section 4 develops links between gradient, curl and the scalar line integral.

These partial derivatives are:
$$\partial F_1/\partial x, \quad \partial F_1/\partial y, \quad \partial F_1/\partial z,$$
$$\partial F_2/\partial x, \quad \partial F_2/\partial y, \quad \partial F_2/\partial z,$$
$$\partial F_3/\partial x, \quad \partial F_3/\partial y, \quad \partial F_3/\partial z.$$

This unit will also build on the concepts of kinetic energy and potential energy, introduced in *Unit 8*, and on the idea of work mentioned briefly in that unit.

1   Divergence of a vector field

We shall approach divergence in two different, but equivalent, ways. In Subsections 1.1 and 1.2 we define divergence mathematically in terms of partial derivatives, using the vector differential operator ∇, and give practice in calculating the divergence of given vector fields. Subsection 1.3 discusses the problem of modelling the flow of heat energy in a uranium fuel rod and predicting the temperature field in the rod. This enables us to develop a physical interpretation of divergence as the rate of heat outflow per unit volume at each point in the rod – one of many examples of divergence in the physical world.

1.1 Defining divergence

The gradient **grad** f of a scalar field f can be expressed as $\boldsymbol{\nabla} f$, where $\boldsymbol{\nabla}$ (del) is the vector differential operator

$$\boldsymbol{\nabla} = \mathbf{i}\frac{\partial}{\partial x} + \mathbf{j}\frac{\partial}{\partial y} + \mathbf{k}\frac{\partial}{\partial z}.$$

We now form the dot product of $\boldsymbol{\nabla}$ with an arbitrary vector field $\mathbf{F}(x, y, z)$, treating $\boldsymbol{\nabla}$ as if it were a vector. We write the order of symbols in the dot product as $\boldsymbol{\nabla} \cdot \mathbf{F}$ so that

$$\boldsymbol{\nabla} \cdot \mathbf{F} = \left(\mathbf{i}\frac{\partial}{\partial x} + \mathbf{j}\frac{\partial}{\partial y} + \mathbf{k}\frac{\partial}{\partial z}\right) \cdot (F_1\mathbf{i} + F_2\mathbf{j} + F_3\mathbf{k}),$$

where we have written the vector field $\mathbf{F}$ in terms of its Cartesian component fields $F_1(x, y, z)$, etc. We can evaluate this expression by multiplying the brackets, letting the differential operators act on the scalar component functions and using the dot product rule for the dot products of the unit vectors. For example, multiplying the first two terms in each bracket yields $(\partial F_1/\partial x)\mathbf{i} \cdot \mathbf{i} = \partial F_1/\partial x$. Terms with dot products of mutually perpendicular unit vectors evaluate to zero, and so we are left with the sum of three terms $\partial F_1/\partial x$, $\partial F_2/\partial y$ and $\partial F_3/\partial z$. This combination of partial derivatives is defined as the *divergence* of the vector field $\mathbf{F}$ or div $\mathbf{F}$ for short. You can see that div $\mathbf{F}$ is a scalar quantity that can be evaluated at each point in the domain of $\mathbf{F}$. Thus div $\mathbf{F}$ is a scalar field.

The order is important here. We do *not* write $\mathbf{F} \cdot \boldsymbol{\nabla}$, since this would result in a differential operator looking for something to operate on.

Definition

The **divergence of a vector field** $\mathbf{F} = F_1\mathbf{i} + F_2\mathbf{j} + F_3\mathbf{k}$ in **Cartesian coordinates** is a scalar field given by

$$\operatorname{div}\mathbf{F} = \boldsymbol{\nabla} \cdot \mathbf{F} = \frac{\partial F_1}{\partial x} + \frac{\partial F_2}{\partial y} + \frac{\partial F_3}{\partial z}. \tag{1.1}$$

---

div $\mathbf{F}$ and $\boldsymbol{\nabla} \cdot \mathbf{F}$ are alternative notations for the divergence of $\mathbf{F}$.

A physical interpretation of divergence will be given in Subsection 1.3. Meanwhile we show how the divergence of a given vector field can be calculated at specified points.

1.2 Calculating divergence

To calculate the divergence of a given vector field $\mathbf{F}$, we need to identify its components F_1, F_2 and F_3, work out the partial derivatives $\partial F_1/\partial x$, $\partial F_2/\partial y$ and $\partial F_3/\partial z$, and add them as in Equation (1.1).

Example 1.1

(a) Determine the divergence of each of the following vector fields:

$$\mathbf{F}(x, y, z) = x^2 \mathbf{i} + y^2 \mathbf{j} + z^2 \mathbf{k},$$
$$\mathbf{r}(x, y, z) = x \mathbf{i} + y \mathbf{j} + z \mathbf{k},$$
$$\mathbf{V}(x, y, z) = -y \mathbf{i} + x \mathbf{j} + 5 \mathbf{k}.$$

(b) Evaluate div $\mathbf{F}$ at the origin and at the point $(1, 2, 3)$.

Solution

(a) The components of $\mathbf{F}$ are $F_1 = x^2$, $F_2 = y^2$, $F_3 = z^2$. Hence
div $\mathbf{F}$ (or $\nabla \cdot \mathbf{F}$) $= 2x + 2y + 2z = 2(x + y + z)$.

Similarly, $r_1 = x$, $r_2 = y$, $r_3 = z$. Hence div $\mathbf{r} = 1 + 1 + 1 = 3$.

Also, $V_1 = -y$, $V_2 = x$, $V_3 = 5$. Hence div $\mathbf{V} = 0 + 0 + 0 = 0$.

(b) The value of div $\mathbf{F}$ at $(0, 0, 0)$ is 0, and its value at $(1, 2, 3)$ is
$2(1 + 2 + 3) = 12$. ∎

---

*Exercise 1.1

Determine the scalar field div $\mathbf{F}$, where $\mathbf{F}(x, y, z) = xy\mathbf{i} - yz\mathbf{k}$, and evaluate div $\mathbf{F}$ at the point $(3, -1, 2)$.

*Exercise 1.2

Consider the three-dimensional vector field $\mathbf{F} = \widehat{\mathbf{r}}/|\mathbf{r}|^n$ $(\mathbf{r} \neq \mathbf{0})$, where $\mathbf{r}$ is the position vector, $\widehat{\mathbf{r}}$ is a unit vector in the direction of $\mathbf{r}$ and n is a positive integer. Express the field in Cartesian form, and show that $\mathbf{F}$ has zero divergence everywhere only when $n = 2$.

When vector fields are given in cylindrical polar coordinates or in spherical polar coordinates, it is not always convenient to use the Cartesian expression for divergence. The polar coordinate expressions for divergence are quite complicated, and we shall derive only the expression for cylindrical polar coordinates.

First recall that the gradient vector operator in cylindrical polar coordinates is given by

See *Unit 23*, Subsection 4.2.

$$\nabla = \mathbf{e}_\rho \frac{\partial}{\partial \rho} + \frac{1}{\rho} \mathbf{e}_\theta \frac{\partial}{\partial \theta} + \mathbf{e}_z \frac{\partial}{\partial z}.$$

To compute the divergence $\nabla \cdot \mathbf{F}$ we must therefore calculate

$$\left(\mathbf{e}_\rho \frac{\partial}{\partial \rho} + \frac{1}{\rho} \mathbf{e}_\theta \frac{\partial}{\partial \theta} + \mathbf{e}_z \frac{\partial}{\partial z} \right) \cdot (F_\rho \mathbf{e}_\rho + F_\theta \mathbf{e}_\theta + F_z \mathbf{e}_z).$$

Now $\mathbf{e}_\rho$ and $\mathbf{e}_\theta$ depend on θ. Indeed, from the relationships

$$\begin{bmatrix} \mathbf{e}_\rho \\ \mathbf{e}_\theta \\ \mathbf{e}_z \end{bmatrix} = \begin{bmatrix} \cos\theta & \sin\theta & 0 \\ -\sin\theta & \cos\theta & 0 \\ 0 & 0 & 1 \end{bmatrix} \begin{bmatrix} \mathbf{i} \\ \mathbf{j} \\ \mathbf{k} \end{bmatrix},$$

Note that $\mathbf{e}_\rho$, $\mathbf{e}_\theta$ and $\mathbf{e}_z$ do not depend on ρ or z.

we see, for example, that

$$\mathbf{e}_\rho = \cos\theta \, \mathbf{i} + \sin\theta \, \mathbf{j}.$$

Therefore

$$\frac{\partial \mathbf{e}_\rho}{\partial \theta} = -\sin\theta \, \mathbf{i} + \cos\theta \, \mathbf{j} = \mathbf{e}_\theta.$$

Exercise 1.3 _____

Find a similar expression for $\dfrac{\partial \mathbf{e}_\theta}{\partial \theta}$.

_____

Now, returning to the calculation of $\boldsymbol{\nabla} \cdot \mathbf{F}$, we proceed term by term as follows:

$$\boldsymbol{\nabla} \cdot \mathbf{F} = \left(\mathbf{e}_\rho \frac{\partial}{\partial \rho} + \frac{1}{\rho} \mathbf{e}_\theta \frac{\partial}{\partial \theta} + \mathbf{e}_z \frac{\partial}{\partial z} \right) \cdot \left(F_\rho \mathbf{e}_\rho + F_\theta \mathbf{e}_\theta + F_z \mathbf{e}_z \right)$$

$$= \mathbf{e}_\rho \cdot \frac{\partial}{\partial \rho} \left(F_\rho \mathbf{e}_\rho + F_\theta \mathbf{e}_\theta + F_z \mathbf{e}_z \right) + \frac{1}{\rho} \mathbf{e}_\theta \cdot \frac{\partial}{\partial \theta} \left(F_\rho \mathbf{e}_\rho + F_\theta \mathbf{e}_\theta + F_z \mathbf{e}_z \right)$$

$$+ \mathbf{e}_z \cdot \frac{\partial}{\partial z} \left(F_\rho \mathbf{e}_\rho + F_\theta \mathbf{e}_\theta + F_z \mathbf{e}_z \right).$$

Since none of $\mathbf{e}_\rho$, $\mathbf{e}_\theta$ or $\mathbf{e}_z$ depends on ρ, we have

$$\frac{\partial}{\partial \rho} \left(F_\rho \mathbf{e}_\rho + F_\theta \mathbf{e}_\theta + F_z \mathbf{e}_z \right) = \frac{\partial F_\rho}{\partial \rho} \mathbf{e}_\rho + \frac{\partial F_\theta}{\partial \rho} \mathbf{e}_\theta + \frac{\partial F_z}{\partial \rho} \mathbf{e}_z,$$

so that

$$\mathbf{e}_\rho \cdot \frac{\partial}{\partial \rho} \left(F_\rho \mathbf{e}_\rho + F_\theta \mathbf{e}_\theta + F_z \mathbf{e}_z \right) = \frac{\partial F_\rho}{\partial \rho}.$$

$\mathbf{e}_\rho$, $\mathbf{e}_\theta$ and $\mathbf{e}_z$ form a right-handed set of unit vectors, and so are mutually perpendicular.

Next, using the results $\partial \mathbf{e}_\rho / \partial \theta = \mathbf{e}_\theta$, $\partial \mathbf{e}_\theta / \partial \theta = -\mathbf{e}_\rho$ and $\partial \mathbf{e}_z / \partial \theta = \mathbf{0}$, we have

$$\frac{\partial}{\partial \theta} \left(F_\rho \mathbf{e}_\rho + F_\theta \mathbf{e}_\theta + F_z \mathbf{e}_z \right) = \frac{\partial F_\rho}{\partial \theta} \mathbf{e}_\rho + F_\rho \frac{\partial \mathbf{e}_\rho}{\partial \theta} + \frac{\partial F_\theta}{\partial \theta} \mathbf{e}_\theta + F_\theta \frac{\partial \mathbf{e}_\theta}{\partial \theta} + \frac{\partial F_z}{\partial \theta} \mathbf{e}_z$$

$$= \frac{\partial F_\rho}{\partial \theta} \mathbf{e}_\rho + F_\rho \mathbf{e}_\theta + \frac{\partial F_\theta}{\partial \theta} \mathbf{e}_\theta - F_\theta \mathbf{e}_\rho + \frac{\partial F_z}{\partial \theta} \mathbf{e}_z.$$

So

$$\frac{1}{\rho} \mathbf{e}_\theta \cdot \frac{\partial}{\partial \theta} \left(F_\rho \mathbf{e}_\rho + F_\theta \mathbf{e}_\theta + F_z \mathbf{e}_z \right) = \frac{1}{\rho} F_\rho + \frac{1}{\rho} \frac{\partial F_\theta}{\partial \theta}.$$

Finally, since none of $\mathbf{e}_\rho$, $\mathbf{e}_\theta$ and $\mathbf{e}_z$ depends on z, the contribution from the z-component of $\boldsymbol{\nabla}$ is

$$\mathbf{e}_z \cdot \frac{\partial}{\partial z} \left(F_\rho \mathbf{e}_\rho + F_\theta \mathbf{e}_\theta + F_z \mathbf{e}_z \right) = \frac{\partial F_z}{\partial z}.$$

So we have finally arrived at the formula for div $\mathbf{F}$ in cylindrical polar coordinates,

$$\text{div } \mathbf{F} = \frac{\partial F_\rho}{\partial \rho} + \frac{1}{\rho} F_\rho + \frac{1}{\rho} \frac{\partial F_\theta}{\partial \theta} + \frac{\partial F_z}{\partial z}.$$

_____

Divergence of a vector field in polar coordinates

The **divergence** of a **vector field** $\mathbf{F}(\rho, \theta, z) = F_\rho \mathbf{e}_\rho + F_\theta \mathbf{e}_\theta + F_z \mathbf{e}_z$ is given in **cylindrical polar coordinates** by

$$\text{div } \mathbf{F} = \boldsymbol{\nabla} \cdot \mathbf{F} = \frac{\partial F_\rho}{\partial \rho} + \frac{1}{\rho} F_\rho + \frac{1}{\rho} \frac{\partial F_\theta}{\partial \theta} + \frac{\partial F_z}{\partial z}. \qquad (1.2)$$

For $\mathbf{F}(r, \theta, \phi) = F_r \mathbf{e}_r + F_\theta \mathbf{e}_\theta + F_\phi \mathbf{e}_\phi$ in **spherical polar coordinates**, the divergence is given by

$$\text{div } \mathbf{F} = \frac{\partial F_r}{\partial r} + \frac{1}{r} \left(\frac{\partial F_\theta}{\partial \theta} + 2 F_r \right) + \frac{1}{r \sin \theta} \left(\frac{\partial F_\phi}{\partial \phi} + F_\theta \cos \theta \right). \qquad (1.3)$$

This follows from a similar but more complicated derivation that we do not consider here.

Example 1.2

Consider the vector field $\mathbf{F} = \hat{\mathbf{r}}/|\mathbf{r}|^n$ $(\mathbf{r} \neq \mathbf{0})$, where $\mathbf{r}$ is the position vector, $\hat{\mathbf{r}}$ is a unit vector in the direction of $\mathbf{r}$ and n is a positive integer. Express $\mathbf{F}$ in spherical polar coordinates, and hence confirm that div $\mathbf{F} = 0$ everywhere only when $n = 2$.

This is the same field as in Exercise 1.2.

Solution

The spherical polar form of the field is $\mathbf{F}(r, \theta, \phi) = \mathbf{e}_r/r^n$ $(r > 0)$, so the field has components $F_r = 1/r^n$ and $F_\theta = F_\phi = 0$. We can use the spherical polar expression for div $\mathbf{F}$ given in Equation (1.3), to obtain

$$\text{div } \mathbf{F} = \frac{\partial \left(1/r^n \right)}{\partial r} + \frac{2}{r} \left(1/r^n \right) \quad (r > 0)$$

$$= (-n)\frac{1}{r^{n+1}} + \frac{2}{r^{n+1}} = \frac{2-n}{r^{n+1}} \quad (r > 0),$$

which is zero only when $n = 2$. ∎

You can see the advantage of using spherical polar coordinates in Example 1.2. (Compare the solution with that for Exercise 1.2.)

1.3 Divergence in physical laws

Our definition of div $\mathbf{F}$ as a sum of partial derivatives gives little clue to the physical meaning of divergence. In this subsection we describe one physical meaning of divergence by considering the flow of heat energy in a uranium fuel rod. In the steady state, the rate of flow of heat energy out of any small region of the rod must be equal to the rate at which heat is generated by fission in that small region. We shall show that this heat-energy balance can be expressed by the equation

Our model assumes that there are no other heat losses or gains.

$$\text{div } \mathbf{J} = S,$$

where div $\mathbf{J}$ represents the *rate of heat outflow per unit volume* at a point in the rod and S is the *rate at which heat is generated per unit volume at that point*. (The scalar field S is sometimes referred to as the *heat source density*.) This equation represents the *law of energy conservation* for heat flow in the rod.

You saw in *Unit 23* that heat flow rate in a conductor may be represented as a vector field, $\mathbf{J}$, where the direction is that of the heat flow, and the magnitude is given by

See *Unit 23*, Subsection 2.3.

$$|\mathbf{J}| = \lim_{A \to 0} \frac{\text{heat flow rate across surface area } A}{A}.$$

In the examples of heat transfer by conduction that you studied in *Unit 15*, the heat source in the conducting material was always zero. No heat was generated within the conducting material itself. Heat flowed *through* the conducting material, but the sources of heat were *outside* it. For example, the hot water flowing through a central heating pipe is the source of the heat that flows radially though the pipe walls — there is no source of heat in the wall of the pipe. For a uranium fuel rod in a nuclear reactor (see Figure 1.1), however, heat is generated throughout the body of the rod by the fission of uranium atoms. The heat generated in the rod flows by conduction through the rod and out into the surrounding coolant, a flowing gas or liquid which takes the heat away to drive turbines. In the steady state, the coolant establishes a uniform, relatively cool, constant temperature Θ_a on the outside surface of the rod. (The radius of the rod is a.) An important question in reactor design is: how does the temperature distribution Θ depend on the heat source and on the constant surface temperature Θ_a established by the coolant? In preparation for this, we now derive the equation $\text{div}\,\mathbf{J} = S$.

When the reactor has been in operation for some time, a steady state is reached where the temperature field in the rod stays constant in time and the net outflow of heat from any region of the rod is balanced by the total heat production by fission in that region. Let us consider this energy balance more closely. If P is a point in a small region of volume V inside the rod and q is the rate at which heat is generated by fission in the region, then the quantity

$$S = \lim_{V \to 0} \frac{q}{V}$$

is the rate (in W m^{-3}) at which heat is generated per unit volume at P. The rate S of heat generation may vary from point to point in the rod and is a scalar field. In Figure 1.2 the point P has position vector $\mathbf{r}$ and lies inside a small region R, with volume V, entirely within the rod. If the region R is small enough, the field S is effectively constant throughout the small region and is approximately equal to $S(\mathbf{r})$. So the net rate at which heat is generated in R is approximately $S(\mathbf{r})V$ (in watts). In the steady state, this rate of heat generation is balanced by the net rate of outflow of heat from the region R into neighbouring regions of the rod. Thus we have

net outflow rate from small region containing $P \simeq S(\mathbf{r})V$.

Dividing both sides by V, we obtain

$$\frac{\text{net outflow rate from small region containing } P}{V} \simeq S(\mathbf{r}). \qquad (1.4)$$

Let us take the limit as the region R becomes smaller and eventually shrinks onto the point P, i.e. as $V \to 0$. Then, while the right-hand side of the approximation (1.4) remains constant, the left-hand side becomes the *net outflow rate per unit volume at P* and the approximation becomes an equality. Thus we have

net outflow rate per unit volume at $P = S(\mathbf{r})$. $\qquad (1.5)$

We can evaluate the net outflow rate per unit volume on the left-hand side of this equation by considering a region R in the shape of a small cube centred on P, as shown in Figure 1.3. We shall determine the net rate of outflow across the three pairs of parallel faces of the cube, and then take the limit as $V \to 0$ to give the net outflow rate per unit volume. Consider first the two parallel faces normal to the x-direction and separated from one another by a distance L, the side length of the cube. Let the left-hand face be in the plane $x = X$, with its midpoint at (X, Y, Z). If $\mathbf{J} = J_1\mathbf{i} + J_2\mathbf{j} + J_3\mathbf{k}$ is the heat flow vector field (in W m^{-2}), only the component of $\mathbf{J}$ normal to this face, in the direction of negative x, will contribute to the outflow rate across this face. (The y- and z-components of $\mathbf{J}$ represent flow in the plane of the face.) If the cube is small enough, we can ignore any variation of $\mathbf{J}$ on the face and take its value $\mathbf{J}(X, Y, Z)$ at the centre of the face. The unit vector in the negative x-direction is $-\mathbf{i}$, so the outflow rate across this face is $-\mathbf{J} \cdot \mathbf{i} = -J_1$ and the outflow rate (in watts) across the area L^2 of the face is approximately $-J_1(X, Y, Z)L^2$. Similarly, the outflow rate across the parallel face in the plane $x = X + L$ is $J_1(X + L, Y, Z)L^2$, since only the component of $\mathbf{J}$ in the positive x-direction contributes. The net outflow rate across the two faces is therefore approximately

$$[-J_1(X, Y, Z) + J_1(X + L, Y, Z)] L^2.$$

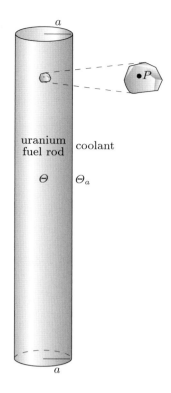

uranium fuel rod   coolant

Θ Θ_a

Figure 1.1

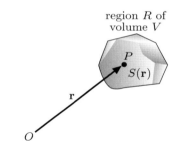

region R of volume V

P

$S(\mathbf{r})$

$\mathbf{r}$

O

Figure 1.2

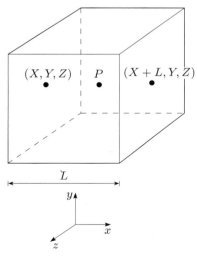

(X, Y, Z) P $(X + L, Y, Z)$

L

y

x

z

Figure 1.3

(In Figure 1.3, the Cartesian coordinate system is oriented so that the coordinate planes are parallel to the plane faces of the cube. We use an orientation of x, y and z that is different from that used generally in this unit.)

Dividing by the volume $V = L^3$ and taking the limit as $L \to 0$ (equivalent to $V \to 0$), gives the contribution from these two parallel faces to the net rate of outflow per unit volume as

The units of outflow rate per unit volume are therefore $\text{W}\,\text{m}^{-3}$.

$$\lim_{L \to 0} \frac{J_1(X + L, Y, Z) - J_1(X, Y, Z)}{L}.$$

You should recognize this limit, from *Unit 12*. It is the partial derivative of J_1 with respect to x at the point (X, Y, Z). In other words, it is the partial derivative $\partial J_1(X, Y, Z)/\partial x$. In the same way, you can see that the contributions to the net rate of outflow per unit volume from the other two pairs of parallel faces of the cube are $\partial J_2(X, Y, Z)/\partial y$ and $\partial J_3(X, Y, Z)/\partial z$. The net rate of heat outflow per unit volume at the point P is the sum of these three partial derivatives, namely,

Taking the limit as $L \to 0$ in all three directions places (X, Y, Z) at the point P.

$$\frac{\partial J_1}{\partial x}(X, Y, Z) + \frac{\partial J_2}{\partial y}(X, Y, Z) + \frac{\partial J_3}{\partial z}(X, Y, Z).$$

You will recognize this expression as the *divergence* of **J**.

Hence, at each point P in the rod, we have

net outflow rate per unit volume $= \operatorname{div} \mathbf{J}$,

and so, from Equation (1.5), energy balance requires

$\operatorname{div} \mathbf{J} = S$

to be satisfied at each point P in the rod.

Note that this equation is dimensionally correct.

The equation $\operatorname{div} \mathbf{J} = S$ is a first-order partial differential equation for the vector field $\mathbf{J} = \mathbf{J}(x, y, z)$. It may be written as

$$\frac{\partial J_1}{\partial x} + \frac{\partial J_2}{\partial y} + \frac{\partial J_3}{\partial z} = S, \tag{1.6}$$

where J_1, J_2, J_3 and S are functions of x, y and z.

You have seen (in *Unit 23*) that we can describe the heat flow vector **J** by Fourier's law as

$\mathbf{J} = -\kappa \operatorname{\mathbf{grad}} \Theta,$

where Θ is the temperature field and κ is the thermal conductivity. If κ is constant throughout the fuel rod, then the divergence of the last equation, divided by $-\kappa$, can be written

$$-\frac{1}{\kappa} \operatorname{div} \mathbf{J} = \operatorname{div}(\operatorname{\mathbf{grad}} \Theta),$$

which, from Equation (1.6), gives us the second-order partial differential equation

This equation for the heat distribution Θ is called *Poisson's equation.*

$$\frac{\partial^2 \Theta}{\partial x^2} + \frac{\partial^2 \Theta}{\partial y^2} + \frac{\partial^2 \Theta}{\partial z^2} = -\frac{S}{\kappa}. \tag{1.7}$$

Knowing S and κ, and the appropriate boundary conditions, Equation (1.7) can be solved for the temperature field Θ.

Example 1.3

Steady-state conductive heat flow is governed by the partial differential equation

$$\operatorname{div} \mathbf{J} = S,$$

where $\mathbf{J}$ (in $\mathrm{W\,m^{-2}}$) is the heat flow per unit area and the scalar field S (in $\mathrm{W\,m^{-3}}$) is the heat generated per unit volume. Fission of uranium atoms in a long cylindrical fuel rod of radius 0.02 metres generates heat at a constant rate S uniformly throughout the rod. When the axis of the rod is along the z-axis, the solution of the equation describing steady-state heat flow in the rod is known to be of the form

$$\mathbf{J}(x, y, z) = A(x\mathbf{i} + y\mathbf{j}),$$

> The description of the rod as 'long' implies that we can ignore any anomalies in the heat flow or generation at the ends of the rod, i.e. we are ignoring any 'end effects'.

where A is a constant. Determine A when $S = 4 \times 10^6\ \mathrm{W\,m^{-3}}$, and hence determine the magnitude and direction of the vector $\mathbf{J}$ at:

(a) points on the z-axis;

(b) a point T with Cartesian coordinates $(0.005, 0, 0)$;

(c) a point Q with Cartesian coordinates $(0.015, 0, 0)$.

Solution

We find that

$$\operatorname{div} \mathbf{J} = \frac{\partial J_1}{\partial x} + \frac{\partial J_2}{\partial y} + \frac{\partial J_3}{\partial z} = \frac{\partial(Ax)}{\partial x} + \frac{\partial(Ay)}{\partial y} = A + A = 2A.$$

Now from Equation (1.6), we have $2A = S$, where S is given as $4 \times 10^6\ \mathrm{W\,m^{-3}}$, so $A = 2 \times 10^6\ \mathrm{W\,m^{-3}}$.

(a) On the z-axis, $x = y = 0$ and so $\mathbf{J} = \mathbf{0}$. The magnitude is zero and there is no direction associated with the zero vector.

(b) At point T, $\mathbf{J}(0.005, 0, 0) = 2 \times 10^6 \times (0.005\mathbf{i}) = 10^4\mathbf{i}$, which is a vector pointing in the positive x-direction, i.e. radially outwards, of magnitude $10^4\ \mathrm{W\,m^{-2}} = 10\,\mathrm{kW\,m^{-2}}$.

(c) Similarly at Q, $\mathbf{J} = 2 \times 10^6 \times (0.015\mathbf{i})$, which is a vector directed in the positive x-direction of magnitude $3 \times 10^4\ \mathrm{W\,m^{-2}} = 30\,\mathrm{kW\,m^{-2}}$. ∎

Figure 1.4 depicts the heat flow vector $\mathbf{J}$ at the points T and Q described in Example 1.3. The vector field $\mathbf{J}(x, y, z)$ can be expressed in cylindrical polar coordinates as $\mathbf{J}(\rho, \theta, z) = A\rho\mathbf{e}_\rho$, so that $\mathbf{J}$ points directly outwards from the z-axis everywhere and $|\mathbf{J}|$ is the same at all points on a cylindrical surface of radius ρ.

> You will be asked to confirm this expression for $\mathbf{J}$ in cylindrical polar coordinates in Exercise 1.8.

*Exercise 1.4

Determine the magnitude of the heat flow field $\mathbf{J} = A(x\mathbf{i} + y\mathbf{j})$ at any point P on the outer cylindrical surface of the rod (See Figure 1.4). Hence deduce the total rate of heat flow out of a one-metre length of the rod. Determine also the total rate of heat generated in the one-metre length.

> This exercise refers to Example 1.3.

Now let us return to the general problem of the fuel rod. Recall that we had arrived at the two equations

$$\operatorname{div} \mathbf{J} = S,$$

$$\mathbf{J} = -\kappa \operatorname{grad} \Theta.$$

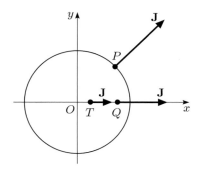

Figure 1.4

The nature of the fuel rod makes it particularly appropriate to use cylindrical polar coordinates, and armed with the formula for div in cylindrical polar coordinates we can make rapid progress. We take the z-axis along the centre of the rod, so that the symmetry of the situation allows us to make further simplifications. The flow rate vector $\mathbf{J} = J_\rho \mathbf{e}_\rho + J_\theta \mathbf{e}_\theta + J_z \mathbf{e}_z$ cannot depend on the angle θ, because we have assumed that the material of the rod is uniform. Hence $J_\theta = 0$. Similarly, if we assume that the rod is very long in comparison with its thickness, then we can neglect the effects of the ends of the rod. In these circumstances $\mathbf{J}$ will not depend on z either, and $J_z = 0$. Thus the formula for $\operatorname{div}\mathbf{J}$ in cylindrical polar coordinates reduces to

$$\operatorname{div}\mathbf{J} = \frac{\partial J_\rho}{\partial \rho} + \frac{1}{\rho}J_\rho,$$

and the above two equations for $\mathbf{J}$ become

$$\frac{\partial J_\rho}{\partial \rho} + \frac{1}{\rho}J_\rho = S \tag{1.8}$$

$$\mathbf{J} = -\kappa \operatorname{grad}\Theta.$$

Now

$$\mathbf{J} = -\kappa \operatorname{grad}\Theta = -\kappa\, \boldsymbol{\nabla}\Theta = -\kappa\left(\mathbf{e}_\rho \frac{\partial \Theta}{\partial \rho} + \frac{1}{\rho}\mathbf{e}_\theta \frac{\partial \Theta}{\partial \theta} + \mathbf{e}_z \frac{\partial \Theta}{\partial z}\right).$$

Since κ is constant, Equation (1.8) leads to the second-order differential equation for Θ:

$$\frac{\partial^2 \Theta}{\partial \rho^2} + \frac{1}{\rho}\frac{\partial \Theta}{\partial \rho} = -\frac{S}{\kappa}.$$

In fact, because Θ does not depend on θ or z, this partial differential equation can be written as a second-order ordinary differential equation,

$$\frac{d^2 \Theta}{d\rho^2} + \frac{1}{\rho}\frac{d\Theta}{d\rho} = -\frac{S}{\kappa}.$$

However, it is not a constant-coefficient equation, so the methods of *Unit 3* are not directly applicable. Fortunately we can reduce the equation to a pair of first-order equations, each of which can be solved. Replacing $d\Theta/d\rho$ by u, we have the two first-order equations

$$\frac{du}{d\rho} + \frac{1}{\rho}u = -\frac{S}{\kappa},$$

$$\frac{d\Theta}{d\rho} = u.$$

The first of these is a linear differential equation, with integrating factor

$$\exp\left(\int \frac{1}{\rho}\,d\rho\right) = \exp(\ln \rho) = \rho.$$

Multiplying through by this factor gives

$$\frac{d}{d\rho}(u\rho) = -\frac{S}{\kappa}\rho,$$

so that

$$u\rho = -\tfrac{1}{2}\frac{S}{\kappa}\rho^2 + C,$$

where C is an arbitrary constant. If we assume that Θ has a maximum at the centre of the rod (which seems eminently reasonable!) then we must have

$$\frac{d\Theta}{d\rho} = u = 0 \quad \text{when} \quad \rho = 0,$$

so $C = 0$. Thus

$$u = \frac{d\Theta}{d\rho} = -\tfrac{1}{2}\frac{S}{\kappa}\rho,$$

and

$$\Theta = -\tfrac{1}{4}\frac{S}{\kappa}\rho^2 + D,$$

where D is another arbitrary constant. Finally, since the temperature on the edge of the rod (when $\rho = a$) is known to be Θ_a, we have

$$\Theta = \Theta_a + \tfrac{1}{4}\frac{S}{\kappa}a^2 - \tfrac{1}{4}\frac{S}{\kappa}\rho^2$$

as the solution to the problem.

Exercise 1.5

(a) A certain laser beam transports energy through air as a cylindrical beam of light, that is, in a uniform parallel beam, at the rate of $5000\,\text{W m}^{-2}$. Taking the z-axis to be in the beam direction, along the axis of the cylinder, we can write the energy flow field as $\mathbf{H}(x, y, z) = 5000\mathbf{k}$, where $\mathbf{k}$ is a unit vector in the direction of the positive z-axis. Determine div $\mathbf{H}$.

(b) When the laser beam shines through fog, it becomes weaker and its intensity falls off exponentially with distance. If the laser is placed so that the beam originates at $z = 0$, the energy flow is given by $\mathbf{H}(x, y, z) = 5000e^{-\alpha z}\mathbf{k}$, where α is a positive constant (the absorption coefficient of the fog). Determine div $\mathbf{H}$.

You have seen that, for steady-state heat flow in a uranium rod with heat flow field $\mathbf{J}$, div $\mathbf{J}$ is equal to the heat source density at each point. In fact, for *any* steady-state heat flow field $\mathbf{J}$, div $\mathbf{J}$ is equal to the heat source density at each point. A similar result applies to the laser beam in Exercise 1.5, where div $\mathbf{H}$ is equal to the source density of light energy in the beam. In Exercise 1.5(a) you found div $\mathbf{H} = 0$. This result represents the fact that there are no light sources or sinks in the air through which the laser beam passes. On the other hand, when the beam passes through fog, which absorbs light and so attenuates the beam (hence the factor $e^{-\alpha z}$), the fog acts as a sink of light. The presence of this sink of light is represented by the fact that div $\mathbf{H}$ is negative.

When a source density S is negative, the source is commonly called a *sink* (cf. the terminology for stability in *Unit 13*).

*Exercise 1.6

Consider the vector field $\mathbf{f}(\rho, \theta, z) = \mathbf{e}_\rho / \rho^n$, where $\rho > 0$ and n is a positive integer. For what value(s) of n is $\operatorname{div} \mathbf{f} = 0$ everywhere?

We have interpreted divergence in terms of net outflow rate from a point. Not all vector fields are associated with flow of material or energy. For example, there is no flow associated with a static magnetic field or an electrostatic field. However, the divergences of such fields can still have physical significance. For example, the divergence of any magnetic field $\mathbf{B}$ is always zero. This law,

$$\operatorname{div} \mathbf{B} = 0, \tag{1.9}$$

is true for all possible magnetic fields and is an expression of the fact that there are no sources or sinks in a magnetic field.

This law is one of four equations called *Maxwell's equations*.

End-of-section Exercises

*Exercise 1.7

Find $\nabla \cdot \mathbf{F}$, where $\mathbf{F}(x, y, z) = xy\mathbf{i} + yz\mathbf{j} + zx\mathbf{k}$, and hence evaluate $\nabla \cdot \mathbf{F}(1, 2, 3)$.

Exercise 1.8

(a) Express the vector field $\mathbf{J}(x, y, z) = A(x\mathbf{i} + y\mathbf{j})$, given in Example 1.3, in cylindrical polar coordinates, and hence determine $\operatorname{div} \mathbf{J}$ using the cylindrical polar expression for divergence.

(b) Express the position vector $\mathbf{r}$ in spherical polar coordinates, and hence determine $\operatorname{div} \mathbf{r}$ using the spherical polar expression for divergence as given by Equation (1.3).

Exercise 1.9

Use Equation (1.9) to decide which of the following vector fields could be magnetic fields:

$$\mathbf{F}(x, y, z) = -y\mathbf{i} + x\mathbf{j} + xy\mathbf{k}; \qquad \mathbf{G}(x, y, z) = x^2\mathbf{i} + y^2\mathbf{j} + z^2\mathbf{k};$$
$$\mathbf{H}(x, y, z) = x\mathbf{i} + y\mathbf{j} - 2z\mathbf{k}.$$

2 Curl of a vector field

You have seen that the divergence of a vector field $\mathbf{F} = F_1\mathbf{i} + F_2\mathbf{j} + F_3\mathbf{k}$ is a scalar field given by the sum of the three partial derivatives $\partial F_1/\partial x$, $\partial F_2/\partial y$ and $\partial F_3/\partial z$. This is one way of differentiating a vector field, resulting in a scalar. We now introduce the curl of a vector field $\mathbf{F}$, written $\mathbf{curl}\,\mathbf{F}$. This new field is a vector field constructed from the other six partial derivatives of F_1, F_2 and F_3 with respect to Cartesian coordinates x, y, z. You can think of these partial derivatives as 'sideways' derivatives. For example, $\partial F_1/\partial y$ describes how the x-component of $\mathbf{F}$ changes with small displacements in the y-direction. Subsections 2.1 and 2.2 introduce the curl of a vector field and show how to calculate it. Subsection 2.3 provides a physical interpretation of curl.

2.1 Defining curl

In this subsection we consider the mathematical definition of **curl F** using the vector differential operator ∇. You have seen that, for any scalar field f and for any vector field **F**, we have:

$$\mathbf{grad}\, f = \nabla f,$$

$$\mathrm{div}\,\mathbf{F} = \nabla \cdot \mathbf{F}.$$

grad f is a vector field.

div **F** is a scalar field.

We now define the vector field **curl F** to be the cross product $\nabla \times \mathbf{F}$ of $\nabla = \mathbf{i}\dfrac{\partial}{\partial x} + \mathbf{j}\dfrac{\partial}{\partial y} + \mathbf{k}\dfrac{\partial}{\partial z}$ and $\mathbf{F} = F_1\mathbf{i} + F_2\mathbf{j} + F_3\mathbf{k}$.

Definition

The **curl of a vector field** $\mathbf{F} = F_1\mathbf{i} + F_2\mathbf{j} + F_3\mathbf{k}$ in **Cartesian coordinates** is

$$\mathbf{curl}\,\mathbf{F} = \nabla \times \mathbf{F}$$

$$= \begin{vmatrix} \mathbf{i} & \mathbf{j} & \mathbf{k} \\ \frac{\partial}{\partial x} & \frac{\partial}{\partial y} & \frac{\partial}{\partial z} \\ F_1 & F_2 & F_3 \end{vmatrix}$$

$$= \left(\frac{\partial F_3}{\partial y} - \frac{\partial F_2}{\partial z}\right)\mathbf{i} + \left(\frac{\partial F_1}{\partial z} - \frac{\partial F_3}{\partial x}\right)\mathbf{j} + \left(\frac{\partial F_2}{\partial x} - \frac{\partial F_1}{\partial y}\right)\mathbf{k}. \quad (2.1)$$

The determinant form of the cross product was given in *Unit 9.*

The name 'curl' comes from the fact that the vector field **curl F** represents the 'local rotation' in the field **F**. Local rotation will be discussed in Subsection 2.3.

When the vector field $\mathbf{F}(x, y)$ is confined to the (x, y)-plane, then F_3 is zero, and F_1 and F_2 do not depend on z. Then you can see from Equation (2.1) that only the z-component of **curl F** can be non-zero and we have the simplified expression

$$\mathbf{curl}\,\mathbf{F} = \left(\frac{\partial F_2}{\partial x} - \frac{\partial F_1}{\partial y}\right)\mathbf{k} \quad (2.2)$$

for the **curl of a two-dimensional vector field** $\mathbf{F}(x, y)$. This means that the curl of a two-dimensional vector field must either be zero or be directed at right angles to the plane of the field.

Examples of both possibilities are given in Example 2.1.

2.2 Calculating curl

To calculate the curl of a given vector field, first identify the component fields, then evaluate the relevant partial derivatives and substitute these partial derivatives into the appropriate expression for curl in Equation (2.1) or Equation (2.2).

Example 2.1

(a) Find the curl of each of the following vector fields.

    (i) $\mathbf{f}(x, y) = x\mathbf{i} + y\mathbf{j}$.

    (ii) $\mathbf{g}(x, y) = -y\mathbf{i} + x\mathbf{j}$.

    (iii) $\mathbf{F}(x, y, z) = \left(xy + z^2\right)\mathbf{i} + x^2\mathbf{j} + (xz - 2)\mathbf{k}$.

(b) (i) Find $\mathbf{curl\,F}(1, -1, 3)$, where $\mathbf{F}$ is the vector field specified in part (a)(iii).

    (ii) Find points where $\mathbf{curl\,F} = \mathbf{0}$, where $\mathbf{F}$ is the vector field specified in part(a)(iii).

Solution

(a) (i) The components of $\mathbf{f}$ are $f_1 = x$ and $f_2 = y$, so

$$\frac{\partial f_2}{\partial x} = 0, \quad \frac{\partial f_1}{\partial y} = 0.$$

The vector field $f(x, y)$ is confined to the (x, y)-plane, so we can use the simplified Equation (2.2). Substituting in Equation (2.2), we find $\mathbf{curl\,f} = \mathbf{0}$.

We write the zero vector here since curl is a vector field.

    (ii) The components of $\mathbf{g}$ are $g_1 = -y$ and $g_2 = x$, so

$$\frac{\partial g_1}{\partial y} = -1, \quad \frac{\partial g_2}{\partial x} = 1.$$

Substituting in Equation (2.2), we obtain

$$\mathbf{curl\,g} = \left(\frac{\partial g_2}{\partial x} - \frac{\partial g_1}{\partial y}\right)\mathbf{k} = (1 - (-1))\mathbf{k} = 2\mathbf{k}.$$

    (iii) We have $F_1 = xy + z^2$, $F_2 = x^2$, $F_3 = xz - 2$, so

$$\frac{\partial F_1}{\partial y} = x, \quad \frac{\partial F_1}{\partial z} = 2z, \quad \frac{\partial F_2}{\partial x} = 2x,$$

$$\frac{\partial F_2}{\partial z} = 0, \quad \frac{\partial F_3}{\partial x} = z, \quad \frac{\partial F_3}{\partial y} = 0.$$

Substituting in Equation (2.1), we obtain

$$\mathbf{curl\,F} = (0 - 0)\mathbf{i} + (2z - z)\mathbf{j} + (2x - x)\mathbf{k} = z\mathbf{j} + x\mathbf{k}.$$

(b) (i) At the point $(1, -1, 3)$, we have $\mathbf{curl\,F} = 3\mathbf{j} + \mathbf{k}$.

    (ii) When $x = 0$ and $z = 0$, and for any value of y, $\mathbf{curl\,F} = \mathbf{0}$, i.e. $\mathbf{curl\,F}$ is $\mathbf{0}$ everywhere on the y-axis. ∎

*Exercise 2.1 _____

Here $\mathbf{r} = x\mathbf{i} + y\mathbf{j} + z\mathbf{k}$, $r = |\mathbf{r}| = \sqrt{x^2 + y^2 + z^2}$ and $\widehat{\mathbf{r}}$ is a unit vector in the direction of $\mathbf{r}$. Find curl $\mathbf{F}$ in each of the following cases.

(a) $\mathbf{F} = \mathbf{r}$.

(b) $\mathbf{F} = f(r)\widehat{\mathbf{r}}$, where f is a function of r only.

(c) $\mathbf{F} = (y^2 + 2z)\mathbf{i} + (xy + 6z)\mathbf{j} + (z^2 + 2xz + y)\mathbf{k}$.

(d) $\mathbf{F} = \mathbf{grad}\, f$, where f is a scalar field.

If a vector field $\mathbf{F}$ has **curl $\mathbf{F} = 0$** everywhere, it is said to be a **conservative field**. Conservative force fields are important in mechanics. When only conservative forces act on a particle, the total mechanical energy of the particle, i.e. potential energy + kinetic energy is conserved.

*Exercise 2.2 _____

Identify conservative fields from those considered in Example 2.1 and Exercise 2.1.

2.3   Curl and local rotation

Whereas the divergence of a vector field represents the outflow rate from a point, the curl of a vector field represents rotation at a point.

Consider the two-dimensional velocity field on the surface of a river. Let the surface be in the (x, y)-plane with the coordinate axes fixed relative to the river bank. Then the water surface flows through fixed points (x, y) with velocity $\mathbf{v}(x, y)$. This surface velocity field can be revealed by watching a floating object such as a small leaf. Then the velocity $\mathbf{v}(x, y)$ is the velocity of the leaf as it passes through the fixed point (x, y).

We are assuming that the flow has settled down so that there are no changes in time. It is steady flow.

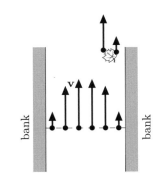

Figure 2.1

If you watch a small leaf floating down a river, you may notice two types of motion. First the leaf floats downstream following a vector field line of the velocity field $\mathbf{v}(x, y)$. Then the leaf may rotate in the plane of the surface. The rate of rotation may be quite fast for an object floating near the bank of a fast flowing river. However, near midstream the rate of rotation is likely to be slow or zero, even when the surface velocity is fast.

The rotation of a floating body is easily explained. It happens whenever the velocity, and hence the drag, is greater on one side of the object than on the other. There is then a torque on the object and so it rotates. Figure 2.1 shows a typical distribution of surface velocities $\mathbf{v}$ on a line across a river. You can see that the velocity magnitude increases quite rapidly as you move out from a river bank, but varies hardly at all near midstream. Hence the difference in drag on the near and far sides of a small floating object may be quite large near a bank and very small near midstream.

A rotation about the z-axis is described by a vector $\boldsymbol{\omega} = \omega\mathbf{k}$, where the magnitude $|\boldsymbol{\omega}| = \omega$ describes the angular speed, and the direction of the vector $\boldsymbol{\omega}$ is at right angles to the plane of rotation in the sense given by the screw rule. In the case of the rotating leaf on a river, the direction of the rotation is at right angles to the river surface, i.e. parallel to the z-axis.

Rotation about an axis was discussed in *Unit 20*.

131

Perhaps you can now begin to see a relationship between the rotation of a small floating object, as described by a vector $\boldsymbol{\omega}$, and the curl of the surface velocity field $\mathbf{curl\,v}$. The curl of any two-dimensional vector field on a surface is directed at right angles to the surface. Hence $\boldsymbol{\omega}$ and $\mathbf{curl\,v}$ are both vectors directed at right angles to the water surface. Furthermore, $\mathbf{curl\,v}$ is built up from the partial derivatives $\partial v_1/\partial y$ and $\partial v_2/\partial x$, which represent variation perpendicular to the directions of the corresponding component vectors $v_1\mathbf{i}$ and $v_2\mathbf{j}$, and so correspond to rotational motion. Furthermore, the angular speed $|\boldsymbol{\omega}|$ is largest where the *downstream* surface velocity varies most rapidly with distance *across* the river. In fact, the rotation of a small floating body can be modelled quite well by

$$\boldsymbol{\omega} = A\,\mathbf{curl\,v},$$

where A is a positive constant that depends on the size and shape of the body, the nature of its surface and the properties of the fluid.

The above relationship applies also in three dimensions and is the basis of experimental techniques for exploring the curl of velocity fields in fluids by using a neutral density probe, i.e. a small object that can float at a point beneath the surface of a fluid without sinking or rising. The magnitude and direction of the rotation of the floating probe provide an indication of the curl of the velocity at that point.

In the next example we consider the surface velocity field on a model river, calculate the curl of the velocity and confirm that it describes the way a small floating object would rotate.

Example 2.2

The surface water velocity on a straight uniform river can often be modelled by a two-dimensional vector field of the form

$$\mathbf{v}(x, y) = Cx(d - x)\mathbf{j} \quad (0 \le x \le d),$$

where the y-axis is along one bank and points downstream, d is the width of the river and C is a positive constant (see Figure 2.2).

(a) What is the surface velocity at the river banks and at midstream? How does the magnitude of the surface velocity change as you move out from one bank towards midstream?

(b) Find the vector field $\mathbf{curl\,v}$. State the magnitude and direction of $\mathbf{curl\,v}$ at the river banks and at midstream.

(c) Explain why the answers to part (b) are consistent with the idea that $\mathbf{curl\,v}$ describes the rate and sense of rotation of a small leaf floating on the river surface.

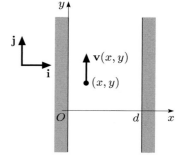

Figure 2.2

Solution

(a) The river banks are the lines $x = 0$ (the y-axis) and $x = d$. We find that $\mathbf{v}(0, y) = \mathbf{v}(d, y) = \mathbf{0}$ and so the river velocity is zero at the banks. At midstream, $x = \frac{1}{2}d$. We find $\mathbf{v}(\frac{1}{2}d, y) = \frac{1}{4}Cd^2\mathbf{j}$. Hence the velocity at midstream is directed downstream (i.e. up the page) and is of magnitude $\frac{1}{4}Cd^2$. The surface speed increases as you move out from either bank towards midstream.

(b) The components of $\mathbf{v}$ are $v_1 = 0$ and $v_2 = Cx(d - x)$. Hence we have $\mathbf{curl\,v} = (Cd - 2Cx)\mathbf{k}$. The value of $\mathbf{curl\,v}$ at the bank $x = 0$ is $Cd\mathbf{k}$. The value of $\mathbf{curl\,v}$ at the bank $x = d$ is $-Cd\mathbf{k}$. The value of $\mathbf{curl\,v}$ at midstream $x = \frac{1}{2}d$ is $\mathbf{0}$.

(c) We have found that at $x = 0$, **curl v** points in the positive z-direction (vertically upwards). A small floating leaf near $x = 0$ would rotate anticlockwise as it floats downstream, since its outer edge is pulled faster than the inner edge by the flow. Similarly, a leaf near the bank $x = d$ would rotate clockwise. This is in accordance with **curl v** being a vector pointing in the negative z-direction at $x = d$. At midstream, the leaf would float without rotating, since both sides of the leaf are pulled equally by the flow. This corresponds to **curl v** = **0** at midstream. ∎

This corresponds to an anticlockwise rotation, by the screw rule of *Unit 4*.

The rotation in the velocity field **v** described by **curl v** is the *local rotation* in the field, as measured by the rotation of a small floating object. Local rotation should be distinguished from bulk rotation, which is simply the movement of material around a circular path.

There is local rotation, but no bulk rotation, in Example 2.2, since the flow is parallel to the y-direction everywhere. There is bulk rotation of water in the velocity fields **u** and **v** that model the surface velocity of water in an emptying bath tub in Exercise 2.3 below, but you will find that there is local rotation in only one of them.

Exercise 2.3 —————————————————————

The velocity field on the surface of an emptying bath tub can be modelled by two functions, the first describing the vigorously swirling vortex of radius a in a central region and the second describing the more gently rotating fluid outside the vortex region. These functions are

$$\mathbf{u}(x, y) = \omega(-y\mathbf{i} + x\mathbf{j}) \quad \left(\sqrt{x^2 + y^2} \leq a\right),$$

$$\mathbf{v}(x, y) = \frac{\omega a^2(-y\mathbf{i} + x\mathbf{j})}{x^2 + y^2} \quad \left(\sqrt{x^2 + y^2} \geq a\right),$$

Note that $\mathbf{u} = \mathbf{v}$ when $(x^2 + y^2)^{1/2} = a$.

where ω is a positive constant and the water surface is assumed to lie in the (x, y)-plane. Find **curl u** and **curl v**.

Exercise 2.4 —————————————————————

Express the two vector fields **u** and **v** of Exercise 2.3 in cylindrical polar coordinates. What shape are the vector field lines of **u** and **v**?

—————————————————————————

Both velocity fields **u** and **v** in Exercise 2.3 have a bulk rotation of fluid around a central point, but field **v** has **curl v** = **0**, showing that there is no local rotation in the field **v**. A small floating object in the region of the field **v** would float around a circular field line, but would not rotate, i.e. it would maintain the same orientation in space.

If you try this experiment next time you have a bath you will probably see some rotation. This is hardly surprising, since the field **v** is a simple model of the flow that assumes that the flow is circular, whereas in reality the flow *spirals into* the plug hole.

In Exercise 2.4 you found that

$$\mathbf{u}(\rho, \theta, z) = \omega\rho\,\mathbf{e}_\theta \quad (\rho \leq a), \quad \mathbf{v}(\rho, \theta, z) = \frac{\omega a^2}{\rho}\mathbf{e}_\theta \quad (\rho \geq a).$$

Hence the fields **u** and **v** have simple forms when expressed in cylindrical polar coordinates. When we are given a vector field in cylindrical polar coordinates, it is usually easier to calculate the curl using the cylindrical polar form of curl rather than converting into Cartesian coordinates.

Curl in polar coordinates

We shall derive the formula for curl only in cylindrical polar coordinates (the method for spherical polar coordinates is similar but the calculations are more complicated). First recall that in cylindrical polar coordinates the gradient vector is given by

$$\nabla = \mathbf{e}_\rho \frac{\partial}{\partial \rho} + \frac{1}{\rho}\,\mathbf{e}_\theta \frac{\partial}{\partial \theta} + \mathbf{e}_z \frac{\partial}{\partial z}.$$

To compute $\mathbf{curl\,F} = \nabla \times \mathbf{F}$ we must therefore calculate

$$\left(\mathbf{e}_\rho \frac{\partial}{\partial \rho} + \frac{1}{\rho}\,\mathbf{e}_\theta \frac{\partial}{\partial \theta} + \mathbf{e}_z \frac{\partial}{\partial z}\right) \times (F_\rho\,\mathbf{e}_\rho + F_\theta\,\mathbf{e}_\theta + F_z\,\mathbf{e}_z),$$

and since this is a complicated expression it is sensible to proceed term by term. Since $\mathbf{e}_\rho$, $\mathbf{e}_\theta$ and $\mathbf{e}_z$ do not depend on ρ, the first term is

$$\mathbf{e}_\rho \frac{\partial}{\partial \rho} \times (F_\rho\,\mathbf{e}_\rho + F_\theta\,\mathbf{e}_\theta + F_z\,\mathbf{e}_z) = \mathbf{e}_\rho \times \frac{\partial}{\partial \rho}(F_\rho\,\mathbf{e}_\rho + F_\theta\,\mathbf{e}_\theta + F_z\,\mathbf{e}_z)$$

The cross product of any vector with itself is $\mathbf{0}$ and
$$\mathbf{e}_\rho \times \mathbf{e}_\theta = \mathbf{e}_z,$$
$$\mathbf{e}_\theta \times \mathbf{e}_z = \mathbf{e}_\rho,$$
$$\mathbf{e}_z \times \mathbf{e}_\rho = \mathbf{e}_\theta.$$

$$= \mathbf{e}_\rho \times \left(\frac{\partial F_\rho}{\partial \rho}\mathbf{e}_\rho + \frac{\partial F_\theta}{\partial \rho}\mathbf{e}_\theta + \frac{\partial F_z}{\partial \rho}\mathbf{e}_z\right)$$

$$= \frac{\partial F_\theta}{\partial \rho}\mathbf{e}_z - \frac{\partial F_z}{\partial \rho}\mathbf{e}_\theta.$$

Next, using the results $\partial\mathbf{e}_\rho/\partial\theta = \mathbf{e}_\theta$, $\partial\mathbf{e}_\theta/\partial\theta = -\mathbf{e}_\rho$ and $\partial\mathbf{e}_z/\partial\theta = \mathbf{0}$, we have

$$\frac{1}{\rho}\mathbf{e}_\theta\frac{\partial}{\partial\theta} \times (F_\rho\,\mathbf{e}_\rho + F_\theta\,\mathbf{e}_\theta + F_z\,\mathbf{e}_z) = \frac{1}{\rho}\mathbf{e}_\theta \times \frac{\partial}{\partial\theta}(F_\rho\mathbf{e}_\rho + F_\theta\,\mathbf{e}_\theta + F_z\,\mathbf{e}_z)$$

$$= \frac{1}{\rho}\mathbf{e}_\theta \times \left(\frac{\partial F_\rho}{\partial\theta}\mathbf{e}_\rho + F_\rho\mathbf{e}_\theta + \frac{\partial F_\theta}{\partial\theta}\mathbf{e}_\theta - F_\theta\mathbf{e}_\rho + \frac{\partial F_z}{\partial\theta}\mathbf{e}_z\right)$$

$$= -\frac{1}{\rho}\frac{\partial F_\rho}{\partial\theta}\mathbf{e}_z + \frac{1}{\rho}F_\theta\mathbf{e}_z + \frac{1}{\rho}\frac{\partial F_z}{\partial\theta}\mathbf{e}_\rho.$$

In the second line of the calculation above, we used the fact that $\partial\mathbf{e}_z/\partial\theta = \mathbf{0}$. Finally, since $\mathbf{e}_\rho$, $\mathbf{e}_\theta$ and $\mathbf{e}_z$ do not depend on z,

$$\mathbf{e}_z\frac{\partial}{\partial z} \times (F_\rho\,\mathbf{e}_\rho + F_\theta\,\mathbf{e}_\theta + F_z\,\mathbf{e}_z) = \mathbf{e}_z \times \frac{\partial}{\partial z}(F_\rho\mathbf{e}_\rho + F_\theta\,\mathbf{e}_\theta + F_z\,\mathbf{e}_z)$$

$$= \mathbf{e}_z \times \left(\frac{\partial F_\rho}{\partial z}\mathbf{e}_\rho + \frac{\partial F_\theta}{\partial z}\mathbf{e}_\theta + \frac{\partial F_z}{\partial z}\mathbf{e}_z\right)$$

$$= \frac{\partial F_\rho}{\partial z}\mathbf{e}_\theta - \frac{\partial F_\theta}{\partial z}\mathbf{e}_\rho.$$

Hence the formula, which we summarize below. A more complicated derivation provides a corresponding formula in spherical polar coordinates.

Curl of a vector field in polar coordinates

The **curl** of a **vector field** $\mathbf{F} = \mathbf{F}(\rho, \theta, z) = F_\rho \mathbf{e}_\rho + F_\theta \mathbf{e}_\theta + F_z \mathbf{e}_z$ in **cylindrical polar coordinates** is

$$\nabla \times \mathbf{F} = \left(\frac{1}{\rho} \frac{\partial F_z}{\partial \theta} - \frac{\partial F_\theta}{\partial z} \right) \mathbf{e}_\rho + \left(\frac{\partial F_\rho}{\partial z} - \frac{\partial F_z}{\partial \rho} \right) \mathbf{e}_\theta$$
$$+ \left(\frac{\partial F_\theta}{\partial \rho} - \frac{1}{\rho} \frac{\partial F_\rho}{\partial \theta} + \frac{1}{\rho} F_\theta \right) \mathbf{e}_z.$$

The curl of a vector field $\mathbf{F}(r, \theta, \phi) = F_r \mathbf{e}_r + F_\theta \mathbf{e}_\theta + F_\phi \mathbf{e}_\phi$ in **spherical polar coordinates** is

$$\nabla \times \mathbf{F} = \left(\frac{1}{r} \frac{\partial F_\phi}{\partial \theta} - \frac{1}{r \sin \theta} \frac{\partial F_\theta}{\partial \phi} + \frac{\cot \theta}{r} F_\phi \right) \mathbf{e}_r$$
$$+ \left(-\frac{\partial F_\phi}{\partial r} + \frac{1}{r \sin \theta} \frac{\partial F_r}{\partial \phi} - \frac{1}{r} F_\phi \right) \mathbf{e}_\theta$$
$$+ \left(\frac{\partial F_\theta}{\partial r} - \frac{1}{r} \frac{\partial F_r}{\partial \theta} + \frac{1}{r} F_\theta \right) \mathbf{e}_\phi.$$

As you can see, the full cylindrical polar expression for curl is quite complicated. However, for vector fields where there is no variation in the z-direction, we have the following.

Curl of a two-dimensional vector field

The **curl** of a two-dimensional **vector field** $\mathbf{F} = \mathbf{F}(\rho, \theta) = F_\rho \mathbf{e}_\rho + F_\theta \mathbf{e}_\theta$ in **cylindrical polar coordinates** is

$$\operatorname{curl} \mathbf{F} = \left(\frac{\partial F_\theta}{\partial \rho} + \frac{F_\theta}{\rho} - \frac{1}{\rho} \frac{\partial F_\rho}{\partial \theta} \right) \mathbf{e}_z. \tag{2.3}$$

Example 2.3

Use Equation (2.3) to calculate **curl u** and **curl v**, where **u** and **v** are the velocity fields in cylindrical polar form that you found in Exercise 2.4.

Solution

For the field **u**, we have $u_\rho = 0$, $u_\theta = \omega \rho$. The only non-zero partial derivative is $\partial u_\theta / \partial \rho = \omega$. Hence

$$\operatorname{curl} \mathbf{u} = \left(\omega + \frac{\omega \rho}{\rho} \right) \mathbf{e}_z = 2\omega \mathbf{e}_z = 2\omega \mathbf{k}.$$

Similarly, we find, $v_\rho = 0$, $v_\theta = \omega a^2 / \rho$. Hence the only non-zero partial derivative is $\partial v_\theta / \partial \rho = -\omega a^2 / \rho^2$. Hence

$$\operatorname{curl} \mathbf{v} = \left(-\frac{\omega a^2}{\rho^2} + \frac{\omega a^2}{\rho^2} \right) \mathbf{e}_z = \mathbf{0}.$$

These results agree with those of Exercise 2.3. ∎

End-of-section Exercises

*Exercise 2.5

Find **curl F**, where $\mathbf{F}(x, y, z) = x(y - z)\mathbf{i} + 3x^2\mathbf{j} + yz\mathbf{k}$. Determine **curl F** at (a) the origin, (b) the point $(1, 2, 3)$ and (c) the point 5 units from the origin on the positive z-axis.

Exercise 2.6

The Earth rotates about its north–south axis at the rate of 2π radians per 24 hours. This rotation has angular velocity $\boldsymbol{\omega} = \omega\mathbf{k}$, where the unit vector **k** points from south to north and $\omega = |\boldsymbol{\omega}|$ is the angular speed. The velocity of a point inside the Earth or on the Earth's surface is given by

$$\mathbf{v} = \boldsymbol{\omega} \times \mathbf{r} \quad (|\mathbf{r}| \leq R),$$

where **r** is the position vector of the point measured from an origin O at the Earth's centre and R is the Earth's radius.

(a) Express the vector field **v** in Cartesian coordinates, taking the z-axis to be directed from south to north along the axis of rotation.

(b) Find **curl v** and determine its magnitude.

(c) Comment on the relationship between the magnitude and direction of **curl v**, and the rate and sense of rotation of your home.

Exercise 2.7

Show that any vector field of the form $\mathbf{F} = f(x)\mathbf{i} + g(y)\mathbf{j}$, where f is a function of x only and g is a function of y only, has zero curl everywhere.

3 The scalar line integral

Scalar line integrals occur whenever we sum scalar values along a line or along a curve in space. An important example of a scalar line integral is the *work done by a force*. Subsection 3.1 defines the work done by a force acting on a particle moving along the x-axis. This definition is then generalized to motion along a curve in space. In Subsection 3.2 we show that the work done by the force is a *scalar line integral* of the force vector along the curve, and we also show how scalar line integrals are evaluated.

We shall often refer to scalar line integrals as just 'line integrals'.

3.1 Work done by forces

We begin with a one-dimensional problem in which a particle is acted upon by a single force $\mathbf{F}$. Suppose a constant force $F\mathbf{i}$ accelerates a particle of mass m in the direction of the positive x-axis. If $a_0\mathbf{i}$ is the constant acceleration of the particle, $x_0\mathbf{i}$ its initial position, and v_0 its initial speed, then the position $x\mathbf{i}$ and velocity $v\mathbf{i}$ of the particle are related by the constant-acceleration equation

$$v^2 = v_0^2 + 2a_0(x - x_0).$$

Multiplying by $\frac{1}{2}m$ and rearranging gives the energy conservation equation

$$\tfrac{1}{2}mv^2 - \tfrac{1}{2}mv_0^2 = ma_0(x - x_0) = F(x - x_0). \tag{3.1}$$

In *Unit 8* this equation was interpreted as stating that the gain (or loss) of kinetic energy equals the loss (or gain) of potential energy. Here we are interested in two other ways of interpreting Equation (3.1). First, since both the force and the displacement of the particle are directed along the x-axis, the right-hand side is just the dot product of $\mathbf{F} = F\mathbf{i}$ and $(x - x_0)\mathbf{i}$, so

$$ma_0(x - x_0) = F(x - x_0) = \mathbf{F} \cdot (x - x_0)\mathbf{i}.$$

Secondly, since F is a constant and the particle is moving in a straight line from x_0 to a general position x, we can write

$$F(x - x_0) = \int_{x_0}^{x} F\,dx,$$

so that the right-hand side of Equation (3.1) is just the integral of F, along the x-axis, from x_0 to x. We call this integral the *work done* by $\mathbf{F}$ in moving the particle along the straight line from x_0 to x.

You can see from this that the work done by the force is equal to the *gain* in kinetic energy of the particle. For a stone falling a distance h from rest, the constant force of gravity, $F_g\mathbf{i} = mg\mathbf{i}$, does work $F_g h = mgh$, which is equal to the *loss* of gravitational potential energy. The work done by the force is equal to the amount of gravitational potential energy that becomes kinetic energy.

We now generalize the work integral, $\int_{x_0}^{x} F\,dx$, to motion that is no longer confined to the x-axis but is either two-dimensional, along a path in a plane, or is in three-dimensional space. In general the force $\mathbf{F}$ will be acting at points $\mathbf{r} = x\mathbf{i} + y\mathbf{j} + z\mathbf{k}$ in space and we use the notation $\mathbf{F}(\mathbf{r})$ instead of $\mathbf{F}(x,y,z)$. We calculate the work done by any force field $\mathbf{F}(\mathbf{r})$ which depends at most on the position vector $\mathbf{r}$. Thus we exclude, for example, forces that depend on velocity, such as friction, or forces that depend explicitly on time as well as position.

We start with Newton's second law, $m\ddot{\mathbf{r}} = \mathbf{F}(\mathbf{r})$, for a particle of mass m. We take the dot product of both sides of the equation with the velocity $\dot{\mathbf{r}} = d\mathbf{r}/dt$ to give $m\ddot{\mathbf{r}} \cdot \dot{\mathbf{r}} = \mathbf{F}(\mathbf{r}) \cdot \dot{\mathbf{r}}$. Since $d(\dot{\mathbf{r}} \cdot \dot{\mathbf{r}})/dt = 2\ddot{\mathbf{r}} \cdot \dot{\mathbf{r}}$, this is equivalent to $\frac{1}{2}m\,d(\dot{\mathbf{r}} \cdot \dot{\mathbf{r}})/dt = \mathbf{F}(\mathbf{r}) \cdot \dot{\mathbf{r}}$. We then integrate both sides of the equation with respect to time over the interval from t_0 to t_1. Thus with $\mathbf{v}_0 = \dot{\mathbf{r}}(t_0)$ and $\mathbf{v}_1 = \dot{\mathbf{r}}(t_1)$ we obtain a generalized form of Equation (3.1),

$$\tfrac{1}{2}m\mathbf{v}_1 \cdot \mathbf{v}_1 - \tfrac{1}{2}m\mathbf{v}_0 \cdot \mathbf{v}_0 = \int_{t_0}^{t_1} \mathbf{F}(\mathbf{r}) \cdot \frac{d\mathbf{r}}{dt}\,dt, \tag{3.2}$$

You met problems of this sort in Unit 6. If F is constant then so is the acceleration $a_0\mathbf{i}$ and $F = ma_0$.

See Subsection 1.2 of Unit 6.

Here $h = x - x_0$, $g = a_0$ and $v_0 = 0$ in Equation (3.1).

We ignore all other forces such as air resistance acting on the stone.

Since it is based on Newton's second law, Equation (3.2) is only valid when $\mathbf{F}$ is the resultant force on the particle. However, when there is more than one force acting simultaneously we can still define the work done by each force separately by an integral of the form of Equation (3.3).

where the left-hand side is the change of kinetic energy and the definite integral

$$W = \int_{t_0}^{t_1} \mathbf{F}(\mathbf{r}) \cdot \frac{d\mathbf{r}}{dt}\, dt \tag{3.3}$$

is the **work done** by the force $\mathbf{F}$ when the particle moves along a path described by the position vector $\mathbf{r}(t)$, in the interval from time t_0 to t_1.

Consider again the case of a particle moving in the positive direction of the x-axis, so that $\mathbf{r} = x\mathbf{i}$ and $\dot{\mathbf{r}} = \dot{x}\mathbf{i}$, but now we allow the magnitude of $\mathbf{F}$ to vary so that $\mathbf{F} = F(x)\mathbf{i}$. Suppose the particle is at $x = a$ at time t_0 and at $x = b$ at time t_1, as shown in Figure 3.1. Since the force $\mathbf{F}$ depends at most on position x, and not on other variables such as velocity, or explicitly on time, the work done by the force, from Equation (3.3), is

The case of a varying force accelerating a particle along the x-axis was considered in Section 1 of *Unit 8*.

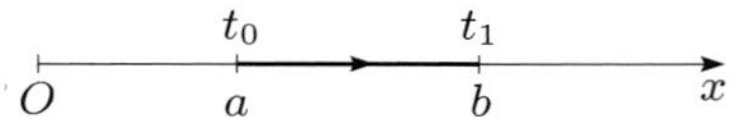

$$W = \int_{t_0}^{t_1} \mathbf{F}(\mathbf{r}) \cdot \frac{d\mathbf{r}}{dt}\, dt = \int_{t_0}^{t_1} F(x)\mathbf{i} \cdot \frac{dx}{dt}\mathbf{i}\, dt = \int_{t_0}^{t_1} F(x)\frac{dx}{dt}\, dt$$

$$= \int_a^b F(x)\, dx. \tag{3.4}$$

Figure 3.1

Example 3.1

A particle moves along the x-axis from $x = 2$ to $x = 5$ under the action of a force $F(x)\mathbf{i}$ given by

$$F(x) = -100(x - 1).$$

Determine the work done by the force and the change in the kinetic energy of the particle.

We use SI units.

Solution

To calculate the work done we can use Equation (3.4), obtaining

$$W = \int_a^b F(x)\, dx = -100 \int_2^5 (x - 1)\, dx$$

$$= -100 \left[\tfrac{1}{2}x^2 - x \right]_2^5 = -750.$$

Hence the work done by the force is 750 J as the particle moves from $x = 5$ to $x = 2$. Assuming $F(x)\mathbf{i}$ is the resultant force acting on the particle, the change in the particle's kinetic energy is -750 J. ∎

The SI units of work (work done) are the same as those of energy (joules).

Exercise 3.1

The force on a particle of mass m moving on an interval of the x-axis is

$$F(x)\mathbf{i} = -\frac{A}{x^2}\mathbf{i} \quad (x \neq 0),$$

where A is a positive constant. Determine the work done by the force when the particle moves from $x = 3$ to $x = 1$, and hence find an expression for the speed v of the particle when it is at $x = 1$, given that its speed at $x = 3$ was u.

Before we give the details of a general method for evaluating integrals like that in Equation (3.3), for the work done by a force, let's first consider two special cases when the integrand, and hence the work done, is zero.

(a) $\mathbf{F} = \mathbf{0}$, which makes sense, since if the force is zero it can do no work.

(b) $\mathbf{F}$ and $d\mathbf{r}/dt$ are perpendicular so that $\mathbf{F} \cdot d\mathbf{r}/dt = 0$. Since the velocity vector $d\mathbf{r}/dt$ points along the tangent to the curve at each point, only the component of the force in this direction contributes to the work done. Hence no work is done if the only force is perpendicular to the direction of motion.

An example of (b) is provided by a particle moving at constant speed along a circular path. In this case the force is directed along the radius, towards the centre; it therefore has zero component along the tangent to the circle at any point and hence does no work. Other examples of situations where forces always act at right angles to the path of a moving particle, and hence do no work, are the tension force in the string of a simple pendulum or the normal reaction on an object moving on an inclined plane.

See Unit 20.

The parameter t (for time) appears in Equation (3.3) because it is often a convenient way of parametrizing the path of the particle. We could equally well describe the path in terms of another parameter, such as the distance s from the point where $\mathbf{r} = \mathbf{r}(t_0)$. For this reason we normally write Equation (3.3) symbolically in parameter-free form as

$$W = \int_C \mathbf{F}(\mathbf{r}) \cdot d\mathbf{r}, \qquad (3.5)$$

where C is the path of the particle. However, when we need to evaluate Equation (3.5), we express the path in terms of a suitable **parameter**, usually t (which may or may not represent time), so that it once again takes the form of Equation (3.3).

To evaluate Equation (3.3) with the dot product in the integrand expressed in Cartesian form, we need to know the functions $\mathbf{F}(\mathbf{r})$ and $d\mathbf{r}/dt$. Now for $\mathbf{r}(t) = x(t)\mathbf{i} + y(t)\mathbf{j} + z(t)\mathbf{k}$, we have

You considered t as a parameter for the position vector $\mathbf{r}$ in Unit 6.

$$\frac{d\mathbf{r}}{dt} = \frac{d}{dt}(x\mathbf{i} + y\mathbf{j} + z\mathbf{k}) = \frac{dx}{dt}\mathbf{i} + \frac{dy}{dt}\mathbf{j} + \frac{dz}{dt}\mathbf{k},$$

and we can express the components of $\mathbf{F}(\mathbf{r})$ at any point on C as functions of t. For example, $F_1(\mathbf{r}) = \mathbf{F}(\mathbf{r}) \cdot \mathbf{i} = F_1(x, y, z) = F_1(x(t), y(t), z(t)) = F_1(t)$, and so

$$\mathbf{F}(t) = F_1(t)\mathbf{i} + F_2(t)\mathbf{j} + F_3(t)\mathbf{k} \quad \text{on } C.$$

Thus the integrand in Equation (3.3) is

Notice that in employing a parameter we also abuse notation by reducing a function of three coordinates $\mathbf{F}(\mathbf{r})$ to a function of one parameter $\mathbf{F}(t)$ where $\mathbf{r}$ is restricted to C.

$$\mathbf{F}(t) \cdot \frac{d\mathbf{r}}{dt} = F_1(t)\frac{dx}{dt} + F_2(t)\frac{dy}{dt} + F_3(t)\frac{dz}{dt}.$$

Work done by a force

The work done by a force $\mathbf{F}(\mathbf{r})$, given in Cartesian coordinates, in moving a particle along a path C, given by $\mathbf{r} = \mathbf{r}(t)$ from $\mathbf{r}(t_0)$ to $\mathbf{r}(t_1)$, is

$$W = \int_C \mathbf{F}(\mathbf{r}) \cdot d\mathbf{r} = \int_{t_0}^{t_1} \left(F_1(t)\frac{dx}{dt} + F_2(t)\frac{dy}{dt} + F_3(t)\frac{dz}{dt} \right) dt. \quad (3.6)$$

Thus we have expressed the work done by a force as an ordinary definite integral which we can try to evaluate by standard integration techniques.

Example 3.2

Find the work done by the force

$$\mathbf{F} = yz\mathbf{i} + zx\mathbf{j} + xy\mathbf{k}$$

when it moves a particle from the point $(0,0,0)$ to the point $(3,1,1)$ along the curve C given by $\mathbf{r} = 3t\mathbf{i} + t^2\mathbf{j} + t^3\mathbf{k}$, from $t_0 = 0$ to $t_1 = 1$.

Solution

The components of $\mathbf{r}$ in terms of t, i.e. the parametric equations for C, are

$$x = 3t, \quad y = t^2, \quad z = t^3, \quad \text{where } t \text{ goes from } t_0 = 0 \text{ to } t_1 = 1,$$

so differentiating these equations yields

$$\frac{dx}{dt} = 3, \quad \frac{dy}{dt} = 2t, \quad \frac{dz}{dt} = 3t^2.$$

The components of $\mathbf{F}$ in terms of t are

$$F_1 = yz = t^5, \quad F_2 = zx = 3t^4, \quad F_3 = xy = 3t^3.$$

Substituting into Equation (3.6) gives

$$W = \int_C \mathbf{F} \cdot d\mathbf{r} = \int_0^1 (3t^5 + 6t^5 + 9t^5)\, dt = \int_0^1 18t^5\, dt = 18 \left[\tfrac{1}{6}t^6\right]_0^1 = 3. \quad \blacksquare$$

*Exercise 3.2

Find the work done by the force

$$\mathbf{F} = (2x + y)\mathbf{i} - x\mathbf{j}$$

as it moves a particle from the point $(2,0)$ to the point $(0,2)$ along the quarter-circle C_1 shown in Figure 3.2. The quarter-circle has centre at the origin and radius 2, and can be parametrized by the equations

$$x = 2\cos t, \quad y = 2\sin t, \quad z = 0, \quad \text{where } t \text{ goes from } t_0 = 0 \text{ to } t_1 = \tfrac{\pi}{2}.$$

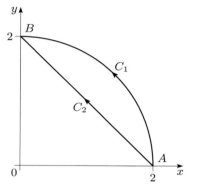

Figure 3.2

Sometimes a curve in the (x, y)-plane is specified by an equation $y = f(x)$. We can then effectively use x as the parameter t in Equation (3.6).

Example 3.3

Find the work done by the vector field $\mathbf{F} = (2x + y)\mathbf{i} - x\mathbf{j}$ acting along the straight line C_2, specified by the equation $y = 2 - x$, from the point $(2, 0)$ to the point $(0, 2)$ (see Figure 3.2).

The force $\mathbf{F}$ is the same as that in Exercise 3.2.

Solution

We put $x = t$, and the parametric equations for C_2 are

$$x = t, \quad y = 2 - t, \quad z = 0,$$

where t runs from $t_0 = 2$ to $t_1 = 0$ (see Figure 3.2). Then we have

$$F_1 = 2x + y = 2 + t, \quad F_2 = -x = -t,$$

$$\frac{dx}{dt} = 1, \quad \frac{dy}{dt} = -1.$$

Substituting into Equation (3.6) yields

$$W = \int_{C_2} \mathbf{F}(\mathbf{r}) \cdot d\mathbf{r} = \int_2^0 ((2 + t) + (-t)(-1))\, dt = \int_2^0 (2t + 2)\, dt = -8. \quad \blacksquare$$

Exercise 3.3

Find the work done by the force $\mathbf{F} = x^2\mathbf{i} + xy\mathbf{j}$ acting along the parabolic segment C specified by the equation $y = 1 - x^2$ from the point $(1, 0)$ to $(0, 1)$ (see Figure 3.3).

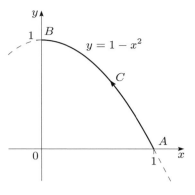

Figure 3.3

Of course there are many paths joining any two given points.

*Exercise 3.4

Find two different paths between the points $(0, 0, 0)$ and $(1, 1, 1)$, giving parametrizations for each.

A parametrization of a particular curve is not unique, nor does the work done depend on the parametrization.

*Exercise 3.5

The straight line C_2 in Example 3.3 can be parametrized by the equations

$$x = 2(1 - t), \quad y = 2t, \quad z = 0, \quad \text{for } t \text{ from 0 to 1.}$$

Find the work done by the force $\mathbf{F} = (2x + y)\mathbf{i} - x\mathbf{j}$ using this parametrization, and compare your answer with that found in Example 3.3.

3.2 Scalar line integrals

You have seen that the work integral in Equation (3.3) may be written as

$$W = \int_C \mathbf{F}(\mathbf{r}) \cdot d\mathbf{r}, \tag{3.7}$$

This is Equation (3.5).

where C specifies the *path* (or directed curve) along which the particle moves, and $\mathbf{r}$ is the position vector of points on C. You can think of the dot product between the force $\mathbf{F}(\mathbf{r})$ and the symbol $d\mathbf{r}$ in Equation (3.7) as representing the fact that we are integrating only the component of the force parallel to the tangent to the curve in the direction of motion. This is illustrated in Figure 3.4, which shows a very short segment PQ of the curve C. The displacement $\delta\mathbf{r}_i = \mathbf{r}_Q - \mathbf{r}_P$ is nearly parallel to the tangents to the path along this segment, and the work done by the force along PQ is approximately the dot product $\mathbf{F}(\mathbf{r}_i) \cdot \delta\mathbf{r}_i$, where $\mathbf{F}(\mathbf{r}_i)$ is the force vector at some point $\mathbf{r}_i$ on PQ. If we divide C up into N such short segments, then adding up the approximations for the work done along all N segments, we obtain an estimate for the work done by $\mathbf{F}$ as it acts along the whole of C, that is,

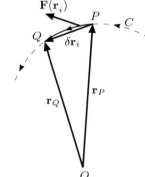

Figure 3.4

$$W \simeq \sum_{i=1}^{N} \mathbf{F}(\mathbf{r}_i) \cdot \delta\mathbf{r}_i.$$

The approximation becomes exact in the limit as $N \to \infty$ and each $|\delta\mathbf{r}_i| \to 0$ to give

The connection between the limit of a sum and integration was introduced in MST121 *Chapter C2.*

$$W = \lim_{N \to \infty} \sum_{i=1}^{N} \mathbf{F}(\mathbf{r}_i) \cdot \delta\mathbf{r}_i = \int_C \mathbf{F}(\mathbf{r}) \cdot d\mathbf{r}.$$

The work integral, Equation (3.3) or Equation (3.7), is an example of a *scalar line integral* of a vector field. We can form the scalar line integral of any vector field $\mathbf{F}(\mathbf{r})$ along a path C.

Definition

The **scalar line integral** of a vector field $\mathbf{F}(\mathbf{r})$ along a path C, given by $\mathbf{r} = \mathbf{r}(t)$ from $\mathbf{r}(t_0)$ to $\mathbf{r}(t_1)$, is

$$\int_C \mathbf{F}(\mathbf{r}) \cdot d\mathbf{r} = \int_{t_0}^{t_1} \mathbf{F}(t) \cdot \frac{d\mathbf{r}}{dt} \, dt.$$

Note that t may be any parameter, not necessarily time.

The physical interpretation of the scalar line integral will depend on the nature of the particular vector field $\mathbf{F}(\mathbf{r})$ being considered. We shall only consider the case of force fields, where the scalar line integral represents the work done by the force.

The path C in a scalar line integral is a directed curve (with starting point A and endpoint B). It is often convenient to denote the scalar line integral by writing it as $\int_{AB} \mathbf{F}(\mathbf{r}) \cdot d\mathbf{r}$ where the order AB indicates the direction along the path.

We indicate the direction by an arrow in diagrams, e.g. Figures 3.2 and 3.3.

We could choose to traverse the *same* path but in the opposite sense, starting at B and ending at A. This would reverse the direction of each displacement $\delta\mathbf{r}$ in Figure 3.4 and therefore change the sign of the scalar line integral. Thus we have

$$\int_{BA} \mathbf{F}(\mathbf{r}) \cdot d\mathbf{r} = - \int_{AB} \mathbf{F}(\mathbf{r}) \cdot d\mathbf{r}. \tag{3.8}$$

Line integrals can be evaluated along segments of **open curves** where the starting point A and the endpoint B are distinct points, as in the examples above, or around **closed curves**. The straight line and quarter-circle of Figure 3.2 are examples of open curves. Suppose now we reverse the direction of the straight line segment in Figure 3.2. Then the reversed line segment together with the quarter-circle make the closed curve shown in Figure 3.5. We can traverse this closed curve in an anticlockwise sense, $APBQA$, by starting at point A, moving along the quarter-circle via P to B, and returning along the straight line BA via Q. The line integral of a vector field $\mathbf{F}$ for one complete anticlockwise traversal of this loop is the sum of the two line integrals. We can write this as

Closed curves are also referred to as *loops*.

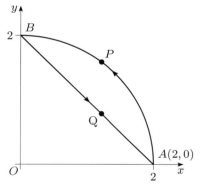

$$\oint_C \mathbf{F} \cdot d\mathbf{r} = \int_{APB} \mathbf{F} \cdot d\mathbf{r} + \int_{BQA} \mathbf{F} \cdot d\mathbf{r},$$

where the circle on the integral sign indicates that the path C is closed. The sense of each of the two line integrals on the right-hand side of the above equation, that is, the direction along the path, is indicated by the order of the letters: APB and BQA.

Figure 3.5

Example 3.4

Evaluate $\oint_C \mathbf{F} \cdot d\mathbf{r}$, where $\mathbf{F} = (2x + y)\mathbf{i} - x\mathbf{j}$ and C is the closed curve $APBQA$ shown in Figure 3.5.

Solution

We sum the line integrals along the two segments APB and BQA of the loop. The line integral of $\mathbf{F}$ along the quarter-circle C_1 ($= APB$) was evaluated in the solution to Exercise 3.2, where you obtained $\int_{C_1} \mathbf{F} \cdot d\mathbf{r} = -4 - 2\pi$. The line integral along the straight line C_2 ($= AQB$) was evaluated in Example 3.3 where we obtained $\int_{AQB} \mathbf{F} \cdot d\mathbf{r} = -8$. But we want the line integral along BQA, i.e. along the same straight-line segment but in the opposite direction. Using Equation (3.8), we just change the sign to obtain $\int_{BQA} \mathbf{F} \cdot d\mathbf{r} = 8$. Thus

$$\oint_C \mathbf{F} \cdot d\mathbf{r} = \int_{APB} \mathbf{F} \cdot d\mathbf{r} + \int_{BQA} \mathbf{F} \cdot d\mathbf{r} = -4 - 2\pi + 8 = 4 - 2\pi. \quad \blacksquare$$

*Exercise 3.6

Evaluate the scalar line integral of the vector field $\mathbf{G} = x^2\mathbf{i} + y\mathbf{j}$ along each of the paths C_1 and C_2 specified in Figure 3.2. (Use the parametrizations of Exercise 3.2 and Example 3.3, respectively.) Evaluate also the scalar line integral of $\mathbf{G}$ around the closed curve $APBQA$ in Figure 3.5.

Example 3.5

A force $\mathbf{F}$ acts along a path C of length L. The tangential component F_t of $\mathbf{F}$ is constant along C. Show that the work done by $\mathbf{F}$ is $F_t L$.

Solution

The component of $\mathbf{F}$ normal to C does no work since it is perpendicular to the tangent to C. So, if the parameter l measures the length along C from $l_0 = 0$ to $l_1 = L$, $F_t = \mathbf{F} \cdot d\mathbf{r}/dl$, and the work done, W, is given by

$$W = \int_C \mathbf{F} \cdot d\mathbf{r} = \int_{l_0}^{l_1} \left(\mathbf{F} \cdot \frac{d\mathbf{r}}{dl} \right) dl$$

$$= \int_{l_0}^{l_1} F_t \, dl = \int_0^L F_t \, dl = F_t L. \quad \blacksquare$$

*Exercise 3.7

Evaluate the scalar line integral of each of the two vector fields $\mathbf{u}$ and $\mathbf{v}$, given below, around the closed circular path C of radius a centred on the origin and defined by the parametric equations

$$x = a\cos t, \quad y = a\sin t, \quad \text{where } t \text{ goes from } 0 \text{ to } 2\pi.$$

(a) $\mathbf{u}(x, y) = (x\mathbf{i} + y\mathbf{j})/(x^2 + y^2)$

(b) $\mathbf{v}(x, y) = \omega(-y\mathbf{i} + x\mathbf{j})$, where ω is a positive constant

You may have spotted that the line integrals in Exercise 3.7 can be evaluated without explicitly carrying out an integration, since in each case the tangential component of the vector field is constant everywhere on the circle. This is obvious in part (a), since $x\mathbf{i} + y\mathbf{j} = \mathbf{r}$ is the position vector, which points radially outwards everywhere, and is therefore always perpendicular to the tangent to any circle centred on the origin. Hence the tangential component of $\mathbf{u}$ is zero everywhere on the circle, and the line integral is zero. It's not so obvious in part (b), but you can see that $\mathbf{r} \cdot \mathbf{v} = 0$, and

The field lines of $\mathbf{v}$ are circles centred on the origin.

so the field **v** is at right angles to the position vector and is therefore directed tangentially to the path. Also the field **v** has a constant magnitude, $\omega((-y)^2 + x^2)^{1/2} = \omega a$, on the circle. Thus the line integral of **v** for one complete traversal of the circle is $\omega a \times 2\pi a = 2\omega\pi a^2$. When evaluating line integrals you can sometimes spot that the tangential component of the vector field is constant and, as this example shows, obtain the value directly using the result of Example 3.5.

Exercise 3.8 _____

Evaluate the scalar line integral of the vector field **v** defined in Exercise 3.7 along the x-axis from $x = 1$ to $x = -1$.

_____

3.3 The length of a curve

Consider the scalar line integral of the vector field **F** along the curve C given by $\mathbf{r} = \mathbf{r}(t)$ from $\mathbf{r}(t_0)$ to $\mathbf{r}(t_1)$, defined by

$$\int_C \mathbf{F}(\mathbf{r}) \cdot d\mathbf{r} = \int_{t_0}^{t_1} \mathbf{F}(t) \cdot \frac{d\mathbf{r}}{dt}\, dt,$$

where t represents time. The expression $\mathbf{r}(t)$ represents the point on the curve corresponding to time t, and $d\mathbf{r}/dt$ represents the velocity of the point as it moves along the curve. Now consider what happens when we choose the vector function

$$\mathbf{F}(t) = \frac{\dot{\mathbf{r}}(t)}{|\dot{\mathbf{r}}(t)|} = \widehat{\dot{\mathbf{r}}(t)},$$

which represents a unit vector in the direction of the velocity vector $\dot{\mathbf{r}}(t)$. In this case

$$\mathbf{F}(t) \cdot \frac{d\mathbf{r}}{dt} = \frac{\dot{\mathbf{r}}(t)}{|\dot{\mathbf{r}}(t)|} \cdot \dot{\mathbf{r}}(t) = |\dot{\mathbf{r}}(t)|,$$

and the scalar line integral becomes

$$\int_C \mathbf{F}(\mathbf{r}) \cdot d\mathbf{r} = \int_{t_0}^{t_1} |\dot{\mathbf{r}}(t)|\, dt = \int_{t_0}^{t_1} \sqrt{\left(\frac{dx}{dt}\right)^2 + \left(\frac{dy}{dt}\right)^2}\, dt. \tag{3.9}$$

This gives the length of the curve C between the two points $\mathbf{r}(t_0)$ and $\mathbf{r}(t_1)$. Indeed, one can see this intuitively by considering what happens to the point which is currently at $\mathbf{r}(t)$ during a small interval of time δt. During this time the point will move along the curve by a distance approximately $|\dot{\mathbf{r}}(t)|\, \delta t$, and so the length of the curve is approximated by the sum

$$\sum_i |\dot{\mathbf{r}}_i(t)|\, \delta t_i.$$

Allowing the intervals δt_i to shrink to zero in the usual way, we can replace the sum by an integral that is precisely Equation (3.9). Let us check this in an example.

Example 3.6

Find the length of a semicircle of radius 1.

Solution

Take the centre of the circle to be at the origin, and consider the semicircle as lying in the upper half-plane $(y \geq 0)$. Then a suitable parametrization is given by $x = \cos t$, $y = \sin t$, $(0 \leq t \leq \pi)$. Thus $\mathbf{r}(t) = \cos t\,\mathbf{i} + \sin t\,\mathbf{j}$, and $\dot{\mathbf{r}}(t) = -\sin t\,\mathbf{i} + \cos t\,\mathbf{j}$.

Therefore

$$|\dot{\mathbf{r}}(t)| = 1,$$

and the integral in Equation (3.9) is

$$\int_0^\pi 1\,dt = \pi,$$

which we know to be the correct answer. ■

Exercise 3.9

Find the length of the curve given by

$$x = t, \qquad y = -\ln(\cos t) \qquad (0 \leq t \leq \pi/4).$$

End-of-section Exercises

Exercise 3.10

Evaluate the scalar line integral of $\mathbf{F} = 2x\mathbf{i} + (xz - 2)\mathbf{j} + xy\mathbf{k}$ along the path C from the point $(0,0,0)$ to the point $(1,1,1)$, defined by the parametrization

$$x = t, \quad y = t^2, \quad z = t^3 \quad (0 \leq t \leq 1).$$

*Exercise 3.11

Determine each of the following line integrals, which you can do without explicitly carrying out an integration.

(a) The line integral of $\mathbf{F} = z^2\mathbf{j}$ along the x-axis from $x = 1$ to $x = 2$

(b) The line integral of $\mathbf{F} = 5\mathbf{k}$ along the z-axis from $z = 0$ to $z = 6$

(c) The line integral of $\mathbf{F} = r^2\mathbf{e}_\theta$ on a semicircle in the (x,y)-plane centred on the origin and of radius 3.

$\mathbf{F}$ is given here in plane polar coordinates.

*Exercise 3.12

Evaluate the scalar line integral of $\mathbf{F} = x^2\mathbf{i} + xy\mathbf{j}$ on the parabolic segment C specified by the equation $y = 1 - x^2$ from the point $(1,0)$ to $(0,1)$.

See Figure 3.3.

4 Linking line integrals, curl and gradient

In this section a connection is established between the properties of scalar line integrals of a vector field and some of the properties of scalar and vector fields that you met in *Unit 23* and earlier in this unit, in particular the curl of the vector field. Subsection 4.2 shows how the properties of scalar line integrals are used for classifying vector fields as *conservative* or *non-conservative*.

4.1 Line integrals and curl

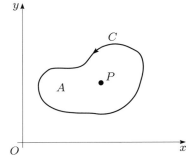

Figure 4.1

In this subsection we are going to make important links between line integrals, the curl of a vector field, potential functions and the gradient of a scalar field. The curl of a vector field was defined in Section 2 in terms of partial derivatives. In fact, it is also possible to define the curl of a vector field in terms of line integrals. This we do below, and in the next subsection you will see that it leads to the *curl test* for conservative fields.

Figure 4.1 shows a closed curve C in the (x, y)-plane enclosing a point P. Let the area enclosed by the curve be A. Consider the line integral of an arbitrary vector field $\mathbf{F} = F_1\mathbf{i} + F_2\mathbf{j}$ for one complete anticlockwise traversal of the curve, then divide the value of the line integral by the area inside the curve to obtain the quotient

$$Q = \frac{1}{A} \oint_C \mathbf{F} \cdot d\mathbf{r}.$$

In general, the value of Q might be expected to depend on the size and shape of the loop enclosing P. But suppose we consider a sequence of loops of smaller and smaller area A, all enclosing P. We then find that the limit of Q for $A \to 0$ is independent of the shapes of the loops and of how the limit is approached, and depends only on the location of the point P, and of course the vector field $\mathbf{F}$. Furthermore, and here's a surprise, the limit turns out to be something familiar:

$$\lim_{A \to 0} \left(\frac{1}{A} \oint_C \mathbf{F} \cdot d\mathbf{r} \right) = \frac{\partial F_2}{\partial x} - \frac{\partial F_1}{\partial y},$$

where the partial derivatives are evaluated at P. You will recognize the right-hand side as the z-component of $\mathbf{curl\,F}$ at P. In other words, we have

$$\lim_{A \to 0} \left(\frac{1}{A} \oint_C \mathbf{F} \cdot d\mathbf{r} \right) = \mathbf{k} \cdot \mathbf{curl\,F}. \qquad (4.1)$$

By considering loops in the (y, z)-plane and in the (z, x)-plane, we can obtain similar relationships for the x- and y-components of $\mathbf{curl\,F}$.

We shall not prove these results for the general case, but ask you to confirm that Equation (4.1) is true in a particular case.

These results are special cases of Stokes' Theorem relating the curl of a vector field to the integral of the field around a closed curve.

Exercise 4.1 _____

Consider the vector field $\mathbf{v} = \omega(-y\mathbf{i} + x\mathbf{j})$, where ω is a positive constant.

(a) Evaluate $\lim_{A \to 0} \left(\frac{1}{A} \oint_C \mathbf{F} \cdot d\mathbf{r} \right)$ for anticlockwise traversal of the circle C of radius a centred on the origin.

The line integral is evaluated in the solution to Exercise 3.7(b).

(b) Evaluate $\mathbf{curl\,v}$ and $\mathbf{k} \cdot \mathbf{curl\,v}$.

It can be shown that if **curl F** = **0** at all points in a vector field then $\oint_C \mathbf{F} \cdot d\mathbf{r}$ must be zero for any closed curve C, and vice versa. You will see later how to make use of this idea, but first we consider how to link line integrals with energy conservation, and the idea of a line integral being independent of the path along which it is evaluated. Suppose a particle can move along paths in the two- or three-dimensional domain of a force field **F**(**r**). In general, a particle may move from one fixed point A to another fixed point B via an infinite number of different paths, and so we might ask: does the work done by the force depend on the particular path taken from A to B? You will see that if the work done by the force is independent of the particular path, then we can define a potential energy function and mechanical energy is conserved.

In fact, we require **curl F** = **0** on some simple region, with no holes in it, before we can show that
$$\oint_C \mathbf{F} \cdot d\mathbf{r} = 0$$
for any closed curve C within the region.

In Example 3.3, we found that the line integral of the vector field $\mathbf{F} = (2x + y)\mathbf{i} - x\mathbf{j}$ on the straight line C_2, from the point $(2, 0)$ to the point $(0, 2)$, has the value -8; but in Exercise 3.2 you found that the line integral of the *same* vector field along the quarter-circle C_1 between the *same* two points $(2, 0)$ and $(0, 2)$ is $-2\pi - 4$. In other words, the value of the line integral of the vector field between the two points depends on the actual path taken between the two points. The line integral of **F** is **path-dependent**. This is not surprising, since different paths between two fixed points will sample different vectors.

In Exercise 3.6, on the other hand, you found that the line integrals of the vector field $\mathbf{G} = x^2\mathbf{i} + y\mathbf{j}$ between the same two points have the same values for each of the two paths C_1 and C_2. In fact, the line integral of **G** between *any* two fixed points has the same value for *any* path between those two points. The line integral of **G** is **path-independent** and depends only on the starting point and endpoint of the path.

We now turn to an idea you met in *Unit 23*, that of the gradient vector. Suppose that the line integral of a vector field **F**(**r**) is path-independent. Given an origin O, we can define a scalar function $U(\mathbf{r})$ at every point P with position vector **r** in the domain of **F**, by putting

$$U(\mathbf{r}) = - \int_{OP} \mathbf{F} \cdot d\mathbf{r},$$

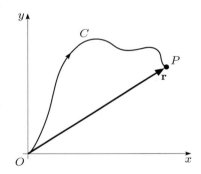

Figure 4.2

where OP is *any* path C from the origin O to P (see Figure 4.2) and the minus sign is a conventional choice consistent with U being a potential energy when **F** is a force field. Then, for any two points A and B in the field,

$$\int_{AB} \mathbf{F} \cdot d\mathbf{r} = \int_{OB} \mathbf{F} \cdot d\mathbf{r} - \int_{OA} \mathbf{F} \cdot d\mathbf{r} = -(U(\mathbf{r}_B) - U(\mathbf{r}_A)), \qquad (4.2)$$

where $U(\mathbf{r}_A)$ and $U(\mathbf{r}_B)$ denote the values of U at the points A and B, respectively. The scalar function $U(\mathbf{r})$ is a scalar field called a **potential field** or simply a **potential** of the vector field **F**.

When the vector field **F** is a force acting on a particle, the potential field U is the potential energy of the particle. Note that only differences of potential are defined by Equation (4.2). As in one dimension, we can choose the value of the potential field to be zero at any convenient point (the *datum*). In this case, the datum is the origin O.

The potential energy of a particle was discussed in *Unit 8*.

Example 4.1

A potential of the two-dimensional field $\mathbf{F} = 2x\mathbf{i} - y\mathbf{j}$ is

$$U(\mathbf{r}) = U(x,y) = -(x^2 - \tfrac{1}{2}y^2).$$

Determine the line integral of $\mathbf{F}$ along a path from the origin to the point $(-3, 7)$.

Solution

Using Equation (4.2), the line integral of $\mathbf{F}$ is given by

$$-\left(U(-3,7) - U(0,0)\right) = -(-((-3)^2 - \tfrac{1}{2} \times 7^2) - 0) = -\tfrac{31}{2}. \quad \blacksquare$$

We can show that any scalar field U is a potential of the vector field $-\mathbf{grad}\,U$, by evaluating the line integral $\int_C(-\mathbf{grad}\,U)\cdot d\mathbf{r}$. We use the Cartesian form of $\mathbf{grad}\,U$,

$$\mathbf{grad}\,U = \frac{\partial U}{\partial x}\mathbf{i} + \frac{\partial U}{\partial y}\mathbf{j} + \frac{\partial U}{\partial z}\mathbf{k},$$

in Equation (3.6). Thus

$$\int_C(-\mathbf{grad}\,U)\cdot d\mathbf{r} = -\int_{t_0}^{t_1}\left(\frac{\partial U}{\partial x}\frac{dx}{dt} + \frac{\partial U}{\partial y}\frac{dy}{dt} + \frac{\partial U}{\partial z}\frac{dz}{dt}\right)dt.$$

The integrand is the expression for dU/dt as given by the Chain Rule. So we have

The Chain Rule was discussed in *Unit 12*.

$$\int_C(-\mathbf{grad}\,U)\cdot d\mathbf{r} = -\int_{t_0}^{t_1}\frac{dU}{dt}\,dt = -(U(t_1) - U(t_0)).$$

Notice again the abuse of notation. Since $\mathbf{r} = \mathbf{r}(t)$, $U(\mathbf{r})$ becomes $U(t)$.

Comparing this result with Equation (4.2), you can see that the scalar field U is a potential of the vector field $\mathbf{F} = -\mathbf{grad}\,U$. If we now choose a datum at the origin, we have

$$\mathbf{F}(\mathbf{r}) = -\mathbf{grad}\,U \quad \text{and} \quad U(\mathbf{r}) = -\int_{OP}\mathbf{F}\cdot d\mathbf{r}, \tag{4.3}$$

where $\mathbf{r}$ is the position vector of P, any point in space. These statements generalize, to two and three dimensions, the one-dimensional relationships

$$F(x) = -\frac{dU}{dx} \quad \text{and} \quad U(a) = -\int_0^a F(x)\,dx,$$

See *Unit 8*.

where a is any point on the x-axis.

*Exercise 4.2

Given that the line integral of the field $\mathbf{F} = 2xyz\mathbf{i} + x^2z\mathbf{j} + x^2y\mathbf{k}$ is path-independent, find a potential function $U(x,y,z)$ for $\mathbf{F}$.

In Subsection 3.1 we considered the one-dimensional case of a force $F\mathbf{i}$ accelerating a particle along the x-axis, and showed that the work done by the force is equal to the change of kinetic energy of the particle. By combining Equations (3.4) and (4.2) we can see that, when F depends on position x, we are able to express the work done by the force as minus the change of potential energy. Furthermore, Equation (3.2) shows that the work done equals the gain in kinetic energy. Thus for any force $F(x)\mathbf{i}$ that acts parallel to the x-axis and depends only on position x, the total mechanical energy is conserved.

Compare the discussion in *Unit 8*.

We now have several links between line integrals of a force **F**, path independence, the curl of **F**, a potential for **F** and conservation of mechanical energy. So in the next subsection we tie all these ideas together with the various definitions of a conservative vector field.

4.2   Conservative vector fields

We classify vector fields according to whether their line integrals are path-dependent or path-independent. Those vector fields for which *all* the line integrals between *all* pairs of points are path-independent are called **conservative fields**. If there is at least one pair of points for which the line integrals of the vector field are path-dependent, then the vector field is *non-conservative*.

Conservative fields: Property (a)

The line integral of a conservative vector field along a path between any two fixed points A and B depends only on the starting point A and the endpoint B of the path. It is independent of the actual path taken between the two points.

Note that in one dimension, where the particle is restricted to the x-axis, the only possibility for varying the path between two fixed points $x = a$ and $x = b$ is when the particle overshoots into the regions $x > b$ or $x < a$ (see Figure 3.1). But then the particle always has to reverse back through these regions to reach $x = a$ or $x = b$ and so the net contribution to the line integral from these forward and reverse motions vanishes. So all one-dimensional vector fields $F(x)\mathbf{i}$ that depend only on position x are conservative.

It follows from the above property that if you are asked to evaluate the line integral of a conservative field between any two given points then you are free to choose the path that produces the simplest possible evaluation.

Example 4.2

Given that the vector field $\mathbf{F} = 2x\mathbf{i} - y\mathbf{j}$ is a conservative field, evaluate the line integral of **F** from the origin to the point $(2, 0)$.

This field was considered in Example 4.1.

Solution

We are free to choose the path for a conservative field. The simplest path to take is the segment of the x-axis from $x = 0$ to $x = 2$. This path can be parametrized by

$$x = t, \quad y = 0, \quad (0 \le t \le 2),$$

and so $dx/dt = 1$ and $dy/dt = 0$. The components of **F** on the path are $F_1 = 2x = 2t$ and $F_2 = -y = 0$, so

$$\int_C \mathbf{F} \cdot d\mathbf{r} = \int_0^2 2t\, dt = 4. \quad \blacksquare$$

The line integral of a conservative field around any closed curve is zero. To see this, consider the loop in Figure 4.3. The two points A and B divide the loop into two segments, an upper segment APB and a lower segment AQB. We know that the line integral of any conservative field $\mathbf{F}$ from A to B has the same value for both segments, i.e.

$$\int_{APB} \mathbf{F} \cdot d\mathbf{r} = \int_{AQB} \mathbf{F} \cdot d\mathbf{r}.$$

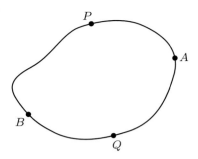

Figure 4.3

Now the line integral for one complete anticlockwise traversal of the loop, starting and ending at A, consists of the line integral along APB plus that along BQA,

$$\oint_{APBQA} \mathbf{F} \cdot d\mathbf{r} = \int_{APB} \mathbf{F} \cdot d\mathbf{r} + \int_{BQA} \mathbf{F} \cdot d\mathbf{r}.$$

But we know from Equation (3.8) that

$$\int_{BQA} \mathbf{F} \cdot d\mathbf{r} = - \int_{AQB} \mathbf{F} \cdot d\mathbf{r}.$$

Hence

$$\oint_{APBQA} \mathbf{F} \cdot d\mathbf{r} = 0.$$

A similar argument applies to any other loop in the domain of $\mathbf{F}$.

This gives us another important property of a conservative field.

Conservative fields: Property (b)

The line integral of any conservative field $\mathbf{F}$ around *any* closed curve C is zero,

$$\oint_C \mathbf{F} \cdot d\mathbf{r} = 0. \tag{4.4}$$

Note that the line integral of a conservative field must be zero for *all possible loops* in its domain. If just one loop has a non-zero line integral, that is sufficient to make the field non-conservative.

*****Exercise 4.3*** _____

State which of the two vector fields $\mathbf{u}$ and $\mathbf{v}$ in Exercise 3.7 is definitely non-conservative.

_____

How can we tell whether or not a given vector field is conservative? To use Property (a) we should need to know that all the line integrals between all possible pairs of fixed points are path-independent. It's obviously not practicable to evaluate all possible line integrals. Alternatively, we could think of using Property (b), but this would seem to require us to evaluate the line integrals around all possible loops! What we need is a simple test for a conservative field. What about the result involving curl that we illustrated via Equation (4.1)? Let's see how this relates to conservative fields. We know that all line integrals around closed loops are zero if $\mathbf{F}$ is a conservative field.

Hence, from Equation (4.1) and the corresponding x- and y-components, **curl F** must be zero for any conservative field.

Conservative fields: Property (c)

If **F** is a conservative field then **curl F = 0**.   (4.5)

Property (c) holds for all conservative fields, but it doesn't provide us with a sufficient test for conservative fields. Perhaps there are vector fields **F** with **curl F = 0** that are non-conservative? However, it can be shown that the converse of Equation (4.5) is also true.

Curl test for a conservative field

If **curl F = 0** then **F** is a conservative field (provided the domain of **F** is simple).

We shall not prove this statement or define what is meant by the domain being 'simple', beyond showing an example (in Exercise 4.8) where the curl test fails. For all other cases in this course you may assume that the curl test is a sufficient test for a conservative field.

We can use the curl test to show that if $\mathbf{F} = -\mathbf{grad}\,U$ for some scalar field U, then **F** is a conservative field. This follows from Exercise 2.1(d) where you found that $\mathbf{curl}(\mathbf{grad}\,U) \equiv \mathbf{0}$ for any scalar field U.

Conservative fields: Property (d)

Any vector field that is a gradient, is conservative. Conversely, any conservative vector field can be expressed as a gradient of a scalar field.

Using Equation (4.3) we can express this last property in terms of potentials.

Conservative fields: Property (e)

For a conservative field **F** and fixed origin O (the datum), there exists a unique potential field defined by $U(\mathbf{r}) = -\int_{OP} \mathbf{F} \cdot d\mathbf{r}$ with $\mathbf{F} = -\mathbf{grad}\,U$, where $\overrightarrow{OP} = \mathbf{r}$.

For a different datum, the potential field will differ from U by a constant.

Property (e) tells us that we can determine line integrals of a conservative field simply by finding its corresponding potential field and using Equation (4.2), as we did in Example 4.1. What is more, Property (e) combined with Equation (3.2) shows that mechanical energy, being the sum of kinetic and potential energies, is conserved when a particle is acted upon by a conservative force field.

*Exercise 4.4

(a) Use the curl test to determine which of the following vector fields are conservative.

$$\mathbf{h} = x\mathbf{i} + y\mathbf{j}$$

$$\mathbf{u} = \omega(-y\mathbf{i} + x\mathbf{j}), \text{ where } \omega \text{ is a positive constant}$$

$$\mathbf{F} = 2x\mathbf{i} + (xz - 2)\mathbf{j} + xy\mathbf{k}$$

(b) Show that $\mathbf{curl}\,\mathbf{G} = \mathbf{0}$ for $\mathbf{G} = kr^n\widehat{\mathbf{r}}$, where k and n are non-zero constants, $\mathbf{r} = x\mathbf{i} + y\mathbf{j} + z\mathbf{k}$, $r = |\mathbf{r}|$ and $\widehat{\mathbf{r}} = \mathbf{r}/r$ $(r \neq 0)$.

The vector field $\mathbf{G}$ (for any n or k) in Exercise 4.4(b) is directed radially, directly towards or away from the origin depending on the sign of the constant k. Such fields are called **central fields**. You have found that $\mathbf{curl}\,\mathbf{G} = \mathbf{0}$ and, though the domain of $\mathbf{G}$ is not simple if $n < 0$ (since $\mathbf{G}$ cannot be defined at the origin), it can be shown that all central fields are conservative. For example, the force of gravity near a large spherical object such as a planet or a star is always directed towards the centre of the sphere. Thus the force of gravity is a central field and is therefore conservative. We can use the law of conservation of mechanical energy for conservative forces for any problem involving gravitational forces only; for example, the motion of planets around the Sun or the motion of artificial Earth satellites.

We can express the law of conservation of mechanical energy as

$$\tfrac{1}{2}mv_B^2 - \tfrac{1}{2}mv_A^2 = U(\mathbf{r}_A) - U(\mathbf{r}_B), \tag{4.6}$$

This equation is a combination of Equations (4.2) and (3.2).

where the left-hand side is the change in kinetic energy when the body moves from A to B, with position vectors $\mathbf{r}_A$ and $\mathbf{r}_B$, and the right-hand side is minus the change in potential energy.

Exercise 4.5

The gravitational potential energy field of a body of mass m in the vicinity of the Earth is given by

$$U(\mathbf{r}) = mgR\left(1 - \frac{R}{|\mathbf{r}|}\right) \quad (|\mathbf{r}| \geq R),$$

where the position vector $\mathbf{r}$ of the body is measured from the centre of the Earth, g is the magnitude of the acceleration due to gravity at the Earth's surface, R is the Earth's radius and the datum is on the Earth's surface. Derive an expression for the Earth's gravitational force $\mathbf{F}(\mathbf{r})$ on the body.

Example 4.3

An Earth satellite moves in an elliptical orbit with its nearest and furthest points from the Earth's surface being $\tfrac{1}{2}R$ and $2R$ where R is the Earth's radius. If its slowest speed is u, find its fastest speed. Assume that the only force acting on the satellite is the Earth's gravity.

Solution

Gravity is a conservative field and so mechanical energy is conserved throughout the motion of the satellite. The potential energy function U is given in Exercise 4.5. We can use the law of conservation of mechanical energy, Equation (4.6), with A the furthest point of the satellite, $|\mathbf{r}_A| = 3R$, and B the nearest point, $|\mathbf{r}_B| = \frac{3}{2}R$, measured from the centre of the Earth. Then the speed at A is given, $v_A = u$, and we need to find v_B, the speed at B. Thus

$$\tfrac{1}{2}mv_B^2 - \tfrac{1}{2}mu^2 = U(\mathbf{r}_A) - U(\mathbf{r}_B)$$
$$= mgR\left(\left(1 - \frac{R}{3R}\right) - \left(1 - \frac{2R}{3R}\right)\right)$$
$$= \tfrac{1}{3}mgR.$$

Hence the fastest speed is $v_B = \sqrt{u^2 + 2gR/3}$. ■

All central fields are conservative, but not all conservative fields are central fields. Consider, for example, the two-dimensional vector field $\mathbf{F}(\mathbf{r}) = -2px\mathbf{i} - py\mathbf{j}$, where p is a constant. The vector $\mathbf{F}(\mathbf{r})$ at any point is not, in general, parallel to the position vector $\mathbf{r} = x\mathbf{i} + y\mathbf{j}$ at that point, and so the field is not a central field. However, this vector field is conservative, as you can confirm in the next exercise.

*Exercise 4.6

The force acting on a particle is given by $\mathbf{F} = -2px\mathbf{i} - py\mathbf{j}$, where p is a constant.

(a) Show that the force is a conservative field.

(b) Confirm that $U(x, y) = p(x^2 + \frac{1}{2}y^2)$ is a potential energy function for $\mathbf{F}$, and hence find the work done by the force, in terms of p, when the particle moves from $(5, 0)$ to $(0, 5)$.

Finally, it is useful to gather together the properties of conservative fields:

Properties of conservative fields

Let $\mathbf{F}$ be a conservative vector field.

(a) All line integrals of $\mathbf{F}$ between any two fixed points in the domain are path-independent.

(b) The line integrals of $\mathbf{F}$ around all closed curves in the domain are zero.

(c) The curl of $\mathbf{F}$ is zero everywhere in the domain.

(d) All gradient fields are conservative and all conservative vector fields can be expressed as the gradient of a scalar field.

(e) For a fixed origin O (the datum), there exists a unique potential field defined by $U(\mathbf{r}) = -\int_{OP} \mathbf{F} \cdot d\mathbf{r}$ with $\mathbf{F} = -\mathbf{grad}\, U$, where $\overrightarrow{OP} = \mathbf{r}$.

We have taken statement (a) as the definition of a conservative field, but statements (b) and (e) are entirely equivalent to statement (a) and may alternatively be taken as the definition. Statement (c) is also equivalent to each of statements (a), (b) and (e) (whenever the domain of $\mathbf{F}$ is simple).

End-of-section Exercises

Exercise 4.7

Show that any vector field of the form $\mathbf{F} = f(x)\mathbf{i} + g(y)\mathbf{j}$, where f is a function of x only and g is a function of y only, is a conservative field. Can a vector field of the form $\mathbf{H} = g(y)\mathbf{i} + f(x)\mathbf{j}$ be conservative?

Exercise 4.8

Consider the two-dimensional vector field

$$\mathbf{B}(x, y) = k(-y\mathbf{i} + x\mathbf{j})/(x^2 + y^2) \quad (x^2 + y^2 > 0),$$

where k is a constant.

(a) Show that $\oint_C \mathbf{B} \cdot d\mathbf{r} = 2\pi k$, where C is a circle of radius a with centre at the origin.

(b) Show that $\mathbf{curl}\,\mathbf{B} = \mathbf{0}$.

Outcomes

After studying this unit you should be able to:

- calculate the divergence of a vector field;
- calculate the curl of a vector field;
- use gradient, divergence and curl to model simple laws and problems involving slopes along paths in scalar fields, heat flow, fluid flow, and local rotation in a vector field.
- evaluate scalar line integrals of vector fields using given parametrizations;
- solve simple problems in one, two and three dimensions involving changes of kinetic energy and potential energy and the work done by a force;
- use the curl test for identifying conservative fields.

Solutions to the exercises

Section 1

1.1 The components of $\mathbf{F}$ are
$$F_1 = xy, \quad F_2 = 0, \quad F_3 = -yz.$$
The relevant partial derivatives are
$$\frac{\partial F_1}{\partial x} = y, \quad \frac{\partial F_2}{\partial y} = 0, \quad \frac{\partial F_3}{\partial z} = -y.$$
Hence div $\mathbf{F} = y + 0 + (-y) = 0$, and so div $\mathbf{F}(3, -1, 2) = 0$.
(The scalar field div $\mathbf{F} = 0$ everywhere.)

1.2 The position vector in Cartesian coordinates is $\mathbf{r} = x\mathbf{i} + y\mathbf{j} + z\mathbf{k}$, so
$$\widehat{\mathbf{r}} = \frac{x\mathbf{i} + y\mathbf{j} + z\mathbf{k}}{\sqrt{x^2 + y^2 + z^2}},$$
$$\mathbf{F}(x, y, z) = \frac{x\mathbf{i} + y\mathbf{j} + z\mathbf{k}}{(x^2 + y^2 + z^2)^{(n+1)/2}}.$$
The x-component is $F_1 = x(x^2 + y^2 + z^2)^{-(n+1)/2}$ and
$$\frac{\partial F_1}{\partial x} =$$
$$\frac{(x^2+y^2+z^2)^{(n+1)/2} - x^2(n+1)(x^2+y^2+z^2)^{(n-1)/2}}{(x^2+y^2+z^2)^{n+1}}.$$
The component F_2 and the partial derivative $\partial F_2/\partial y$ are obtained from F_1 and $\partial F_1/\partial x$ by replacing x by y. Similarly, F_3 and $\partial F_3/\partial z$ are obtained by replacing x by z. When this is done, we obtain div $\mathbf{F} =$

$$\frac{3(x^2+y^2+z^2)^{(n+1)/2} - (x^2+y^2+z^2)(n+1)(x^2+y^2+z^2)^{(n-1)/2}}{(x^2+y^2+z^2)^{n+1}}$$
$$= \frac{(3 - (n+1))(x^2+y^2+z^2)^{(n+1)/2}}{(x^2+y^2+z^2)^{n+1}}$$
$$= \frac{2 - n}{(x^2+y^2+z^2)^{(n+1)/2}} \text{ which is zero everywhere only}$$

when $n = 2$. Hence div $\mathbf{F} = 0$ everywhere only when $n = 2$.

1.3 We have
$$\mathbf{e}_\theta = -\sin\theta\,\mathbf{i} + \cos\theta\,\mathbf{j}$$
so that
$$\frac{\partial \mathbf{e}_\theta}{\partial \theta} = -\cos\theta\,\mathbf{i} - \sin\theta\,\mathbf{j} = -\mathbf{e}_\rho.$$

1.4 The heat flow vector field $\mathbf{J}$ has cylindrical symmetry. Anywhere on the outer surface, $\mathbf{J}$ is directed radially outwards and has a magnitude of $2 \times 10^6 \times 0.02$ $= 4 \times 10^4\,\mathrm{W\,m^{-2}}$.

The total surface area of a $1\,\mathrm{m}$ length of rod is $2\pi \times 0.02 \times 1 = 4\pi \times 10^{-2}\,\mathrm{m^2}$. Hence the total outward heat flow rate from a $1\,\mathrm{m}$ length is given by $(4 \times 10^4) \times (4\pi \times 10^{-2}) = 1600\pi\,\mathrm{W}$. This is also the rate of heat generated in the $1\,\mathrm{m}$ length, since the heat flow is steady. Alternatively,
$$S \times \text{volume} = (4 \times 10^6) \times \pi(0.02)^2 \times 1$$
$$= 1600\pi\,\mathrm{W}.$$

1.5 **(a)** The components of $\mathbf{H}$ are (in $\mathrm{W\,m^{-2}}$)
$$H_1 = H_2 = 0, \quad H_3 = 5000,$$
so that
$$\frac{\partial H_1}{\partial x} = \frac{\partial H_2}{\partial y} = \frac{\partial H_3}{\partial z} = 0.$$
Thus div $\mathbf{H} = 0$.

(b) The only non-zero component of $\mathbf{H}$ is $H_3 = 5000e^{-\alpha z}$, so
$$\frac{\partial H_1}{\partial x} = \frac{\partial H_2}{\partial y} = 0, \quad \frac{\partial H_3}{\partial z} = 5000(-\alpha)e^{-\alpha z}.$$
Hence div $\mathbf{H} = -5000\alpha e^{-\alpha z}$.

1.6 The only non-zero component of $\mathbf{f}$ is $f_\rho = \rho^{-n}$, so $\partial f_\rho/\partial\rho = -n\rho^{-(n+1)}$. From Equation (1.2), we obtain
$$\text{div}\,\mathbf{f} = \frac{-n}{\rho^{n+1}} + \left(\frac{1}{\rho}\right)\left(\frac{1}{\rho^n}\right) = \frac{1-n}{\rho^{n+1}}.$$
This is zero everywhere only when $n = 1$.

1.7 The components of $\mathbf{F}$ are $F_1 = xy$, $F_2 = yz$ and $F_3 = zx$, so that
$$\frac{\partial F_1}{\partial x} = y, \quad \frac{\partial F_2}{\partial y} = z, \quad \frac{\partial F_3}{\partial z} = x.$$
Thus $\boldsymbol{\nabla} \cdot \mathbf{F}\,(= \text{div}\,\mathbf{F}) = y + z + x$. The divergence at $(1, 2, 3)$ is $\boldsymbol{\nabla} \cdot \mathbf{F}(1, 2, 3) = 2 + 3 + 1 = 6$.

1.8 **(a)** In cylindrical polar coordinates, $\rho = \sqrt{x^2 + y^2}$ and $\mathbf{e}_\rho = (x\mathbf{i} + y\mathbf{j})/\sqrt{x^2 + y^2}$. Hence $\mathbf{J}(\rho, \theta, z) = A\rho\mathbf{e}_\rho$, and the cylindrical polar components of $\mathbf{J}$ are $J_\rho = A\rho$, $J_\theta = J_z = 0$. The only non-zero partial derivative is $\partial J_\rho/\partial\rho = A$. Hence, using Equation (1.2), we have div $\mathbf{J} = A + \left(\frac{1}{\rho}\right)(A\rho) = 2A$, which is in agreement with the result of Example 1.3.

(b) In spherical polar coordinates, $\mathbf{r} = r\mathbf{e}_r$. Hence, using Equation (1.3),
$$\text{div}\,\mathbf{r} = \frac{\partial r}{\partial r} + \frac{2r}{r} = 3.$$

1.9 We have
$$\text{div}\,\mathbf{F} = 0 + 0 + 0 = 0,$$
$$\text{div}\,\mathbf{G} = 2x + 2y + 2z,$$
$$\text{div}\,\mathbf{H} = 1 + 1 - 2 = 0.$$
So $\mathbf{F}$ and $\mathbf{H}$ could be magnetic fields, but $\mathbf{G}$ could not, since the divergence of a magnetic field is always zero.

Section 2

2.1 (a) The components of $\mathbf{F} = \mathbf{r} = x\mathbf{i} + y\mathbf{j} + z\mathbf{k}$ are
$$F_1 = x, \quad F_2 = y, \quad F_3 = z,$$
so that
$$\frac{\partial F_1}{\partial z} = \frac{\partial F_1}{\partial y} = \frac{\partial F_2}{\partial z} = \frac{\partial F_2}{\partial x} = \frac{\partial F_3}{\partial y} = \frac{\partial F_3}{\partial x} = 0.$$
Hence, substituting into Equation (2.1),
$$\mathbf{curl\, F} = \mathbf{0}.$$

(b) The components of $\mathbf{F} = f(r)\hat{\mathbf{r}} = (f(r)/r)\mathbf{r}$ are
$$F_1 = f(r)\frac{x}{r}, \quad F_2 = f(r)\frac{y}{r}, \quad F_3 = f(r)\frac{z}{r}.$$
The x-component of $\mathbf{curl\, F}$ (using the Chain Rule) is
$$\frac{\partial F_3}{\partial y} - \frac{\partial F_2}{\partial z} = z\frac{d}{dr}\left(\frac{f(r)}{r}\right)\frac{\partial r}{\partial y} - y\frac{d}{dr}\left(\frac{f(r)}{r}\right)\frac{\partial r}{\partial z}$$
$$= z\frac{d}{dr}\left(\frac{f(r)}{r}\right)\frac{y}{r} - y\frac{d}{dr}\left(\frac{f(r)}{r}\right)\frac{z}{r} = 0.$$
Similarly, the y- and z-components of $\mathbf{curl\, F}$ are zero, so $\mathbf{curl}\,(f(r)\hat{\mathbf{r}}) = \mathbf{0}$ for all functions f of r only.

(c) We have
$$\mathbf{F} = (y^2 + 2z)\mathbf{i} + (xy + 6z)\mathbf{j} + (z^2 + 2xz + y)\mathbf{k},$$
so the x-, y- and z-components of $\mathbf{curl\, F}$ are
$$\frac{\partial F_3}{\partial y} - \frac{\partial F_2}{\partial z} = 1 - 6 = -5,$$
$$\frac{\partial F_1}{\partial z} - \frac{\partial F_3}{\partial x} = 2 - 2z = 2(1 - z),$$
$$\frac{\partial F_2}{\partial x} - \frac{\partial F_1}{\partial y} = y - 2y = -y,$$
so $\mathbf{curl\, F} = -5\mathbf{i} + 2(1 - z)\mathbf{j} - y\mathbf{k}$.

(d) Since $\mathbf{F} = \mathbf{grad}\, f = \frac{\partial f}{\partial x}\mathbf{i} + \frac{\partial f}{\partial y}\mathbf{j} + \frac{\partial f}{\partial z}\mathbf{k}$, we have
$$\frac{\partial F_3}{\partial y} - \frac{\partial F_2}{\partial z} = \frac{\partial}{\partial y}\left(\frac{\partial f}{\partial z}\right) - \frac{\partial}{\partial z}\left(\frac{\partial f}{\partial y}\right)$$
$$= \frac{\partial^2 f}{\partial y \partial z} - \frac{\partial^2 f}{\partial z \partial y} = 0.$$
Similarly, the y- and z-components are zero. Hence $\mathbf{curl}(\mathbf{grad}\, f) \equiv \mathbf{0}$.

2.2 Any vector field having zero curl everywhere is a conservative field. Fields (a), (b) and (d) of Exercise 2.1 and field (a)(i) of Example 2.1 are conservative.

2.3 Both $\mathbf{u}$ and $\mathbf{v}$ are two-dimensional fields in the (x, y)-plane.
For the field $\mathbf{u}$, $u_1 = -\omega y$ and $u_2 = \omega x$, so
$$\frac{\partial u_2}{\partial x} = \omega, \quad \frac{\partial u_1}{\partial y} = -\omega.$$
Hence $\mathbf{curl\, u} = \left(\frac{\partial u_2}{\partial x} - \frac{\partial u_1}{\partial y}\right)\mathbf{k} = 2\omega\mathbf{k}$.

For the field $\mathbf{v}$, $v_1 = -\dfrac{\omega a^2 y}{x^2 + y^2}$ and $v_2 = \dfrac{\omega a^2 x}{x^2 + y^2}$, so
$$\frac{\partial v_2}{\partial x} = \frac{(x^2 + y^2)\omega a^2 - \omega a^2 x(2x)}{(x^2 + y^2)^2} = \frac{\omega a^2(y^2 - x^2)}{(x^2 + y^2)^2},$$
$$\frac{\partial v_1}{\partial y} = \frac{(x^2 + y^2)(-\omega a^2) + \omega a^2 y(2y)}{(x^2 + y^2)^2} = \frac{\omega a^2(y^2 - x^2)}{(x^2 + y^2)^2}.$$

Hence $\mathbf{curl\, v} = \left(\dfrac{\partial v_2}{\partial x} - \dfrac{\partial v_1}{\partial y}\right)\mathbf{k} = \mathbf{0}$.
Note that at the boundary, $\mathbf{curl\, u} \neq \mathbf{curl\, v}$.

2.4 In cylindrical polar coordinates we have
$$x = \rho\cos\theta, \qquad y = \rho\sin\theta.$$
Hence
$$\mathbf{u}(\rho, \theta, z) = -\rho\omega\sin\theta\,\mathbf{i} + \rho\omega\cos\theta\,\mathbf{j} = \omega\rho\mathbf{e}_\theta \quad (\rho \leq a),$$
and, since $x^2 + y^2 = \rho^2$,
$$\mathbf{v}(\rho, \theta, z) = \frac{\omega a^2}{\rho}\mathbf{e}_\theta \quad (\rho \geq a).$$
The vector field lines of $\mathbf{u}$ and $\mathbf{v}$ are circles.

2.5 The components of
$$\mathbf{F}(x, y, z) = x(y - z)\mathbf{i} + 3x^2\mathbf{j} + yz\mathbf{k}$$
are $F_1 = x(y - z)$, $F_2 = 3x^2$ and $F_3 = yz$.
The partial derivatives required for substitution in Equation (2.1) are
$$\frac{\partial F_3}{\partial y} = z, \quad \frac{\partial F_2}{\partial z} = 0, \quad \frac{\partial F_1}{\partial z} = -x,$$
$$\frac{\partial F_3}{\partial x} = 0, \quad \frac{\partial F_2}{\partial x} = 6x, \quad \frac{\partial F_1}{\partial y} = x.$$
Hence, using Equation (2.1),
$$\mathbf{curl\, F} = z\mathbf{i} - x\mathbf{j} + 5x\mathbf{k}.$$

(a) At the origin, $\mathbf{curl\, F} = \mathbf{0}$.

(b) At $(1, 2, 3)$, $\mathbf{curl\, F} = 3\mathbf{i} - \mathbf{j} + 5\mathbf{k}$.

(c) At $(0, 0, 5)$, $\mathbf{curl\, F} = 5\mathbf{i}$.

2.6 (a) We have $\mathbf{v} = \boldsymbol{\omega} \times \mathbf{r}$, where $\boldsymbol{\omega} = \omega\mathbf{k}$. Using a Cartesian coordinate system with the z-axis lying on the axis of the Earth's rotation and in the direction of the angular velocity, we have
$$\boldsymbol{\omega} = \omega\mathbf{k}, \quad \mathbf{r} = x\mathbf{i} + y\mathbf{j} + z\mathbf{k}.$$
Hence $\mathbf{v}(x, y, z) = \omega\mathbf{k} \times (x\mathbf{i} + y\mathbf{j} + z\mathbf{k}) = \omega(x\mathbf{j} - y\mathbf{i})$.

(b) Now $v_1 = -\omega y$, $v_2 = \omega x$ and $v_3 = 0$, so
$$\mathbf{curl\, v} = \left(\frac{\partial}{\partial x}(\omega x) - \frac{\partial}{\partial y}(-\omega y)\right)\mathbf{k} = 2\omega\mathbf{k} = 2\boldsymbol{\omega}.$$
Hence
$$|\mathbf{curl\, v}| = 2\omega = 2 \times \frac{2\pi}{24 \times 60 \times 60}$$
$$= 1.454 \times 10^{-4}\text{ rad s}^{-1}.$$

(c) Every object fixed on the Earth rotates with angular velocity $\boldsymbol{\omega}$. The rate of rotation is
$$\tfrac{1}{2}\mathbf{curl\, v} = 7.272 \times 10^{-5}\text{ rad s}^{-1}.$$

2.7 The field $\mathbf{F}$ is confined to the (x, y)-plane, so
$$\mathbf{curl\, F} = \left(\frac{\partial}{\partial x}(g(y)) - \frac{\partial}{\partial y}(f(x))\right)\mathbf{k} = \mathbf{0}.$$

Section 3

3.1 The work done is

$$W = -A \int_3^1 \frac{1}{x^2}\, dx = -A \left[-\frac{1}{x}\right]_3^1 = A\left(\frac{1}{1} - \frac{1}{3}\right) = \frac{2}{3}A.$$

The change in kinetic energy is $\frac{2}{3}A$,

and so $\frac{1}{2}mv^2 - \frac{1}{2}mu^2 = \frac{2}{3}A$ and $v = \left(\frac{4}{3}(A/m) + u^2\right)^{1/2}$.

3.2 We have $dx/dt = -2\sin t$, $dy/dt = 2\cos t$;
$F_1 = 2x + y = 4\cos t + 2\sin t$, $F_2 = -x = -2\cos t$.
Hence

$$\int_{C_1} \mathbf{F} \cdot d\mathbf{r} = \int_0^{\pi/2} [(4\cos t + 2\sin t)(-2\sin t)$$
$$+ (-2\cos t)2\cos t]\, dt$$
$$= \int_0^{\pi/2} (-4\sin(2t) - 4)\, dt$$
$$= [2\cos(2t) - 4t]_0^{\pi/2} = -4 - 2\pi.$$

3.3 Put $x = t$. Then $y = 1 - t^2$, with t going from 1 to 0. The components of the vector field $\mathbf{F}$ are $F_1 = x^2 = t^2$ and $F_2 = xy = t(1 - t^2)$. The derivatives are $dx/dt = 1$ and $dy/dt = -2t$. Hence

$$\int_C \mathbf{F} \cdot d\mathbf{r} = \int_1^0 (t^2 - 2t^2(1 - t^2))\, dt = -\frac{1}{15}.$$

3.4 There are an infinite number of paths between the points $(0, 0, 0)$ and $(1, 1, 1)$, so we choose two examples. The first moves from the origin along the x-axis to $(1, 0, 0)$, then parallel to the y-axis to $(1, 1, 0)$ and finally parallel to the z-axis to $(1, 1, 1)$. We can parametrize this as

$$\mathbf{r}(t) = \begin{cases} t\mathbf{i} & 0 \le t \le 1 \\ \mathbf{i} + (t-1)\mathbf{j} & 1 \le t \le 2 \\ \mathbf{i} + \mathbf{j} + (t-2)\mathbf{k} & 2 \le t \le 3. \end{cases}$$

Another alternative is the straight line joining the two points, which can be parametrized much more easily as

$$\mathbf{r}(t) = t\mathbf{i} + t\mathbf{j} + t\mathbf{k} \quad (0 \le t \le 1).$$

3.5 With $x = 2(1 - t)$, $y = 2t$ and $z = 0$, we have $dx/dt = -2$, $dy/dt = 2$, $dz/dt = 0$, and $F_1 = 2x + y = 4 - 2t$, $F_2 = -x = -2(1 - t)$. Hence

$$\int_{C_2} \mathbf{F} \cdot d\mathbf{r} = \int_0^1 ((4 - 2t)(-2) - 2(1 - t)2)\, dt$$
$$= \int_0^1 (8t - 12)\, dt = -8,$$

which is the same value as that found in Example 3.3.

3.6 C_1 is parametrized by $x = 2\cos t$, $y = 2\sin t$. Thus $dx/dt = -2\sin t$, $dy/dt = 2\cos t$.
$G_1 = x^2 = 4\cos^2 t$, $G_2 = y = 2\sin t$. Hence

$$\int_{C_1} \mathbf{G} \cdot d\mathbf{r} = \int_0^{\pi/2} [(4\cos^2 t)(-2\sin t) + 2\sin t(2\cos t)]\, dt$$
$$= \int_0^{\pi/2} (-8\cos^2 t \sin t + 2\sin(2t))\, dt$$
$$= [\tfrac{8}{3}\cos^3 t - \cos(2t)]_0^{\pi/2} = -\frac{2}{3}.$$

C_2 is parametrized by $x = t$, $y = 2 - t$. Thus we have $dx/dt = 1$, $dy/dt = -1$. $G_1 = x^2 = t^2$, $G_2 = y = 2 - t$.
Thus $\displaystyle\int_{C_2} \mathbf{G} \cdot d\mathbf{r} = \int_2^0 [t^2 + (2 - t)(-1)]\, dt = -\frac{2}{3}$.
The closed curve $APBQA$ is the path C_1 plus the reverse of path C_2. Hence the line integral of $\mathbf{G}$ along the closed curve $APBQA$ is $-\frac{2}{3} - (-\frac{2}{3}) = 0$.

3.7 (a) $\displaystyle\oint_C \mathbf{u} \cdot d\mathbf{r} = \int_0^{2\pi} ((a\cos t/a^2)(-a\sin t)$
$$+ (a\sin t/a^2)(a\cos t))\, dt = 0.$$

(b) $\displaystyle\oint_C \mathbf{v} \cdot d\mathbf{r} = \omega \int_0^{2\pi} ((-a\sin t)(-a\sin t)$
$$+ (a\cos t)(a\cos t))\, dt = 2\omega\pi a^2.$$

3.8 The x-axis is the line $y = 0$, and so the vector field $\mathbf{v}$ on the x-axis is $\mathbf{v} = \omega x\mathbf{j}$, which has no component along the x-axis. So the tangential component of $\mathbf{v}$ along the line is zero. Thus the scalar line integral along the line segment on the x-axis is zero.

3.9 We have

$$\mathbf{r}(t) = t\,\mathbf{i} - \ln\cos t\,\mathbf{j},$$

so that

$$\dot{\mathbf{r}}(t) = \mathbf{i} + \tan t\,\mathbf{j}.$$

Thus the required length is given by

$$\int_0^{\pi/4} \sqrt{1 + \tan^2 t}\, dt = \int_0^{\pi/4} \sec t\, dt$$
$$= [\ln(\sec t + \tan t)]_0^{\pi/4}$$
$$= \ln(\sqrt{2} + 1) - \ln(1)$$
$$= \ln(\sqrt{2} + 1).$$

In practice, although Equation (3.9) is a very useful formula, the actual computations can involve complicated integrals. (This is often a task for which the computer algebra package can be used.)

3.10 $x = t$, $y = t^2$, $z = t^3$; $t_0 = 0$, $t_1 = 1$;
$F_1 = 2t$, $F_2 = t^4 - 2$, $F_3 = t^3$;
$dx/dt = 1$, $dy/dt = 2t$, $dz/dt = 3t^2$;

$$\int_C \mathbf{F} \cdot d\mathbf{r} = \int_0^1 (5t^5 - 2t)\, dt = -\frac{1}{6}.$$

3.11 In these examples, the component of the vector field $\mathbf{F}$ in the direction tangential to the curve is constant.

(a) The curve C here is a segment of the x-axis, on which $\mathbf{i} \cdot \mathbf{F} = 0$, and so the line integral is zero.

(b) Here the curve C is a segment of the z-axis, on which $\mathbf{k} \cdot \mathbf{F} = 5$, a constant, and so the line integral is $5 \times (6 - 0) = 30$.

(c) The tangential component of $\mathbf{F}$ on the semicircle is $\mathbf{e}_\theta \cdot \mathbf{F}(3, \theta) = 3^2 = 9$, a constant, and so the line integral is $9 \times 3\pi = 27\pi$.

3.12 Let $x = t$ and $y = 1 - t^2$. Then $dx/dt = 1$ and $dy/dt = -2t$. The components of the vector field $\mathbf{F}$ are

$$F_1 = x^2 = t^2 \quad \text{and} \quad F_2 = xy = t(1 - t^2).$$

The starting and endpoints of the curve are specified by $t = 1$ and $t = 0$, respectively. Hence

$$\int_C \mathbf{F} \cdot d\mathbf{r} = \int_1^0 (t^2 - 2t^2(1 - t^2))\, dt = -\tfrac{1}{15}.$$

Section 4

4.1 (a) The line integral was found in the solution to Exercise 3.7(b) to have the value $2\omega\pi a^2$. The area of the circle is πa^2, and so the required limit is $2\omega\pi a^2/\pi a^2 = 2\omega$.

(b) From Equation (2.1),
$\mathbf{curl\, v} = (\partial(\omega x)/\partial x - \partial(-\omega y)/\partial y)\mathbf{k} = 2\omega\mathbf{k}$, and $\mathbf{k} \cdot \mathbf{curl\, v} = 2\omega$.

4.2 We have $\mathbf{F} = 2xyz\mathbf{i} + x^2z\mathbf{j} + x^2y\mathbf{k}$. Since the line integral is path-independent, take the direct path from $(0, 0, 0)$ to (a, b, c) parametrized by

$$\mathbf{r}(t) = ta\mathbf{i} + tb\mathbf{j} + tc\mathbf{k} \qquad (0 \le t \le 1),$$

so that

$$\frac{d\mathbf{r}}{dt} = a\mathbf{i} + b\mathbf{j} + c\mathbf{k}.$$

Then

$$\int_C \mathbf{F} \cdot d\mathbf{r} = \int_0^1 (2atbtct\mathbf{i} + (at)^2ct\mathbf{j} + (at)^2bt\mathbf{k}) \cdot \frac{d\mathbf{r}}{dt}\, dt$$

$$= \int_0^1 (2a^2bc + a^2bc + a^2bc)t^3\, dt$$

$$= 4a^2bc \left[\frac{t^4}{4} \right]_0^1$$

$$= a^2bc$$

$$= U(0, 0, 0) - U(a, b, c).$$

Setting the datum for the potential energy function at the origin, so that $U(0, 0, 0) = 0$, we can deduce that a potential function for $\mathbf{F}$ is

$$U(x, y, z) = -x^2yz.$$

4.3 The field $\mathbf{v}$ is non-conservative, because its line integral around the closed loop C is non-zero. We cannot yet say from the solution to Exercise 3.7 that the field $\mathbf{u}$ is conservative, since there may be loops on which the line integral of $\mathbf{u}$ is non-zero. (In fact, $\mathbf{u}$ *is* conservative.)

4.4 (a) $\mathbf{curl\, h} = \mathbf{0}$, $\mathbf{curl\, u} = 2\omega\mathbf{k}$, $\mathbf{curl\, F} = -y\mathbf{j} + z\mathbf{k}$. Field $\mathbf{h}$ is conservative and the other two are non-conservative.

(b) The $\mathbf{i}$-component of $\mathbf{curl\, G}$ is $k(n - 1)(zr^{n-2}y/r - yr^{n-2}z/r) = 0$. Similarly the $\mathbf{j}$- and the $\mathbf{k}$-components are zero, and so $\mathbf{curl\, G} = \mathbf{0}$. Alternatively, put $\hat{\mathbf{r}} = \mathbf{e}_r$ and use the expression for curl in spherical polar coordinates given earlier. Since $G_r = kr^n$, $G_\theta = G_\phi = 0$, this gives $\mathbf{curl\, G} = \mathbf{0}$.

4.5 Express $U(\mathbf{r})$ in Cartesian or spherical polar coordinates and use $\mathbf{F} = -\mathbf{grad\,} U$, where the coordinate forms of $\mathbf{grad\,} U$ are given in *Unit 23*. It is easiest to use spherical polar coordinates, since U depends only on the distance $r = |\mathbf{r}|$. (It is a spherically symmetric scalar field.) Thus we have

$$U(r, \theta, \phi) = mgR\left(1 - \frac{R}{r}\right),$$

and

$$\mathbf{grad\,} U = \frac{\partial U}{\partial r}\mathbf{e}_r = \frac{mgR^2}{r^2}\mathbf{e}_r.$$

Thus the gravitational force in spherical polar coordinates is

$$\mathbf{F}(r, \theta, \phi) = -\mathbf{grad\,} U = -\frac{mgR^2}{r^2}\mathbf{e}_r,$$

or in coordinate-free form,

$$\mathbf{F}(\mathbf{r}) = -\frac{mgR^2}{|\mathbf{r}|^2}\hat{\mathbf{r}}.$$

4.6 (a) The field $\mathbf{F}$ is confined to the (x, y)-plane and so

$$\mathbf{curl\, F} = \left(\frac{\partial F_2}{\partial x} - \frac{\partial F_1}{\partial y}\right)\mathbf{k} = \left(\frac{\partial(-py)}{\partial x} - \frac{\partial(-2px)}{\partial y}\right)\mathbf{k}$$

$$= \mathbf{0}.$$

Hence $\mathbf{F}$ is conservative.

(b) $\mathbf{grad\,} U = (\partial U/\partial x)\mathbf{i} + (\partial U/\partial y)\mathbf{j} = 2px\mathbf{i} + py\mathbf{j}$. Hence $\mathbf{F} = -\mathbf{grad\,} U$, and so U is a potential energy function for $\mathbf{F}$. The work done by the force is the line integral of $\mathbf{F}$ for any path from $(5, 0)$ to $(0, 5)$. From Equation (4.2), this line integral is simply the difference between potential energies, $-(U(0, 5) - U(5, 0)) = 25p - \frac{25}{2}p = \frac{25}{2}p$.

4.7 Use the curl test.
$\mathbf{curl\, F} = [(\partial g(y)/\partial x - \partial f(x)/\partial y)]\mathbf{k}$, where $\partial g/\partial x = \partial f/\partial y = 0$. Hence $\mathbf{curl\, F} = \mathbf{0}$ and so $\mathbf{F}$ is conservative.
$\mathbf{curl\, H} = [(\partial f(x)/\partial x - \partial g(y)/\partial y)]\mathbf{k}$. This can be zero, and hence $\mathbf{H}$ conservative, only if $f(x) = mx + c_1$ and $g(y) = my + c_2$, for constants m, c_1 and c_2. Otherwise the curl is non-zero and $\mathbf{H}$ is non-conservative.

4.8 (a) The circle can be parametrized by $x = a\cos t$, $y = a\sin t$. Hence, $B_1 = -(k/a)\sin t$, $B_2 = (k/a)\cos t$, $dx/dt = -a\sin t$, $dy/dt = a\cos t$. So

$$\oint_C \mathbf{B} \cdot d\mathbf{r} = \int_0^{2\pi} k\, dt = 2\pi k.$$

Alternatively: the field can be expressed in plane polars as

$$\mathbf{B}(r, \phi) = \frac{k}{r}\mathbf{e}_\phi \qquad (r \ne 0).$$

Hence the field is directed tangentially, and the tangential component of $\mathbf{B}$ on the circle of radius $r = a$ is k/a, which is constant. Hence the line integral around the circle is $(k/a)2\pi a = 2\pi k$.

(b) It is easiest to use the cylindrical polar form of curl given in Subsection 2.3. With $B_\theta = k/\rho$, $B_\rho = 0$, we have

$$\mathbf{curl\, B} = [-k/\rho^2 + k/\rho^2]\mathbf{e}_z = \mathbf{0}.$$

(So part (a) shows that the vector field **B** is not a conservative field, since it has a non-zero line integral for the circle, but part (b) shows that **curl B** is zero. This failure of the curl test occurs because the domain of **B** is not simple. The origin $x^2 + y^2 = 0$ is excluded. Whenever there is a hole in the domain of the vector field, there is a possibility that the curl test will fail. You may take it that the curl test can be applied to all vector fields we ask you to work with in this course, other than **B** here.)

Index